GUIDE TO FOOD STORAGE

Follow this guide for food storage, and you can be sure that what's in your freezer, refrigerator, and pantry is fresh-tasting and ready to use in recipes.

In the Freezer (at -10° to 0° F)

Dairy and Eggs

Item	Time
Cheese, hard	6 months
Cheese, soft	6 months
Egg substitute, unopened	1 year
Egg whites	1 year
Egg yolks	1 year
Ice cream, sherbet	1 month

Fruits and Vegetables

Item	Time
Commercially frozen fruits	1 year
Commercially frozen vegetables	8 to 12 months

Meats, Poultry, and Seafood

Beef, Lamb, Pork, and Veal

Item	Time
Chops, uncooked	4 to 6 months
Ground and stew meat, uncooked	3 to 4 months
Ham, fully cooked, half	1 to 2 months
Roasts, uncooked	4 to 12 months
Steaks, uncooked	6 to 12 months

Poultry

Item	Time
All cuts, cooked	4 months
Boneless or bone-in pieces, uncooked	9 months

Seafood

Item	Time
Fish, fatty, uncooked	2 to 3 months
Fish, lean, uncooked	6 months

In the Refrigerator (at 34° to 40° F)

Dairy and Eggs

Item	Time
Butter	1 to 3 months
Buttermilk	1 to 2 weeks
Cheese, hard, wedge, opened	6 months
Cheese, semihard, block, opened	3 to 4 weeks
Cream cheese, fat-free, light, and ⅓-less-fat	2 weeks
Egg substitute, opened	3 days
Fresh eggs in shell	3 to 5 weeks

Meats, Poultry, and Seafood

Beef, Lamb, Pork, and Veal

Item	Time
Ground and stew meat, uncooked	1 to 2 days
Roasts, uncooked	3 to 5 days
Steaks and chops, uncooked	3 to 5 days

Chicken, Turkey, and Seafood

Item	Time
All cuts, uncooked	1 to 2 days

Fruits and Vegetables

Item	Time
Apples, beets, cabbage, carrots, celery, citrus fruits, eggplant, and parsnips	2 to 3 weeks
Apricots, asparagus, berries, cauliflower, cucumbers, mushrooms, okra, peaches, pears, peas, peppers, plums, salad greens, and summer squash	2 to 4 days
Corn, husked	1 day

In the Pantry (keep these at room temperature for 6 to 12 months)

Baking and Cooking Staples

- Baking powder
- Biscuit and baking mixes
- Broth, canned
- Cooking spray
- Honey
- Mayonnaise, fat-free, low-fat, and light (unopened)
- Milk, canned evaporated fat-free
- Milk, nonfat dry powder
- Mustard, prepared (unopened)
- Oils, olive and vegetable
- Pasta, dried
- Peanut butter
- Rice, instant and regular
- Salad dressings, bottled (unopened)
- Seasoning sauces, bottled
- Tuna, canned

Fruits, Legumes, and Vegetables

- Fruits, canned
- Legumes (beans, lentils, peas), dried or canned
- Tomato products, canned
- Vegetables, canned

weightwatchers® annual recipes *for success* 2014

ISBN-13: 978-0-8487-3981-2
ISBN-10: 0-8487-3981-7

Printed in the United States of America
First Printing 2013

Be sure to check with your health-care provider before making any changes to your diet. *Weight Watchers* and ***PointsPlus***® are the registered trademarks of Weight Watchers International, Inc., and are used under license by Time Home Entertainment Inc.

OXMOOR HOUSE
VP, Brand Publishing: Laura Sappington
Editorial Director: Leah McLaughlin
Creative Director: Felicity Keane
Brand Manager: Katie McHugh
Senior Editor: Andrea C. Kirkland
Managing Editor: Elizabeth Tyler Austin

WEIGHT WATCHERS® ANNUAL RECIPES FOR SUCCESS 2014
Editor: Rachel Quinlivan West, RD
Project Editor: Megan McSwain Yeatts
Recipe Editor: Alyson Moreland Haynes
Recipe Developers and Testers: Wendy Ball, RD; Victoria E. Cox; Tamara Goldis, RD; Stefanie Maloney; Callie Nash; Karen Rankin; Leah Van Deren
Photography Director: Jim Bathie
Senior Photo Stylist: Kay E. Clarke
Photo Stylist: Mindi Shapiro Levine
Assistant Photo Stylist: Mary Louise Menendez
Senior Production Manager: Theresa Beste-Farley
Production Manager: Tamara Nall Wilder

CONTRIBUTORS
Project Editor: Sarah Waller
Editor: Carolyn Land Williams, PhD, RD
Designer: Carol Damsky
Copy Editor: Deri Reed
Proofreaders: Carmine Loper, Lauren Brooks
Indexer: Mary Ann Laurens
Interns: Ali Carruba, Elizabeth Laseter, Laura Medlin, Amy Pinney, April Smitherman, Frances Gunnells, Madison Taylor Pozzo, Deanna Sakal, Tonya West

Photographers: Daniel Taylor, Beau Gustafson
Food Stylists: Erica Hopper, Ana Price Kelly

TIME HOME ENTERTAINMENT INC.
Publisher: Jim Childs
VP, Brand & Digital Strategy: Steven Sandonato
Executive Director, Marketing Services: Carol Pittard
Executive Director, Retail & Special Sales: Tom Mifsud
Director, Bookazine Development & Marketing: Laura Adam
Executive Publishing Director: Joy Butts
Finance Director: Glenn Buonocore
Associate General Counsel: Helen Wan

Cover: Chicken Alfredo, page 68

weightwatchers®
annual recipes
for success
2014

Pomegranate Sorbet,
page 167

contents

Layered Cobb Salad,
page 100

Weight Watchers®

At Weight Watchers, weight management is a partnership that combines our knowledge with your efforts. We help you on your weight-loss journey to make positive behavioral changes in your life, inspiring you with our belief in your power to succeed and motivating you every step of the way.

WEIGHT WATCHERS INTERNATIONAL BACKGROUND

SINCE ITS FOUNDING IN 1963, Weight Watchers has helped millions achieve healthy, sustainable weight loss. Weight Watchers International, Inc., is the world's leading provider of weight-management services, operating globally through a network of company-owned and franchise operations. Weight Watchers holds more than 40,000 weekly meetings where members receive group support and learn about healthy eating patterns, behavior modification, and physical activity. **WeightWatchers.com** provides innovative subscription weight-management products over the Internet and is the leading Internet-based weight-management provider in the world. In addition, Weight Watchers offers a wide range of products, publications, and programs for those interested in weight loss and weight control.

For more information about the Weight Watchers program and a meeting near you, call 1-800-651-6000 or visit **weightwatchers.com**

THE WEIGHT WATCHERS COMMITMENT TO SCIENCE

Weight Watchers backs up its weight-management plans with a strong commitment to the science of weight loss. The research and conclusions of experts and health organizations worldwide, including the World Health Organization and the National Institutes of Health, are incorporated into the Weight Watchers offerings. Weight Watchers also conducts its own research on weight-loss methods. As scientific findings change, the Weight Watchers plans evolve.

Weight Watchers®
ANNUAL RECIPES FOR SUCCESS 2014

Full of fresh and healthy recipes, this cookbook makes losing weight easy and delicious. You'll find all you need to successfully follow the Weight Watchers *PointsPlus®* plan, from everyday favorites to special occasion dishes and treats. Here's a snapshot of what's inside:

- Over 270 quick, mouth-watering recipes
- A ***PointsPlus*** value per serving for each recipe
- Nutritional analysis with every recipe (see "About Our Recipes" on page 16)
- More than 40 color photographs of recipes
- Step-by-step instructions, how-to photographs, prep and cook times, and helpful hints from our Test Kitchens
- Four weeks of 7-Day Menu Planners that incorporate recipes from the cookbook as well as quick and easy new recipes, too

PIMIENTO CHEESE GRILLED CHEESE

PointsPlus value per serving: 6

Two types of cheese go into this sandwich's homemade filling before it's layered with bacon and grilled. (page 104)

OUR FAVORITE RECIPES

All of our recipes are rigorously tested to ensure ease of preparation and excellent taste. But some are a cut above the rest. Here are our favorites from this year. We hope you enjoy them just as much as we do.

► SALMON CORN CHOWDER

PointsPlus value per serving: 6

Creamed corn is the secret ingredient in this quick chowder that's topped with cheddar cheese and crumbled bacon. This chowder is a perfect dish on cold winter days. (page 121)

▼ ASIAN SLAW

PointsPlus value per serving: 2

This Asian-inspired slaw gets some kick from the creamy wasabi dressing. It's an ideal make-ahead dish since extra marinating time only enhances the flavors. (page 85)

OUR FAVORITE RECIPES

▸ PLUM-SAUCED CHICKEN THIGHS

PointsPlus value per serving: 8

Sometimes the simplest ingredients can create the most delicious dishes. In this skillet recipe, basic chicken thighs, green onions and bell pepper are transformed when cooked in a thick sauce made with canned plums and soy sauce. (page 76)

▸▸ SPICY PORK CHOPPED SALAD

PointsPlus value per serving: 7

Napa cabbage, mandarin oranges, and bell pepper form this salad's base; it's topped with seasoned pork and garnished with almonds. (page 92)

▸▸▸ CHIPOTLE CHICKEN–STUFFED JALAPEÑOS

PointsPlus value per serving: 1

Cream cheese, cilantro, and shredded chicken are mixed together to make a creamy filling for these individual appetizers. (page 20)

▾ GREEN BEANS WITH PANCETTA

PointsPlus value per serving: 2

Crisply cooked pancetta and toasted walnuts transform ordinary green beans into a side that's worthy of a special night. (page 148)

OUR FAVORITE RECIPES

► SALSA VERDE CHICKEN ENCHILADAS

PointsPlus value per serving: 7

Filled with a creamy salsa-chicken mixture and then topped with melted cheese, this Mexican comfort food takes less than 15 minutes to prepare. (page 81)

▼ FLANK STEAK WITH RED ONION–SHERRY MARMALADE

PointsPlus value per serving: 7

Caramelized onions cooked in a sweet yet tangy vinegar sauce are the perfect accompaniment for lean flank steak. (page 36)

▲SWEET AND SOUR SALMON

PointsPlus value per serving: 9

Fresh salmon is browned in the skillet with simple Mexican seasonings and then topped with a sweet pineapple glaze creating the perfect balance of sweet and sour. Pair with simple sides such as couscous and a steamed vegetable for a satisfying meal. (page 31)

◄LINGUINE WITH SPICY BEEF AND OLIVES

PointsPlus value per serving: 8

Olives, capers, red wine, and ground beef are simmered together to create a robust sauce for pasta. You control the spice by increasing or decreasing the red pepper. (page 38)

OUR FAVORITE RECIPES

▸SLUSHY WATERMELON MOJITOS

PointsPlus value per serving: 4

Mix fresh melon cubes with frozen limeade to get a slushy, refreshing beverage. Dress these cocktails up with lime slices and mint sprigs for a special occasion. (page 26)

▸▸ DARK CHOCOLATE–BLUEBERRY BARK

PointsPlus value per serving: 4

This test kitchen favorite can't get any easier to prepare—dried blueberries and cherries are stirred into melted chocolate, allowed to harden, and topped with dried fruit and pistachios. (page 174)

▾BANANAS FOSTER SUNDAES

PointsPlus value per serving: 8

Brown sugar and butter caramelize and coat banana slices as part of a decadent sauce that's served over light vanilla ice cream. (page 165)

ABOUT OUR RECIPES

Weight Watchers® Annual Recipes for Success 2014

gives you the nutrition facts you need to stay on track. Every recipe in this book includes a *PointsPlus®* value per serving. For more information on Weight Watchers, see page 7.

Each recipe has a list of nutrients—including fat, carbohydrates, fiber, and protein. You'll also find calories, saturated fat, monounsaturated fat, polyunsaturated fat, cholesterol, iron, sodium, and calcium as well as a serving size and the number of servings. Measurements are abbreviated g (grams) and mg (milligrams). Nutritional values used in our calculations either come from The Food Processor, Version 10.4 (ESHA Research), or are provided by food manufacturers.

NUTRITIONAL ANALYSIS IS BASED ON THESE ASSUMPTIONS:

- Unless otherwise indicated, meat, poultry, and fish always refer to skinned, boned, and cooked servings.
- When we give a range for an ingredient (3 to 3½ cups flour, for instance), we calculate using the lesser amount.
- Some alcohol calories evaporate during heating; the analysis reflects this.
- Only the amount of marinade absorbed by the food is used in calculations.
- Garnishes and optional ingredients are not included in an analysis.

Safety Note: Cooking spray should never be used near direct heat. Always remove a pan from heat before spraying it with cooking spray.

A NOTE ON USE FOR DIABETICS:

Almost all of our recipes can be incorporated into a diabetic diet by using the carbohydrate amount in the nutrient analysis and incorporating that into the carbohydrate amount recommended by your physician.

appetizers & beverages

Black-Eyed Pea and Tomato Salsa, *page 18*

CREAMY SPINACH DIP

PointsPlus value per serving: 2

HANDS-ON TIME: 14 min. ▪ **TOTAL TIME:** 14 min.

The skillet will be very full initially when the spinach is added; as it wilts, though, the spinach will reduce greatly in size. Serve with fresh vegetables like carrots, cucumbers, or broccoli florets that have a ***PointsPlus*** value per serving of 0.

- 1 teaspoon canola oil
- 2 garlic cloves, minced
- 4 cups loosely packed fresh baby spinach
- 3 ounces ⅓-less-fat cream cheese (about ⅓ cup), softened
- 2 ounces finely shredded Asiago cheese (about ½ cup)
- ½ teaspoon hot sauce
- ¼ teaspoon salt
- ¼ teaspoon freshly ground black pepper
- ½ cup fat-free sour cream

1. Heat oil in a large nonstick skillet over medium-high heat 1 minute. Add garlic to pan; cook 30 seconds. Add spinach to pan; cook 2 minutes or until spinach begins to wilt, stirring frequently. Remove from heat. Add cream cheese and next 4 ingredients, stirring until cheese melts. Transfer to a bowl; stir in sour cream. **YIELD: 8 SERVINGS (SERVING SIZE: 2 TABLESPOONS).**

PER SERVING: Calories 81; Fat 5.3g (sat 2.7g, mono 1.7g, poly 0.4g); Protein 3.8g; Carb 4.7g; Fiber 0.7g; Chol 17mg; Iron 0.4mg; Sodium 217mg; Calc 103mg

BLACK-EYED PEA AND TOMATO SALSA

PointsPlus value per serving: 1 *(pictured on page 50)*

HANDS-ON TIME: 15 min. ▪ **TOTAL TIME:** 15 min.

- 1 cup chopped tomato
- ¼ cup chopped red onion
- 3 tablespoons chopped poblano chile
- 2 tablespoons chopped fresh cilantro
- 2½ tablespoons fresh lime juice
- ¼ teaspoon minced fresh garlic
- ⅛ teaspoon salt
- ⅛ teaspoon ground cumin
- ⅛ teaspoon freshly ground black pepper
- 1 (15.8-ounce) can black-eyed peas, rinsed and drained

1. Place all ingredients in a large bowl, and toss to combine. **YIELD: 8 SERVINGS (SERVING SIZE: ABOUT ⅓ CUP).**

PER SERVING: Calories 35; Fat 0.3g (sat 0.1g, mono 0g, poly 0.1g); Protein 1.9g; Carb 6.6g; Fiber 1.5g; Chol 0mg; Iron 0.4mg; Sodium 139mg; Calc 11mg

HOW TO SEED CHILE PEPPERS

Chile peppers can add flavor depth to a recipe, but they can also set your taste buds on fire. To modify their scorch, follow these tips for removing the seeds and veins—the source of capsaicin, the chemical that gives peppers their kick. You can control the heat by removing as many or as few of the seeds as you'd like. Since capsaicin can stick to your hands, be sure to wear gloves when handling hot peppers.

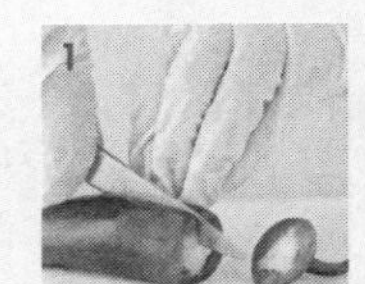

1. Use a paring knife to cut off the stem and slice the chile in half lengthwise.
2. Next, cut each half lengthwise to create four separate strips.
3. Lay the strips skin sides down, and slide the knife against the pepper to cut away the vein and seeds.

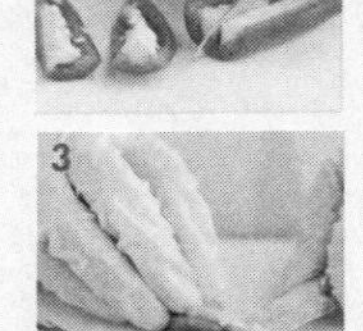

CAJUN HOT CRAB DIP

PointsPlus value per serving: 2

HANDS-ON TIME: 30 min. ▪ **TOTAL TIME:** 1 hr. 5 min.

Spoon this dip into a baking dish up to a day ahead, but top with panko and chives just before baking. If it's chilled, leave the dish out at room temperature while the oven preheats.

Cooking spray
2 tablespoons minced shallots
1 teaspoon minced fresh garlic
1 pound lump crabmeat, shell pieces removed and divided
¼ cup water
1 tablespoon hot pepper sauce
2 teaspoons salt-free Cajun seasoning
½ cup mayonnaise
3 ounces ⅓-less-fat cream cheese (about ⅓ cup), softened
¼ cup minced red bell pepper
2 tablespoons lemon juice
¼ teaspoon salt
¼ teaspoon freshly ground black pepper
3 tablespoons panko
3 tablespoons minced fresh chives

1. Preheat oven to 450°.
2. Heat a small saucepan over medium heat. Coat pan with cooking spray. Add shallots and garlic to pan; cook 2 minutes, stirring frequently. Place 1 cup crab in a food processor. Add shallot mixture, ¼ cup water, pepper sauce, and Cajun seasoning to crab; process until smooth. Spoon mixture into a large bowl, and stir in remaining crab, mayonnaise, and next 5 ingredients (through black pepper).
3. Transfer mixture to a 1-quart glass or ceramic casserole dish coated lightly with cooking spray. Combine panko and chives in a small bowl; sprinkle over crab mixture. Coat panko mixture with cooking spray. Bake at 450° for 30 minutes or until browned and bubbly. Let stand 5 minutes. **YIELD: 12 SERVINGS (SERVING SIZE: ¼ CUP).**

PER SERVING: Calories 95; Fat 5.3g (sat 1.1g, mono 1.8g, poly 1.3g); Protein 8.4g; Carb 2g; Fiber 0.1g; Chol 43mg; Iron 0.4mg; Sodium 253mg; Calc 46mg

CRABMEAT

Crab is a great source of lean protein, B_{12}, iron, and omega-3 fatty acids that have been shown to boost heart health. If you're going the easier route and purchasing meat that has already been removed from the crab instead of picking your own, the types of crabmeat—jumbo lump, lump, claw, surimi—can get a little confusing. Jumbo lump crabmeat is often considered the highest grade and is usually the most expensive. It's from the large pieces of meat from the muscles in the legs of the crab used for swimming and is bright white in color. Lump crabmeat is made of the smaller pieces that break off of the jumbo lump meat and is what is commonly used to make crab cakes. The darker pink meat that comes from the fins and claws of the crab is called claw meat. Claw meat is less expensive than lump but tends to have a stronger flavor. Dishes where you want the crab flavor to really come through such as in a bisque or soup are good uses for claw meat. Lastly, there is imitation crabmeat that's actually not made from crab at all but rather from surimi, a paste of finely minced fish that is flavored and shaped to resemble crabmeat.

LAYERED BUFFALO CHICKEN DIP

PointsPlus value per serving: 1

HANDS-ON TIME: 8 min. ▪ **TOTAL TIME:** 8 min.

Serve this with white corn chips or crisp celery sticks. Raw celery has a *PointsPlus* value per serving of 0 while a serving of 7 corn chips (about ½ ounce) has a *PointsPlus* value of 2.

2 teaspoons olive oil
1½ cups shredded cooked chicken breast
1 tablespoon paprika
2 tablespoons hot sauce
⅓ cup light blue cheese dressing
1 ounce crumbled blue cheese (about ¼ cup)
⅓ cup chopped green onions

1. Heat a large nonstick skillet over medium-high heat. Add oil to pan; swirl to coat. Add chicken to pan; sprinkle with paprika and hot sauce, tossing to coat chicken. Cook 3 minutes or until thoroughly heated, stirring constantly.
2. Transfer chicken to a 1-quart serving dish. Drizzle dressing over chicken; sprinkle with cheese and green onions. **YIELD: 16 SERVINGS (SERVING SIZE: 2 TABLESPOONS).**

PER SERVING: Calories 48; Fat 2.8g (sat 0.7g, mono 1.2g, poly 0.7g); Protein 4.7g; Carb 1.1g; Fiber 0.2g; Chol 13mg; Iron 0.3mg; Sodium 144mg; Calc 14mg

BLUE CHEESE AND CHIVE STRAWS

PointsPlus value per serving: 1

HANDS-ON TIME: 18 min. ▪ **TOTAL TIME:** 4 hr. 43 min.

6.75 ounces all-purpose flour (about 1½ cups)
¼ cup chilled butter, cut into small pieces
4 ounces crumbled blue cheese (about 1 cup)
⅓ cup finely chopped chives
¼ teaspoon salt
¼ teaspoon freshly ground black pepper
1 to 2 tablespoons cold water

1. Weigh or lightly spoon flour into dry measuring cups; level with a knife. Place flour and butter in a food processor; pulse to blend. Add cheese, chives, salt, and pepper; pulse until mixture resembles coarse meal. Drizzle water into flour mixture, and pulse until dough forms a ball. Roll dough into a 16 x 8–inch rectangle. Wrap dough in plastic wrap; refrigerate 4 hours or until firm.

2. Preheat oven to 350°.

3. Cut dough crosswise into 64 (¼-inch-wide) slices. Place ½ inch apart on a baking sheet lined with parchment paper. Bake at 350° for 10 minutes or until edges are lightly browned. Cool straws completely on wire racks. **YIELD: 32 SERVINGS (SERVING SIZE: 2 STRAWS).**

PER SERVING: Calories 47; Fat 2.5g (sat 1.6g, mono 0.7g, poly 0.1g); Protein 1.4g; Carb 4.7g; Fiber 0.2g; Chol 6mg; Iron 0.3mg; Sodium 78mg; Calc 21mg

MINI TOMATO-PARMESAN TARTS

PointsPlus value per serving: 3

HANDS-ON TIME: 40 min. ▪ **TOTAL TIME:** 1 hr. 5 min.

If you don't have a pastry cutter, use the rim of a drinking glass to cut rounds from the puff pastry.

1½ cups finely diced seeded plum tomato (about 4)
¼ cup minced shallots
1 tablespoon extra-virgin olive oil
1 teaspoon chopped fresh thyme
2 teaspoons champagne or white wine vinegar
¼ teaspoon freshly ground black pepper
2 sheets frozen puff pastry dough, thawed
Cooking spray
2.5 ounces grated fresh Parmesan cheese (about ⅔ cup)
¼ teaspoon kosher salt
Fresh small basil leaves (optional)

1. Preheat oven to 400°.
2. Combine first 6 ingredients in a medium bowl. Place 1 sheet of pastry dough on a work surface lightly dusted with flour. Gently roll to a 10 x 12½–inch rectangle. Cut dough with a 2½-inch round cutter into 20 rounds. Place on a baking sheet coated with cooking spray. Prick dough liberally with a fork. Top each round with about ¾ teaspoon cheese and about 2 teaspoons tomato mixture. Repeat procedure with remaining dough, cheese, and tomato mixture. Bake at 400° for 25 minutes or until golden, rotating pans once during baking. Sprinkle tarts evenly with salt. Sprinkle with basil leaves, if desired. **YIELD: 20 SERVINGS (SERVING SIZE: 2 TARTS).**

PER SERVING: Calories 105; Fat 7.2g (sat 1.5g, mono 2.1g, poly 3.3g); Protein 2.6g; Carb 7.6g; Fiber 0.4g; Chol 3mg; Iron 0.5mg; Sodium 115mg; Calc 44mg

CHIPOTLE CHICKEN–STUFFED JALAPEÑOS

PointsPlus value per serving: 1 *(pictured on page 11)*

HANDS-ON TIME: 23 min. ▪ **TOTAL TIME:** 32 min.

If you don't like things super spicy, use only 1 teaspoon of the chipotle chiles in these stuffed jalapeños.

Cooking spray
8 large jalapeño peppers
½ cup shredded cooked chicken breast
4 ounces ⅓-less-fat cream cheese (about ½ cup), softened
1 tablespoon chopped fresh cilantro
2 teaspoons finely chopped chipotle chiles, canned in adobo sauce

1. Preheat oven to 400°.
2. Heat a grill pan over medium-high heat. Coat pan with cooking spray. Add peppers to pan; cook 14 minutes or until tender and blackened, turning occasionally. Cool 2 minutes.
3. While peppers cook, combine chicken and next 3 ingredients. Cut a lengthwise slit in each pepper; discard stems, seeds, and membranes. Fill each pepper with about 2 tablespoons chicken mixture.
4. Place peppers on a baking sheet coated with cooking spray. Bake at 400° for 7 minutes or until cheese is lightly browned. **YIELD: 8 SERVINGS (SERVING SIZE: 1 STUFFED PEPPER).**

PER SERVING: Calories 56; Fat 3.6g (sat 1.9g, mono 0.9g, poly 0.2g); Protein 4.1g; Carb 1.8g; Fiber 0.7g; Chol 18mg; Iron 0.2mg; Sodium 95mg; Calc 20mg

BEEF TENDERLOIN BRUSCHETTA WITH BROWN BUTTER

PointsPlus value per serving: 2

HANDS-ON TIME: 21 min. ▪ **TOTAL TIME:** 46 min.

Mustard seeds are toasted when they begin to pop. Similar to microwave popcorn, when a second of time passes between pops, the seeds are done.

½ cup diced mango
2 tablespoons chopped fresh cilantro
2 tablespoons lime juice
2 teaspoons finely chopped serrano chile
½ teaspoon sugar
¼ teaspoon salt
⅛ teaspoon ground turmeric
1½ teaspoons canola oil
½ teaspoon yellow mustard seeds, divided
1½ teaspoons butter, melted
Cooking spray
1 (4-ounce) beef tenderloin steak, trimmed (1 inch thick)
⅛ teaspoon salt
⅛ teaspoon freshly ground black pepper
16 (½-inch-thick) slices diagonally cut French bread baguette, toasted

1. Combine first 7 ingredients in a small bowl; cover and let stand at room temperature 15 minutes.
2. Heat a small nonstick skillet over medium-high heat. Add oil to pan; swirl to coat. Add 1 mustard seed to pan; cook until seed pops (about 90 seconds). Add remaining seeds; stir to coat with oil. Cover and cook seeds 30 seconds or until they begin to pop, gently shaking pan. Stir in butter and cover. Cook until 1 second passes between pops, shaking pan constantly (about 30 seconds). Remove from heat. Scrape mustard seed mixture into mango mixture; stir gently. Let stand 5 minutes.
3. Heat pan over medium-high heat. Coat pan with cooking spray. Sprinkle beef with ⅛ teaspoon salt and pepper. Add beef to pan; cook 3 minutes on each side or until desired degree of doneness. Let rest 5 minutes. Slice across the grain into very thin slices.
4. Divide beef slices evenly among baguette slices. Top each bruschetta with 1½ teaspoons mango mixture. Serve immediately. **YIELD: 8 SERVINGS (SERVING SIZE: 2 BRUSCHETTA).**

PER SERVING: Calories 88; Fat 2.8g (sat 1g, mono 1.2g, poly 0.4g); Protein 4.4g; Carb 12.1g; Fiber 0.6g; Chol 11mg; Iron 0.9mg; Sodium 216mg; Calc 5mg

LEMON-ARTICHOKE CHICKEN BRUSCHETTA

PointsPlus value per serving: 2

HANDS-ON TIME: 10 min. ▪ **TOTAL TIME:** 15 min.

Purchase the long, skinny French bread baguettes for this appetizer instead of the wide French bread that's also available.

12 (½-inch-thick) slices diagonally cut French bread baguette
1 ounce crumbled feta cheese (about ¼ cup)
¼ cup light mayonnaise
¼ teaspoon grated fresh lemon rind
½ cup shredded cooked chicken breast
½ cup drained canned artichoke hearts, coarsely chopped
1 tablespoon chopped fresh parsley
⅛ teaspoon freshly ground black pepper

1. Preheat oven to 450°.
2. Place baguette slices on a large baking sheet. Bake slices at 450° for 3 minutes or until toasted.
3. While baguette slices bake, combine cheese, mayonnaise, and lemon rind in a small bowl. Combine chicken and next 3 ingredients in a separate bowl. Spread baguette slices with mayonnaise mixture, and top with chicken mixture.
4. Bake at 450° for 5 minutes or until thoroughly heated. **YIELD: 12 SERVINGS (SERVING SIZE: 1 BRUSCHETTA).**

PER SERVING: Calories 58; Fat 2.6g (sat 0.8g, mono 0.6g, poly 1g); Protein 3.4g; Carb 5.1g; Fiber 0.3g; Chol 9mg; Iron 0.5mg; Sodium 134mg; Calc 13mg

BRUSCHETTA

The term bruschetta refers to an Italian appetizer where toasted bread is topped with various combinations of olive oil, garlic, herbs, cured meats, cheese, beans, and finely chopped vegetables like tomatoes and red peppers. Traditionally, the bread is rubbed with garlic and brushed with olive oil before being grilled or toasted. Brushetta has become a common appetizer in the United States with the most popular toppings consisting of a mixture of chopped tomatoes, fresh basil, garlic, olive oil, and Parmesan cheese. No time to chop? There are now prepared bruschetta toppings available for purchase so bread simply has to be toasted and topped. Look for these prepared toppings in your grocery near the jarred pesto.

CASHEW CHICKEN POT STICKERS

PointsPlus value per serving: 2 *(pictured on page 49)*

HANDS-ON TIME: 28 min. ▪ **TOTAL TIME:** 28 min.

¾ cup coarsely chopped cooked chicken
½ cup chopped dry-roasted cashews
½ cup chopped broccoli slaw
½ cup garlic and green onion teriyaki sauce
24 round wonton wrappers
1 tablespoon canola oil
1 cup water

1. Combine first 4 ingredients in a medium bowl.
2. Working with 1 wonton wrapper at a time (cover remaining wrappers with a damp towel to keep them from drying), spoon about 1 tablespoon chicken mixture into center of each wrapper. Moisten edges of dough with water; bring opposite sides together, pinching edges to seal.
3. Heat a large nonstick skillet over medium heat. Add oil to pan; swirl to coat. Arrange pot stickers in pan in a single layer; cook 2 minutes or until browned on bottom. Add 1 cup water to pan; cover and cook 5 minutes. Uncover and cook 1 minute or until liquid evaporates. Serve immediately. **YIELD: 24 SERVINGS (SERVING SIZE: 1 POT STICKER).**

PER SERVING: Calories 63; Fat 2.5g (sat 0.4g, mono 1.4g, poly 0.6g); Protein 3.6g; Carb 6.3g; Fiber 0.3g; Chol 7mg; Iron 0.5mg; Sodium 143mg; Calc 6mg

MAKING POT STICKERS

Work with one wonton wrapper at a time and keep the remaining wrappers covered with a damp towel since they can dry out before you've had time to shape all of the pot stickers. Cook pot stickers soon after they're formed, and eat soon after they're cooked. Little pockets of steam trapped inside make them tender. Once the steam dissipates, the pot stickers toughen and become dense.

TINY CHICKEN TOSTADAS

PointsPlus value per serving: 2

HANDS-ON TIME: 10 min. ▪ **TOTAL TIME:** 10 min.

These tiny tostadas are perfect for any party or family gathering. Each bite includes all your favorite Mexican flavors—guacamole, chicken, cheese, and pico de gallo.

36 round tortilla chips
Cooking spray
1 (7-ounce) package refrigerated guacamole
1 cup chopped skinless, boneless rotisserie chicken breast
3 ounces preshredded reduced-fat 4-cheese Mexican blend cheese (about ¾ cup)
1 cup fresh pico de gallo

1. Preheat broiler.
2. Place tortilla chips on a large foil-lined baking sheet coated with cooking spray. Spread about 2 teaspoons guacamole on each chip; top with about 1 tablespoon chicken. Sprinkle with cheese.
3. Broil 2 to 3 minutes or until cheese melts. Serve immediately with pico de gallo. **YIELD: 18 SERVINGS (SERVING SIZE: 2 TOSTADAS AND ABOUT 1 TABLESPOON PICO DE GALLO).**

PER SERVING: Calories 74; Fat 4.2g (sat 1.1g, mono 1.8g, poly 0.8g); Protein 4.4g; Carb 5.4g; Fiber 0.9g; Chol 10mg; Iron 0.1mg; Sodium 181mg; Calc 50mg

BBQ CHICKEN CUPS

PointsPlus value per serving: 2

HANDS-ON TIME: 16 min. ▪ **TOTAL TIME:** 31 min.

Use fresh pizza dough from the supermarket deli to make these barbecue-flavored snacks in a flash.

Cooking spray
½ cup chopped red onion
1 pound refrigerated fresh pizza dough
1¾ cups shredded cooked chicken breast
¾ cup lower-sodium barbecue sauce
3 ounces shredded part-skim mozzarella cheese (¾ cup)

1. Preheat oven to 375°.
2. Heat a small skillet over medium-high heat. Coat pan with cooking spray. Add onion to pan; sauté 5 minutes or until tender.
3. Press pizza dough into a 14 x 12–inch rectangle; cut into 18 (2½-inch) circles. Press circles into 18 muffin cups coated with cooking spray.
4. Combine onion, chicken, and barbecue sauce in a

large bowl. Divide chicken mixture among dough cups. Sprinkle with cheese. Bake at 375° for 15 minutes or until golden. **YIELD: 18 SERVINGS (SERVING SIZE: 1 CUP).**

PER SERVING: Calories 92; Fat 2.8g (sat 0.9g, mono 0.7g, poly 0.5g); Protein 6.4g; Carb 10.6g; Fiber 0.3g; Chol 16mg; Iron 0.7mg; Sodium 185mg; Calc 49mg

SMOKED ALMOND CHICKEN SALAD BITES

PointsPlus value per serving: 1

HANDS-ON TIME: 13 min. ▪ **TOTAL TIME:** 13 min.

For the best flavor, make the chicken salad ahead so it has time to chill thoroughly before serving it on the crackers.

1½ cups finely chopped skinless, boneless rotisserie chicken breast
¼ cup chopped green onions
2 tablespoons chopped smoked almonds
2 tablespoons plain fat-free yogurt
2 tablespoons light mayonnaise
1½ teaspoons chopped fresh rosemary
½ teaspoon Dijon mustard
⅛ teaspoon freshly ground black pepper
½ cup seedless red grapes, divided
25 baked pita crackers

1. Combine first 8 ingredients in a large bowl. Chop ¼ cup grapes; stir into chicken mixture. Spoon chicken mixture onto crackers. Slice ¼ cup grapes lengthwise; top each cracker with a grape half. **YIELD: 25 SERVINGS (SERVING SIZE: 1 TOPPED CRACKER).**

PER SERVING: Calories 42; Fat 1.7g (sat 0.2g, mono 0.8g, poly 0.4g); Protein 3.4g; Carb 3.2g; Fiber 0.3g; Chol 8mg; Iron 0.3mg; Sodium 49mg; Calc 9mg

GREEK YOGURT

Greek yogurt is thicker and slightly more sour compared to other yogurts. This makes it the perfect replacement for some calorie-dense condiments like mayonnaise and sour cream. In addition to being lower in fat, Greek yogurt is also a great source of protein, calcium, and good bacteria that help keep your digestive system healthy—assets that mayo nor sour cream can offer. When eating by itself, try flavoring plain Greek yogurt with honey, fresh fruit, or nuts.

MIDDLE EASTERN CHICKEN SALAD BITES

PointsPlus value per serving: 1

HANDS-ON TIME: 6 min. ▪ **TOTAL TIME:** 6 min.

¼ cup light mayonnaise
¼ cup plain 2% reduced-fat Greek yogurt
1 tablespoon tahini (roasted sesame seed paste)
2 teaspoons chopped fresh dill
1 teaspoon fresh lemon juice
2 cups chopped skinless, boneless rotisserie chicken breast
1 ounce crumbled reduced-fat feta cheese (about ¼ cup)
24 baked pita crackers

1. Combine first 5 ingredients in a medium bowl. Add chicken and cheese to mayonnaise mixture; stir until blended. Spoon chicken mixture onto crackers. **YIELD: 24 SERVINGS (SERVING SIZE: 1 TOPPED CRACKER).**

PER SERVING: Calories 49; Fat 2.2g (sat 0.5g, mono 0.9g, poly 0.8g); Protein 4.7g; Carb 2.6g; Fiber 0.2g; Chol 12mg; Iron 0.4mg; Sodium 109mg; Calc 11mg

TARRAGON CHICKEN SALAD CUPS

PointsPlus value per serving: 2

HANDS-ON TIME: 16 min. ▪ **TOTAL TIME:** 16 min.

Fat-free Greek yogurt and light mayonnaise provide a creamy base for the salad and make for a healthy alternative to store-bought chicken salad.

2 (1.9-ounce) packages mini phyllo shells
¼ cup plain fat-free Greek yogurt
¼ cup light mayonnaise
1 tablespoon minced fresh tarragon
1½ teaspoons Dijon mustard
¼ teaspoon kosher salt
¼ teaspoon freshly ground black pepper
2 cups chopped skinless, boneless rotisserie chicken breast

1. Preheat oven to 350°.
2. Bake phyllo shells at 350° for 5 minutes.
3. While phyllo shells bake, combine yogurt and next 5 ingredients in a medium bowl. Add chicken, tossing to coat. Spoon 1 tablespoon chicken salad into each phyllo shell. Serve immediately. **YIELD: 15 SERVINGS (SERVING SIZE: 2 FILLED SHELLS).**

PER SERVING: Calories 78; Fat 3.8g (sat 0.5g, mono 1.6g, poly 1.3g); Protein 6.1g; Carb 4.2g; Fiber 0g; Chol 17mg; Iron 0.5mg; Sodium 169mg; Calc 6mg

BUILDING A HEALTHY PIZZA

Most pizza is high in calories and fat making it an occasional treat when trying to lose weight, but not all pizza is off limits. The trick is choosing healthier toppings that are lower in fat and sodium and that add nutrients. By making smart choices, you can make pizza be a nutritionally balanced meal and part of your weight-loss plan. Here are five toppings to add to your next pie:

Ham: Choose this meat in place of bacon, sausage or pepperoni, and you'll get protein that's much lower in fat, calories, and POINTS. Chicken is also a great substitute as well.

Pineapple: This sweet, juicy fruit pairs well with mozzerella cheese and mild meats like ham.

Fresh basil: Adding a sprinkling of fresh basil is an easy way to enhance the flavor of the pizza's sauce and cheese.

Spinach: Although not your usual pizza staple, spinach is a low-calorie vegetable that adds fiber, vitamins, and minerals. You can also load up on other veggies like onions, peppers, zucchini, mushrooms, tomatoes, or eggplant.

Olives: A light sprinkling of sliced olives is a great way to add a salty and savory kick to pizza. While olives are mostly fat, it's primarily the heart-healthy unsaturated type.

MINI PITA CHICKEN PIZZAS

PointsPlus value per serving: 2

HANDS-ON TIME: 7 min. ■ **TOTAL TIME:** 10 min.

Grapes add a sweet surprise in these mini chicken pizzas, which pairs well with the mozzarella cheese.

¼ cup reduced-fat pesto with basil
4 (0.4-ounce) whole-wheat mini pitas, split and toasted
½ cup shredded cooked chicken breast
¼ cup chopped seedless red grapes
2 ounces shredded part-skim mozzarella cheese (about ½ cup)

1. Preheat oven to 450°.
2. Spread pesto over mini pita halves. Top with chicken and grapes. Sprinkle with cheese. Place pizzas on baking sheet. Bake at 450° for 3 minutes or until cheese melts. **YIELD: 8 SERVINGS (SERVING SIZE: 1 MINI PIZZA).**

PER SERVING: Calories 81; Fat 4g (sat 1.5g, mono 1.7g, poly 0.3g); Protein 5.9g; Carb 4.7g; Fiber 0.6g; Chol 13mg; Iron 0.3mg; Sodium 147mg; Calc 81mg

TERIYAKI CHICKEN SLIDERS

PointsPlus value per serving: 5

HANDS-ON TIME: 12 min. ■ **TOTAL TIME:** 1 hr. 12 min.

These fun, miniature chicken sandwiches are a great option for backyard cookouts or tailgates—just keep the chicken in your refrigerator or cooler until ready to grill.

2 (6-ounce) skinless, boneless chicken breast halves
¼ cup garlic and green onion teriyaki sauce
Cooking spray
6 (¼-inch-thick) slices cored fresh pineapple
6 (0.67-ounce) slices Swiss cheese, halved diagonally into triangles
12 (1-ounce) Hawaiian sweet dinner rolls, split
Chopped fresh cilantro (optional)

1. Slice chicken breasts in half horizontally to make cutlets; cut each cutlet crosswise into thirds. Place chicken and teriyaki sauce in a large heavy-duty zip-top plastic bag. Seal bag, and marinate in refrigerator 1 hour.
2. Preheat grill to 400°.
3. Remove chicken from bag; discard marinade. Place chicken on grill rack coated with cooking spray; grill 3 minutes. Turn chicken over; add pineapple to grill rack. Grill chicken and pineapple 2 minutes. Turn pineapple over; place 1 cheese triangle on each piece of chicken. Grill chicken and pineapple 2 minutes or until cheese melts and chicken is done. Remove chicken and pineapple from grill. Cut pineapple slices into quarters.
4. Place 1 piece of chicken on bottom half of each roll. Top each with 2 pieces of pineapple, and sprinkle with cilantro, if desired; cover with roll tops. Serve immediately. **YIELD: 12 SERVINGS (SERVING SIZE: 1 SLIDER).**

PER SERVING: Calories 178; Fat 6.5g (sat 3.5g, mono 1.5g, poly 0.3g); Protein 12.1g; Carb 20.2g; Fiber 0.3g; Chol 42mg; Iron 0.9mg; Sodium 209mg; Calc 94mg

CURRIED CHICKEN LETTUCE WRAPS

PointsPlus value per serving: 3

HANDS-ON TIME: 10 min. ■ **TOTAL TIME:** 15 min.

Feel free to substitute hot mango chutney if you want lettuce wraps with a little extra kick. The *PointsPlus* value per serving for the wraps remains the same.

1 teaspoon canola oil
1 pound ground chicken breast
½ teaspoon curry powder
½ cup mango chutney
2 tablespoons chopped fresh cilantro
9 Bibb lettuce leaves
¼ cup sliced almonds, toasted
6 tablespoons plain fat-free Greek yogurt

1. Heat a large nonstick skillet over medium-high heat. Add oil to pan; swirl to coat. Add chicken and curry powder to pan; cook 6 minutes or until chicken is done, stirring to crumble. Remove from heat. Let stand 5 minutes.
2. Stir in chutney and cilantro. Spoon about ⅓ cup mixture into each lettuce leaf. Sprinkle with almonds, and dollop each with 2 teaspoons yogurt. **YIELD: 9 SERVINGS (SERVING SIZE: 1 LETTUCE WRAP).**

PER SERVING: Calories 129; Fat 3.1g (sat 0.4g, mono 1.5g, poly 0.7g); Protein 12.3g; Carb 12g; Fiber 0.5g; Chol 32mg; Iron 0.5mg; Sodium 205mg; Calc 21mg

BARBECUE CHICKEN AND PINEAPPLE SKEWERS

PointsPlus value per serving: 2

HANDS-ON TIME: 18 min. ■ **TOTAL TIME:** 48 min.

Don't be tempted to skip the soaking step. Soaking the wooden skewers prevents them from drying out and catching fire during the grilling process.

8 (6-inch) wooden skewers
1 pound skinless, boneless chicken breast, cut into 16 (1-inch) cubes
1 medium-sized red onion, cut into 16 wedges
16 (1-inch) cubes fresh pineapple
¼ cup barbecue sauce
1 tablespoon chopped fresh cilantro
½ teaspoon freshly ground black pepper
Cooking spray

1. Soak wooden skewers in water 30 minutes.
2. Preheat grill to 400°.
3. Divide chicken cubes, onion wedges, and pineapple cubes among skewers. Combine barbecue sauce, cilantro, and pepper in a small bowl.
4. Place skewers on grill rack coated with cooking spray. Brush skewers with sauce mixture. Grill 4 minutes, brushing occasionally with sauce mixture. Turn skewers over; brush with sauce mixture. Grill 4 minutes or until chicken is done and onion is tender. **YIELD: 8 SERVINGS (SERVING SIZE: 1 SKEWER).**

PER SERVING: Calories 96; Fat 1.5g (sat 0.3g, mono 0.4g, poly 0.2g); Protein 12.5g; Carb 7.7g; Fiber 0.9g; Chol 36mg; Iron 0.5mg; Sodium 152mg; Calc 14mg

ITALIAN CHICKEN MEATBALLS WITH MARINARA

PointsPlus value per serving: 2

HANDS-ON TIME: 7 min. ■ **TOTAL TIME:** 17 min.

These meatballs also make a great main dish when served over pasta or spaghetti squash. Six meatballs and ⅓ cup of sauce have a *PointsPlus* value per serving of 6. Use a 1½-inch scoop to easily portion the meatballs into a uniform size, which ensures they'll cook evenly.

Cooking spray
1 ounce grated fresh Parmesan cheese (about ¼ cup)
1 tablespoon salt-free Italian medley seasoning
¼ teaspoon salt
¼ teaspoon freshly ground black pepper
1 pound ground chicken
1 large egg, lightly beaten
1½ cups fire-roasted tomato and garlic pasta sauce

1. Preheat oven to 450°.
2. Line a 15 x 10–inch jelly-roll pan with foil. Coat foil with cooking spray. Combine Parmesan cheese and next 5 ingredients (through egg) in a medium bowl. Shape mixture into 24 (1½-inch) balls. Place meatballs on prepared pan.
3. Bake at 450° for 10 to 12 minutes or until done.
4. While meatballs cook, place pasta sauce in a 4-cup glass measure. Cover with heavy-duty plastic wrap, and microwave at HIGH 2 to 3 minutes or until heated. Serve meatballs with pasta sauce. **YIELD: 12 SERVINGS (SERVING SIZE: 2 MEATBALLS AND 2 TABLESPOONS SAUCE).**

PER SERVING: Calories 79; Fat 4.2g (sat 1.3g, mono 1.7g, poly 0.7g); Protein 8g; Carb 2.6g; Fiber 0.5g; Chol 42mg; Iron 0.3mg; Sodium 199mg; Calc 46mg

FRESH RASPBERRY LEMONADE

PointsPlus value per serving: 3

HANDS-ON TIME: 10 min. ▪ **TOTAL TIME:** 32 min.

¾ cup sugar
2 cups water, divided
2 cups fresh raspberries
½ cup fresh orange juice (about 1 orange)
1¾ cups fresh lemon juice (about 13 medium lemons)
16 ounces sparkling water, chilled

1. Combine sugar and ¾ cup water in a small saucepan; bring to a boil. Cook 2 minutes, stirring until sugar dissolves. Cool to room temperature.
2. Place 1¼ cups water and raspberries in a blender, and pulse 10 times or until well blended. Strain mixture through a fine sieve into a large pitcher; discard solids. Add orange juice, lemon juice, sparkling water, and cooled syrup to pitcher; stir to combine. Serve immediately over ice. YIELD: 8 SERVINGS (SERVING SIZE: ABOUT 1 CUP)

PER SERVING: Calories 115; Fat 0.3g (sat 0g, mono 0g, poly 0.2g); Protein 0.8g; Carb 30g; Fiber 0.5g; Chol 0mg; Iron 0.4mg; Sodium 15mg; Calc 21mg

SLUSHY WATERMELON MOJITOS

PointsPlus value per serving: 4 *(pictured on page 14)*

HANDS-ON TIME: 4 min. ▪ **TOTAL TIME:** 2 hr. 4 min.

The classic Cuban mojito cocktail is the inspiration for this ruby-hued watermelon version. Be sure to keep the limeade frozen so the beverage will be slushy.

5 cups cubed seeded watermelon
1 cup sparkling water, chilled
¾ cup white rum
¼ cup chopped fresh mint
1 (6-ounce) can frozen limeade concentrate, undiluted
Mint sprigs (optional)
Lime slices (optional)

1. Arrange watermelon in a single layer on a baking sheet; freeze 2 hours or until completely frozen.
2. Place frozen watermelon, sparkling water, rum, mint, and limeade in a blender; process until smooth. Garnish with mint sprigs and lime slices, if desired. Serve immediately. YIELD: 8 SERVINGS (SERVING SIZE: ABOUT ¾ CUP).

PER SERVING: Calories 119; Fat 0.4g (sat 0.1g, mono 0.1g, poly 0.2g); Protein 0.7g; Carb 17.5g; Fiber 0.6g; Chol 0mg; Iron 0.3mg; Sodium 2mg; Calc 11mg

CRANBERRY-APPLE-ORANGE CIDER

PointsPlus value per serving: 2 *(pictured on page 51)*

HANDS-ON TIME: 7 min. ▪ **TOTAL TIME:** 37 min.

This cider is great for any winter gathering. Keep warm on the stove top or in a slow cooker. Garnish with fresh orange or apple slices.

4 cups diet cranberry juice cocktail
4 cups apple cider
1 cup orange juice
2 (3-inch) cinnamon sticks
4 whole cloves

1. Combine all ingredients in a large saucepan. Bring to a boil; cover, reduce heat, and simmer 30 minutes. Strain mixture through a fine sieve, discarding solids. Serve warm. YIELD: 8 SERVINGS (SERVING SIZE: 1 CUP).

PER SERVING: Calories 76; Fat 0.1g (sat 0g, mono 0g, poly 0g); Protein 0.2g; Carb 19.2g; Fiber 0.1g; Chol 0mg; Iron 0.1mg; Sodium 38mg; Calc 3mg

MOCHA HOT CHOCOLATE

PointsPlus value per serving: 4

HANDS-ON TIME: 14 min. ▪ **TOTAL TIME:** 14 min.

Adding the optional whipped topping doesn't increase the *PointPlus* value of each serving and adds a little extra creaminess and froth to this cocoa.

4 cups 1% low-fat milk
¼ cup sugar
2 teaspoons instant espresso granules
⅛ teaspoon salt
2 ounces bittersweet chocolate, chopped
½ teaspoon vanilla extract
⅓ cup frozen fat-free whipped topping, thawed (optional)

1. Combine first 5 ingredients in a medium saucepan. Cook over medium heat 6 minutes or until sugar dissolves and chocolate melts, stirring constantly with a whisk. Reduce heat to low; cook 5 minutes or until thoroughly heated, stirring occasionally. Remove from heat; stir in vanilla. Pour about ¾ cup milk mixture into each of 6 glasses. Dollop with whipped topping, if desired. YIELD: 6 SERVINGS (SERVING SIZE: ¾ CUP).

PER SERVING: Calories 159; Fat 5.5g (sat 3.4g, mono 1.7g, poly 0.2g); Protein 6.2g; Carb 21.3g; Fiber 0.1g; Chol 8mg; Iron 0.4mg; Sodium 121mg; Calc 207mg

main dishes

SPINACH AND WHITE BEAN ROTINI

PointsPlus value per serving: 7

HANDS-ON TIME: 11 min. ■ **TOTAL TIME:** 11 min.

This easy meal comes together in no time at all and uses many things that are already in your pantry. For additional color, toss in veggies like chopped roasted red peppers or ripe tomatoes that have a *PointsPlus* value of 0.

8 ounces uncooked rotini (corkscrew pasta)
1 teaspoon olive oil
4 garlic cloves, minced
1 (15.8-ounce) can Great Northern beans or other white beans, rinsed and drained
¼ teaspoon freshly ground black pepper
2 (6-ounce) packages baby spinach
5 tablespoons freshly grated Parmesan cheese

1. Cook pasta according to package directions, omitting salt and fat. Drain and keep warm.
2. While pasta cooks, heat a large nonstick skillet over medium-high heat. Add oil to pan; swirl to coat. Add garlic to pan; sauté 1 minute. Add beans and pepper; cook 2 minutes or until thoroughly heated. Add spinach; cook until just wilted, stirring occasionally. Combine pasta and spinach mixture, tossing gently. Sprinkle with Parmesan cheese. **YIELD: 5 SERVINGS (SERVING SIZE: ABOUT 1¼ CUPS PASTA MIXTURE AND 1 TABLESPOON CHEESE).**

PER SERVING: Calories 281; Fat 3.8g (sat 1.3g, mono 1.4g, poly 0.4g); Protein 13.8g; Carb 49.3g; Fiber 7.6g; Chol 5mg; Iron 4.3mg; Sodium 401mg; Calc 178mg

KALE

Kale is an often overlooked nutritional powerhouse—naturally low in calories and fat and rich in fiber, vitamins, and minerals. In fact, 1 cup of this dark leafy green provides more than 100% of your daily vitamin A and vitamin C needs. If you're unsure of what to do with it, think of kale as a substitute for spinach or collard greens, and use it in place of either of these. Kale leaves can be tossed into salads; sautéed or stir-fried with a little garlic and olive oil; steamed; or added to casseroles, soups, or pasta dishes. Kale thrives in cold weather making it a great option when other leafy greens may not be in season. Store kale in an airtight plastic bag in the refrigerator for up to five days, and wash just before using.

BLACK BEAN AND KALE QUESADILLAS

PointsPlus value per serving: 8 *(pictured on page 57)*

HANDS-ON TIME: 14 min. ■ **TOTAL TIME:** 14 min.

Draining the pico de gallo gets rid of extra moisture that could make your quesadillas soggy. Feel free to up the spice of this quick meal by adding hot sauce or extra pico de gallo.

1 cup drained pico de gallo
1 (15-ounce) can unsalted black beans, rinsed and drained
¼ cup minced fresh cilantro
1 tablespoon fresh lime juice
1/16 teaspoon salt
1/16 teaspoon freshly ground black pepper
1 diced peeled avocado
1 teaspoon olive oil
1 tablespoon bottled minced garlic
1 (5-ounce) package prewashed baby kale and spinach mix
4 (7-inch) fat-free flour tortillas
4 ounces shredded light Monterey Jack cheese with jalapeño peppers (about 1 cup)
Cooking spray
Lime wedges (optional)

1. Place pico de gallo and black beans in a medium bowl; mash with a potato masher, leaving some beans whole.
2. Combine cilantro and next 4 ingredients (through avocado) in a small bowl.
3. Heat a large nonstick skillet over medium-high heat. Add oil to pan; swirl to coat. Add garlic and kale mixture to pan; sauté 1 minute or until greens wilt. Drain kale mixture on paper towels; set aside.
4. Spread bean mixture evenly on 1 side of each tortilla. Top half of each tortilla with kale mixture and cheese. Fold each tortilla in half.
5. Preheat a nonstick griddle to 375°; coat with cooking spray. Place tortillas on griddle; coat tops of tortillas with cooking spray. Cook 2 to 3 minutes on each side or until lightly browned and cheese melts. Cut each quesadilla in half; serve with avocado mixture and lime wedges, if desired. **YIELD: 4 SERVINGS (SERVING SIZE: 1 QUESADILLA AND 3 TABLESPOONS AVOCADO MIXTURE).**

PER SERVING: Calories 318; Fat 11.2g (sat 3.9g, mono 5.4g, poly 1g); Protein 18.6g; Carb 39g; Fiber 10.8g; Chol 15mg; Iron 2.7mg; Sodium 825mg; Calc 355mg

HERBED MUSHROOM RAGOUT OVER CHEESY POLENTA

PointsPlus value per serving: 9

HANDS-ON TIME: 27 min. ▪ **TOTAL TIME:** 27 min.

Use your favorite types of mushrooms in this creamy, protein-packed dish that both vegetarians and non-vegetarians will enjoy.

1 tablespoon olive oil
3 garlic cloves, chopped
1 shallot, thinly sliced
2 (8-ounce) packages presliced portobello mushrooms
2 teaspoons chopped fresh thyme
¾ teaspoon freshly ground black pepper, divided
¼ teaspoon salt, divided
1 (14.5-ounce) can fire-roasted diced tomatoes, undrained
2 cups fat-free milk
½ cup quick-cooking polenta
1 ounce shredded Manchego cheese (about ¼ cup)
1 ounce goat cheese, crumbled (about ¼ cup)
2 cups frozen meatless crumbles
Thyme sprigs (optional)

1. Heat a large nonstick skillet over medium-high heat. Add oil to pan; swirl to coat. Add garlic and shallot; sauté 1 minute. Add mushrooms; sauté 2 minutes or until tender. Stir in thyme, ½ teaspoon pepper, ⅛ teaspoon salt, and tomatoes. Cover, reduce heat, and simmer 5 minutes.
2. While mushrooms simmer, bring milk to a boil in a large saucepan over medium-high heat; reduce heat to medium-low. Gradually stir in polenta; cook 2 minutes or until thick, stirring constantly. Remove from heat; add cheeses, ¼ teaspoon pepper, and ⅛ teaspoon salt, stirring until cheese melts.
3. Stir crumbles into mushroom mixture; cook 3 minutes or until slightly thick. Spoon polenta into bowls, and top with crumble mixture. Garnish with thyme sprigs, if desired. **YIELD: 4 SERVINGS (SERVING SIZE: ½ CUP POLENTA AND 1 CUP CRUMBLE MIXTURE).**

PER SERVING: Calories 351; Fat 9.5g (sat 3.1g, mono 4.0g, poly 2.1g); Protein 24.2g; Carb 42.5g; Fiber 7.7g; Chol 11mg; Iron 5.1mg; Sodium 824mg; Calc 303mg

MEATLESS TEX-MEX TOSTADAS

PointsPlus value per serving: 9

HANDS-ON TIME: 10 min. ▪ **TOTAL TIME:** 15 min.

Seasoned, meatless crumbles taste quite similar to lean ground beef.

1 (12-ounce) package frozen meatless crumbles, thawed
½ cup frozen whole kernel corn
½ cup refrigerated prechopped onion
Cooking spray
1 tablespoon 25%-less-sodium taco seasoning
1 (8.5-ounce) pouch microwaveable precooked brown rice
6 (0.4-ounce) tostada shells
1 (16-ounce) can 99%-fat-free refried black beans
4 ounces preshredded reduced-fat 4-cheese Mexican blend cheese (about 1 cup)
3 cups shredded iceberg lettuce
6 tablespoons light sour cream
Fresh salsa (optional)
Lime wedges (optional)

1. Preheat oven to 425°.
2. Heat a large nonstick skillet over medium heat. Add meatless crumbles, corn, and onion to pan; coat with cooking spray. Cook 5 minutes or until onion is tender, stirring occasionally. Stir in taco seasoning, and cook 1 minute.
3. While meatless crumbles cook, heat rice according to package directions. Place tostada shells on a baking sheet. Spread black beans evenly over tostada shells. Top evenly with rice, meatless crumble mixture, and cheese. Bake at 425° for 5 minutes or until cheese melts. Top each tostada evenly with lettuce and sour cream. Serve with fresh salsa and lime wedges, if desired. **YIELD: 6 SERVINGS (SERVING SIZE: 1 TOSTADA, ½ CUP LETTUCE, AND 1 TABLESPOON SOUR CREAM).**

PER SERVING: Calories 345; Fat 12.4g (sat 3.5g, mono 3.3g, poly 3.5g); Protein 20.4g; Carb 38.9g; Fiber 8.5g; Chol 19mg; Iron 3.4mg; Sodium 539mg; Calc 242mg

MISO-GLAZED BLACK COD

PointsPlus value per serving: 10

HANDS-ON TIME: 12 min. ■ **TOTAL TIME:** 12 min.

Loaded with omega-3 fats, black cod (also known as sablefish) has a rich, buttery flesh that pairs well with the sweet and salty glaze. If you can't find black cod, substitute halibut. Serve this quick dish with steamed brown rice and snap peas.

¼ cup white or yellow miso (soybean paste)
3 tablespoons mirin (sweet rice wine)
2 tablespoons rice vinegar
1 teaspoon grated peeled fresh ginger
4 (6-ounce) skinless black cod fillets
2 tablespoons diagonally cut green onions
1 teaspoon sesame seeds, toasted

1. Preheat broiler.
2. Combine first 4 ingredients in a shallow dish. Dip fish in miso mixture, coating all sides. Place fish on a foil-lined baking sheet; discard any remaining miso mixture. Broil fish 8 to 10 minutes or until fish flakes easily when tested with a fork. Sprinkle fish with green onions and sesame seeds. YIELD: 4 SERVINGS (SERVING SIZE: 1 FILLET, 1½ TEASPOONS GREEN ONIONS, AND ¼ TEASPOON SESAME SEEDS).

PER SERVING: Calories 367; Fat 26.9g (sat 5.4g, mono 13.9g, poly 4g); Protein 24.1g; Carb 4g; Fiber 0.4g; Chol 83mg; Iron 2.3mg; Sodium 505mg; Calc 64mg

MISO

A staple in Japanese cuisine, miso is a salty paste made by fermenting soybeans with another grain, often wheat or rice. Miso varies in color and flavor based on how long it was fermented, where it was fermented, and what is was fermented with. The end result though is a salty paste that's used throughout Japanese cooking, most notably in miso soup where the miso is mixed with broth. Miso can be used in place of soy sauce and is a flavorful base for marinades, salad dressings, and stir-fry mixtures.

MEDITERRANEAN HALIBUT

PointsPlus value per serving: 7

HANDS-ON TIME: 9 min. ■ **TOTAL TIME:** 15 min.

Tangy sun-dried tomatoes, olives, and zucchini are simmered together to create a tasty topping for fish. If you can't find halibut, grouper or haddock can be substituted.

2 teaspoons olive oil
4 (6-ounce) halibut fillets
½ teaspoon salt
½ teaspoon freshly ground black pepper
1 cup dry white wine
½ cup sliced sun-dried tomatoes, packed without oil
¼ cup chopped pitted kalamata olives
1 medium zucchini, halved lengthwise and sliced
Basil sprigs (optional)
Lemon wedges (optional)

1. Heat a large nonstick skillet over medium-high heat. Add oil to pan; swirl to coat. Sprinkle fish with salt and pepper. Add fish to pan; cook 3 minutes on each side.
2. Add wine and next 3 ingredients (through zucchini) to pan; cover and simmer 6 minutes or until fish flakes easily when tested with a fork. Garnish with basil sprigs and lemon wedges, if desired. YIELD: 4 SERVINGS (SERVING SIZE: 1 FILLET AND ½ CUP ZUCCHINI MIXTURE).

PER SERVING: Calories 254; Fat 7.2g (sat 1.2g, mono 4.3g, poly 1.1g); Protein 33.2g; Carb 7g; Fiber 1.4g; Chol 83mg; Iron 1.2mg; Sodium 577mg; Calc 34mg

SALMON

Quick cooking and easy to season, salmon is one of the most versatile fish options around. Tasty when smoked, grilled, poached, roasted, or baked, salmon usually takes just 10 to 15 minutes to cook making it a great weeknight option. Salmon has a higher fat content than most fish—most all of which are the heart healthy fats—and this keeps salmon moist and tender when cooking. The fat content and mild flavor is also what makes it so easy to pair with different flavors and seasonings. Salmon seasonings will range from dry spice rubs, to pastes made with fresh herbs, to sweet and tangy marinades, to simple seasonings like lemon juice and salt and pepper. While fresh is most always best in quality, frozen salmon is easy to keep on hand. Look for frozen varieties that say they have been flash-frozen which means frozen quickly after being caught and skinned. To thaw, place salmon fillets in the refrigerator overnight.

SWEET AND SOUR SALMON

PointsPlus value per serving: 9 *(pictured on page 13)*

HANDS-ON TIME: 13 min. ■ **TOTAL TIME:** 13 min.

Adobo seasoning is a mix of garlic, oregano, salt, and other spices and can be found in either the spice or Mexican section of most grocery stores. Serve with Moroccan Couscous on page 154.

Cooking spray
4 (6-ounce) salmon fillets
1 teaspoon adobo seasoning
⅓ cup honey
¼ cup cider vinegar
¼ cup pineapple juice
Sliced green onions (optional)

1. Heat a grill pan over medium heat. Coat pan with cooking spray. Sprinkle skinless sides of fish with adobo seasoning. Add fish, seasoned sides down, to pan; cook 4 minutes. Coat fish with cooking spray; turn fish over, and cook 4 minutes or until fish flakes easily when tested with a fork or until desired degree of doneness.

2. While fish cooks, combine honey, cider vinegar, and pineapple juice in a small saucepan over medium-high heat; bring to a boil. Reduce heat, and simmer 10 minutes or until sauce is syrupy and reduced to about ⅓ cup. Spoon sauce over fish; sprinkle with green onions, if desired. **YIELD: 4 SERVINGS (SERVING SIZE: 1 FILLET AND ABOUT 4 TEASPOONS SAUCE).**

PER SERVING: Calories 370; Fat 13g (sat 3.1g, mono 5.7g, poly 3.2g); Protein 36.2g; Carb 24.4g; Fiber 0g; Chol 87mg; Iron 0.6mg; Sodium 440mg; Calc 23mg

ROASTED SALMON WITH MAPLE-DIJON SAUCE

PointsPlus value per serving: 8

HANDS-ON TIME: 6 min. ■ **TOTAL TIME:** 13 min.

Sweet maple syrup and sharp Dijon mustard bring out the best in nutrient-rich salmon. Serve with wilted greens such as spinach or kale and some lentils or brown rice for a quick meal.

¼ cup whole-grain Dijon mustard
1 tablespoon finely chopped shallots
2 tablespoons maple syrup
2 teaspoons chopped fresh thyme
¼ teaspoon freshly ground black pepper
4 (6-ounce) salmon fillets
Cooking spray
¼ teaspoon salt

1. Preheat oven to 425°.
2. Combine first 5 ingredients in a small bowl; set aside.
3. Heat a large ovenproof skillet over medium-high heat. Coat fish with cooking spray; sprinkle with salt. Add fish, skin sides up, to pan; cook 3 minutes. Turn fish over. Bake at 425° for 7 minutes or until fish flakes easily when tested with a fork or until desired degree of doneness. Spoon mustard sauce over fish. **YIELD: 4 SERVINGS (SERVING SIZE: 1 FILLET AND ABOUT 4 TEASPOONS MUSTARD SAUCE).**

PER SERVING: Calories 316; Fat 13.1g (sat 3.1g, mono 5.7g, poly 3.2g); Protein 36.3g; Carb 10.3g; Fiber 0.2g; Chol 87mg; Iron 0.7mg; Sodium 589mg; Calc 34mg

SPICE-RUBBED SALMON WITH CUCUMBER-YOGURT SAUCE

PointsPlus value per serving: 8 *(pictured on page 59)*

HANDS-ON TIME: 13 min. ▪ **TOTAL TIME:** 13 min.

Most Moroccan seasoning blends are salt-free, but if your blend has salt in the ingredient list, omit the ¼ teaspoon of salt in Step 1. If you can't find Moroccan seasoning, try making your own by combining ½ teaspoon each of cinnamon, ground ginger, cumin, coriander, black pepper, and paprika.

1 tablespoon Moroccan seasoning
2 teaspoons brown sugar
½ teaspoon salt, divided
4 (6-ounce) salmon fillets
2 teaspoons olive oil
1 cup chopped seeded peeled cucumber
½ cup plain fat-free Greek yogurt
1 tablespoon fresh lemon juice
2 garlic cloves, minced

1. Combine Moroccan seasoning, brown sugar, and ¼ teaspoon salt in a small bowl. Rub evenly over fish.
2. Heat a large nonstick skillet over medium-high heat. Add oil to pan; swirl to coat. Add fish; cook 4 to 5 minutes on each side or until fish flakes easily when tested with a fork or until desired degree of doneness.
3. While fish cooks, combine cucumber, yogurt, lemon juice, garlic, and ¼ teaspoon salt in a bowl; stir well. Spoon sauce evenly over fish. **YIELD: 4 SERVINGS (SERVING SIZE: 1 FILLET AND ABOUT ⅓ CUP SAUCE).**

PER SERVING: Calories 326; Fat 15.4g (sat 3.4g, mono 7.3g, poly 3.4g); Protein 39.4g; Carb 5g; Fiber 0.3g; Chol 87mg; Iron 0.7mg; Sodium 390mg; Calc 69mg

HOW TO SEED A CUCUMBER

When purchasing cucumbers, remember that the smaller the cucumber, the smaller the seeds and the better the flavor. To seed a cucumber, simply cut it in half lengthwise, and scrape out the seeds with a spoon.

BROILED TILAPIA WITH AVOCADO-RADISH SALSA

PointsPlus value per serving: 6

HANDS-ON TIME: 7 min. ▪ **TOTAL TIME:** 12 min.

Radishes add color, crunch, and a healthy dose of vitamin C to this quick salsa. Serve the fish and salsa over quinoa for a wholesome meal with fresh flavors. A ½-cup serving of cooked quinoa has a *PointsPlus* value of 3.

4 (6-ounce) tilapia fillets
½ teaspoon ground cumin
¼ teaspoon kosher salt
¼ teaspoon ground red pepper
¼ teaspoon freshly ground black pepper
Cooking spray
1 cup chopped radishes
½ cup diced peeled avocado
¼ cup chopped red onion
2 tablespoons chopped fresh cilantro
2 tablespoons fresh lime juice
2 teaspoons canola oil
⅛ teaspoon kosher salt
Lime wedges (optional)

1. Preheat broiler.
2. Sprinkle fish with cumin, ¼ teaspoon salt, red pepper, and black pepper. Place fish on a broiler pan coated with cooking spray; broil 10 to 11 minutes or until fish flakes easily when tested with a fork.
3. While fish cooks, combine radishes and next 6 ingredients (through kosher salt); toss well. Spoon salsa over fish; serve with lime wedges, if desired. **YIELD: 4 SERVINGS (SERVING SIZE: 1 FILLET AND ABOUT ⅓ CUP SALSA).**

PER SERVING: Calories 226; Fat 8g (sat 1.6g, mono 4.1g, poly 1.6g); Protein 34.9g; Carb 4.4g; Fiber 2.1g; Chol 85mg; Iron 1.3mg; Sodium 282mg; Calc 33mg

MISO-GLAZED SCALLOPS WITH WILTED KALE

PointsPlus value per serving: 7

HANDS-ON TIME: 15 min. ▪ **TOTAL TIME:** 15 min.

This entrée could also be served as a small plated appetizer at your next dinner party.

2 tablespoons yellow miso (soybean paste)
2 tablespoons mirin (sweet rice wine)
2 tablespoons rice vinegar
1 teaspoon minced peeled fresh ginger
1 garlic clove, minced
12 large sea scallops (about 1½ pounds)
2 tablespoons canola oil, divided
1 (16-ounce) package cut prewashed kale
¼ cup water
1 teaspoon black sesame seeds (optional)

1. Combine first 5 ingredients in a medium bowl; reserve 2 tablespoons miso mixture. Add scallops to remaining miso mixture in bowl; toss gently to coat. Let stand 5 minutes.
2. While scallops stand, heat a large Dutch oven over medium-high heat. Add 1 tablespoon canola oil, reserved miso mixture, and kale to pan. Cover, reduce heat to low, and cook 1 to 2 minutes or until kale is wilted. Keep warm.
3. Drain scallops, reserving marinade. Heat a large skillet over medium-high heat. Add 1 tablespoon canola oil to pan; swirl to coat. Add scallops to pan; cook 3 minutes on each side or until done. Remove scallops from pan; keep warm. Add reserved marinade and ¼ cup water to pan; cook 1 minute, scraping pan to loosen browned bits.
4. Divide kale among 4 plates. Top evenly with scallops and sauce; sprinkle with sesame seeds, if desired. **YIELD: 4 SERVINGS (SERVING SIZE: ¾ CUP KALE, 3 SCALLOPS, AND 1 TABLESPOON SAUCE).**

PER SERVING: Calories 267; Fat 9.3g (sat 0.8g, mono 4.7g, poly 2.9g); Protein 26.4g; Carb 19.5g; Fiber 2.5g; Chol 41mg; Iron 2.4mg; Sodium 687mg; Calc 182mg

FETA SHRIMP

PointsPlus value per serving: 7 *(pictured on page 52)*

HANDS-ON TIME: 15 min. ▪ **TOTAL TIME:** 15 min.

Oregano, garlic, tomatoes, and feta cheese combine to make a dish full of Mediterranean flavor. Serve with crusty whole-grain French bread or over hot cooked couscous.

1¼ pounds peeled and deveined large shrimp
1 tablespoon olive oil, divided
1 (16-ounce) container grape tomatoes
½ cup sliced green onions
3 garlic cloves, minced
½ cup dry white wine
1 tablespoon chopped fresh oregano
2 teaspoons butter
½ teaspoon freshly ground black pepper
¼ teaspoon kosher salt
2 ounces crumbled feta cheese (about ½ cup)

1. Pat shrimp dry with paper towels. Heat a large nonstick skillet over medium-high heat. Add 1½ teaspoons oil to pan; swirl to coat. Add shrimp to pan; sauté 3 minutes or until lightly browned. Remove shrimp from pan; drain.
2. Add 1½ teaspoons oil to pan; swirl to coat. Add tomatoes; sauté 3 minutes. Add green onions and garlic; cook 1 minute, stirring occasionally. Add wine and oregano; cook 3 minutes or until wine is reduced by half, scraping pan to loosen browned bits.
3. Add butter, pepper, and salt to tomato mixture, stirring until butter melts. Return shrimp to pan; cook 2 minutes or until thoroughly heated. Sprinkle with cheese before serving. **YIELD: 4 SERVINGS (SERVING SIZE: ABOUT 1⅓ CUPS SHRIMP MIXTURE AND 2 TABLESPOONS CHEESE).**

PER SERVING: Calories 230; Fat 9.9g (sat 4g, mono 3.7g, poly 0.8g); Protein 23.5g; Carb 9.1g; Fiber 2.3g; Chol 194mg; Iron 1.2mg; Sodium 522mg; Calc 152mg

HOW TO PEEL AND DEVEIN SHRIMP

A while back, shrimp were given a bad name because of their high cholesterol content, but shrimp are a low-fat protein source rich in nutrients. So what's the real story on shrimp, and are they good for us or not? The overall consensus is that shrimp can be part of a healthy diet and are a good way to consume more seafood. Shrimp are very low in calories but high in protein—making them a great option if you're watching your caloric intake. In fact, a 3-ounce serving of cooked shrimp has approximately 85 calories and 18 grams of protein. Shrimp are also a great source of B_{12}, iron, zinc, iodine, and selenium. But, yes, that 3-ounce serving also has about 166mg of cholesterol—a little more than half of the daily recommended limit of 300mg. However, recent research has suggested that the cholesterol in shrimp and other seafood may not have the same harmful effect on our bodies that the cholesterol in meat and cheese has. This combined with all the positive nutrition benefits has helped redeem shrimp's name. Recipes often call for shrimp to be peeled and deveined. Except for the largest shrimp, however, there's neither danger nor distaste in leaving the thin black line (vein) right where it is, but many people prefer to take it out. If you're butterflying shrimp, deveining occurs anyway.

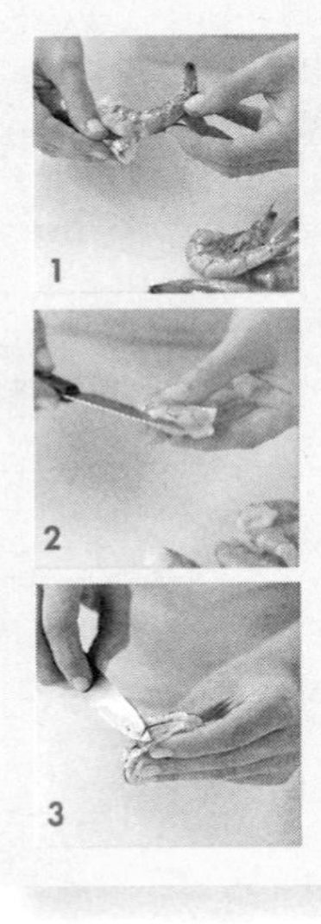

1. Peel the shell off the shrimp.
2. Cut a shallow slit along the back using a sharp paring knife.
3. Remove the dark vein using a sharp knife or deveining tool. Rinse under cold water, and drain.

THAI SHRIMP WITH PAN SLAW

PointsPlus value per serving: 3

HANDS-ON TIME: 14 min. ■ **TOTAL TIME:** 14 min.

Preshredded coleslaw makes this one-dish meal with exotic flavor quick and easy to prepare.

1½ teaspoons olive oil
1 tablespoon fresh minced garlic
1 tablespoon minced jalapeño pepper
5 tablespoons rice wine vinegar, divided
1 tablespoon fish sauce
1 tablespoon fresh lime juice
1 teaspoon sugar, divided
½ teaspoon Sriracha (hot chile sauce)
32 peeled and deveined medium shrimp (about 1 pound)
1 (10-ounce) package angel hair coleslaw
Cooking spray

1. Heat a large nonstick skillet over medium-high heat. Add oil to pan; swirl to coat. Add garlic and jalapeño to pan; sauté 1 minute. Stir in 1 tablespoon vinegar, fish sauce, lime juice, ½ teaspoon sugar, and Sriracha. Add shrimp; sauté 6 minutes or until shrimp are done. Remove shrimp mixture from pan; set aside, and keep warm.
2. Return pan to heat. Add slaw, and coat with cooking spray. Toss well; coat slaw again with cooking spray. Stir-fry over medium-high heat 4 minutes. Stir in ¼ cup vinegar and ½ teaspoon sugar.
3. Divide slaw evenly among 4 plates; top with shrimp and sauce. YIELD: 4 SERVINGS (SERVING SIZE: ABOUT ⅔ CUP SLAW, 8 SHRIMP, AND ABOUT 1 TABLESPOON SAUCE).

PER SERVING: Calories 127; Fat 2.9g (sat 0.4g, mono 1.3g, poly 0.3g); Protein 16.7g; Carb 7.7g; Fiber 1.8g; Chol 143mg; Iron 0.3mg; Sodium 554mg; Calc 101mg

GRILLED BEEF FILETS WITH TOMATO-OLIVE TOPPING

PointsPlus value per serving: 8

HANDS-ON TIME: 11 min. ■ **TOTAL TIME:** 11 min.

Spoon briny olives, sweet cherry tomatoes, and tangy goat cheese over grilled beef filets for a quick, high-flavor entrée.

2 tablespoons olive oil, divided
2 teaspoons Mediterranean herb seasoning
4 (4-ounce) beef tenderloin steaks, trimmed (about 1 inch thick)
Cooking spray
1 cup halved cherry tomatoes
2 tablespoons chopped fresh basil
2 tablespoons chopped pitted kalamata olives
1 teaspoon balsamic vinegar
¼ teaspoon salt
¼ teaspoon freshly ground black pepper
2 ounces crumbled goat cheese (about ½ cup)

1. Preheat grill to medium-high heat.
2. Combine 1 tablespoon oil and herb seasoning. Rub evenly on both sides of steaks. Place steaks on grill rack coated with cooking spray. Grill 3 minutes on each side or until desired degree of doneness.
3. While steaks cook, combine 1 tablespoon oil, tomatoes, and next 5 ingredients (through black pepper) in a medium bowl. Top steaks evenly with tomato mixture. Sprinkle evenly with cheese. YIELD: 4 SERVINGS (SERVING SIZE: 1 STEAK, ¼ CUP TOMATO TOPPING, AND 2 TABLESPOONS CHEESE).

PER SERVING: Calories 322; Fat 18.5g (sat 6g, mono 9.5g, poly 1.2g); Protein 34.9g; Carb 2.3g; Fiber 0.5g; Chol 94mg; Iron 2.5mg; Sodium 471mg; Calc 51mg

BEEF FILETS WITH CARAMEL BRANDY-ROSEMARY SAUCE

PointsPlus value per serving: 5

HANDS-ON TIME: 14 min. ■ **TOTAL TIME:** 14 min.

Reducing the broth mixture creates a thick, velvety sauce worthy of a special dinner.

4 (4-ounce) beef tenderloin steaks, trimmed (about 1 inch thick)
1 teaspoon freshly ground black pepper
½ teaspoon salt
Cooking spray
2 tablespoons finely chopped shallots
1½ teaspoons turbinado sugar
2 tablespoons cognac
½ cup fat-free, lower-sodium beef broth
½ cup fat-free half-and-half
1 teaspoon chopped fresh rosemary

1. Heat a large nonstick skillet over medium-high heat. Sprinkle steaks with pepper and salt; coat steaks with cooking spray. Add steaks to pan; cook 3 minutes on each side or until desired degree of doneness. Transfer steaks to a serving platter; keep warm.
2. Add shallots and sugar to pan; sauté 30 seconds or until shallots are tender. Add cognac; cook 20 seconds. Add broth; cook 4 minutes or until liquid is reduced by half. Add half-and-half and rosemary; simmer 3 minutes or until slightly thick. Spoon sauce evenly over steaks. YIELD: 4 SERVINGS (SERVING SIZE: 1 STEAK AND 2 TABLESPOONS SAUCE).

PER SERVING: Calories 196; Fat 5.6g (sat 2.1g, mono 2.2g, poly 0.2g); Protein 25.4g; Carb 5.5g; Fiber 0.3g; Chol 66mg; Iron 1.6mg; Sodium 426mg; Calc 62mg

FLANK STEAK WITH RED ONION–SHERRY MARMALADE

PointsPlus value per serving: 7 *(pictured on page 12)*

HANDS-ON TIME: 15 min. ■ **TOTAL TIME:** 15 min.

Sweet and tangy onion marmalade complements the flavor of dry-rubbed flank steak. Serve with brown rice and steamed or roasted green beans.

1 tablespoon brown sugar
2 teaspoons dried rosemary, crushed
1 teaspoon dry mustard
1 teaspoon garlic powder
½ teaspoon ground red pepper
½ teaspoon salt
1 (1-pound) flank steak, trimmed
Cooking spray
1½ tablespoons canola oil
3 tablespoons granulated sugar
1 large red onion, sliced
¼ cup sherry vinegar
¼ cup water
⅜ teaspoon crushed red pepper
Chopped fresh parsley (optional)

1. Preheat oven to 450°.
2. Combine first 6 ingredients in a small bowl; rub over both sides of steak. Heat a large ovenproof skillet over medium-high heat. Coat pan with cooking spray. Add steak; cook 2 minutes on each side or until browned. Place skillet in oven. Bake at 450° for 4 to 5 minutes or until desired degree of doneness. Let stand 5 minutes. Cut steak diagonally across grain into thin slices.
3. While steak cooks, heat a large nonstick skillet over medium-high heat. Add oil to pan; swirl to coat. Add granulated sugar and onion; cook 6 minutes or until onion is tender and lightly browned, stirring frequently. Stir in vinegar, ¼ cup water, and red pepper; bring to a boil. Cook 3 minutes, and remove from heat. Serve steak slices with onion marmalade. Garnish with parsley, if desired. **YIELD: 4 SERVINGS (SERVING SIZE: 3 OUNCES STEAK AND ABOUT ⅓ CUP ONION MARMALADE).**

PER SERVING: Calories 279; Fat 11.9g (sat 2.8g, mono 5.6g, poly 1.7g); Protein 25.2g; Carb 17.4g; Fiber 1.2g; Chol 70mg; Iron 2.5mg; Sodium 361mg; Calc 51mg

BEEF CHOW MEIN

PointsPlus value per serving: 6 *(pictured on page 56)*

HANDS-ON TIME: 15 min ■ **TOTAL TIME:** 15 min.

Make sure to purchase the chow mein noodles in a plastic wrapper that have to be cooked and not the crunchy, ready-to-eat noodles in a canister.

1 cup matchstick-cut carrots
1 cup sugar snap peas, trimmed
1 (6-ounce) package chow mein or Chinese curly noodles
½ pound flank steak, trimmed
1 tablespoon dark sesame oil, divided
2 tablespoons lower-sodium soy sauce, divided
¾ cup fat-free, lower-sodium beef broth
2 tablespoons oyster sauce
¼ teaspoon freshly ground black pepper
1 cup presliced mushrooms
2 teaspoons bottled ground fresh ginger

1. Cook carrots, sugar snap peas, and noodles in boiling water 3 minutes; drain.
2. Cut steak diagonally across grain into thin slices. Heat a large nonstick skillet over medium-high heat. Add 2 teaspoons oil to pan; swirl to coat. Add beef to pan; stir-fry 3 minutes or until done. Stir in 1 tablespoon soy sauce, scraping pan to loosen browned bits. Remove beef mixture from pan; keep warm.
3. Combine 1 tablespoon soy sauce, broth, oyster sauce, and pepper in a small bowl, stirring with a whisk. Add 1 teaspoon oil to pan; swirl to coat. Add mushrooms and ginger; stir-fry 2 minutes. Add broth mixture; cook 1 minute. Add noodle mixture and beef; cook 1 minute or until thoroughly heated. **YIELD: 5 SERVINGS (SERVING SIZE: 1 CUP).**

PER SERVING: Calories 236; Fat 6g (sat 1.4g, mono 2.3g, poly 1.7g); Protein 16.4g; Carb 28.3g; Fiber 2.9g; Chol 29mg; Iron 2.2mg; Sodium 743mg; Calc 27mg

FLANK STEAK

Flank steak is a lean, flavorful cut of beef that often gets overlooked. It's a flat cut of meat good for marinating and is often cut against the grain and grilled, baked, broiled, or sautéed for fajitas or stir-fries. Flank steak is also one of the less expensive cuts of red meat making it an economical choice when feeding a crowd.

THAI BEEF IN BROWN SAUCE

PointsPlus value per serving: 7 *(pictured on page 55)*

HANDS-ON TIME: 11 min. ▪ **TOTAL TIME:** 11 min.

Fish sauce adds a unique depth of flavor to this dish. Make sure to microwave broccoli for only 2 minutes and not the full length listed on the package. It will finish cooking when added to the skillet. Serve over hot cooked rice.

1 (12-ounce) bag steam-in-the-bag fresh frozen broccoli florets
1 pound flank steak, trimmed
1 tablespoon cornstarch
4 teaspoons canola oil
1 cup red bell pepper strips
2 teaspoons bottled minced garlic
1 teaspoon bottled ground fresh ginger
½ cup light coconut milk
2 tablespoons Sriracha (hot chile sauce)
1 tablespoon fish sauce
1 tablespoon fresh lime juice

1. Cut slits in broccoli bag; steam broccoli in microwave at HIGH 2 minutes.
2. Cut steak diagonally across grain into thin slices. Combine beef and cornstarch in a medium bowl, tossing to coat.
3. Heat a large nonstick skillet over medium-high heat. Add oil to pan; swirl to coat. Add beef to pan; sauté 3 minutes. Push beef to one side of pan. Add bell pepper, garlic, and ginger; sauté 2 minutes. Stir in cooked broccoli, coconut milk, and remaining ingredients; cook 1 minute or until thoroughly heated, stirring frequently. **YIELD: 4 SERVINGS (SERVING SIZE: ABOUT 1¼ CUPS).**

PER SERVING: Calories 278; Fat 13.2g (sat 4.4g, mono 5.3g, poly 1.7g); Protein 28.1g; Carb 11.9g; Fiber 3.4g; Chol 70mg; Iron 2.8mg; Sodium 597mg; Calc 76mg

TEX-MEX HAMBURGER STEAKS

PointsPlus value per serving: 8

HANDS-ON TIME: 12 min. ▪ **TOTAL TIME:** 22 min.

Serve these easy hamburger steaks with brown rice to soak up the flavorful sauce. A serving of steak and sauce without rice has a *PointsPlus* value of 5.

1 pound ground sirloin
¾ teaspoon salt-free Southwest chipotle seasoning, divided
⅛ teaspoon salt
1 (16-ounce) jar black bean and corn salsa
½ cup no-salt-added tomato sauce
1 (8.8-ounce) pouch microwaveable precooked whole-grain brown rice
2 tablespoons chopped fresh cilantro (optional)

1. Combine beef, ½ teaspoon seasoning, and salt in a medium bowl. Using moist hands, shape beef mixture into 4 (½-inch thick) patties.
2. Cook patties in a large nonstick skillet over medium-high heat 2 minutes on each side or just until browned. Combine salsa, tomato sauce, and ¼ teaspoon seasoning; pour over patties. Bring to a boil; cover, reduce heat, and simmer 10 minutes or just until patties are no longer pink in center (do not overcook).
3. While patties cook, heat rice according to package directions. Serve patties and sauce over rice, and garnish with cilantro, if desired. **YIELD: 4 SERVINGS (SERVING SIZE: 1 PATTY, ABOUT ½ CUP RICE, AND ABOUT ½ CUP SAUCE).**

PER SERVING: Calories 320; Fat 6.3g (sat 2.5g, mono 2g, poly 1g); Protein 27.9g; Carb 34g; Fiber 3.9g; Chol 60mg; Iron 3.8mg; Sodium 649mg; Calc 0mg

CILANTRO

Cilantro is a leafy green herb typically used in Mexican and Indian dishes that complements spicier flavors well. It comes from the leaves of the coriander plant (and is sometimes referred to as coriander), and it has a unique flavor that people tend to love or hate. Cilantro wilts quickly, so purchase a bunch that has perky green stems and leaves and a fragrant aroma. Store in a vase of water as you would flowers, place in the refrigerator, and cover the leaves with a plastic bag until ready to use.

SKILLET ENCHILADA CASSEROLE

PointsPlus value per serving: 9

HANDS-ON TIME: 15 min. ▪ **TOTAL TIME:** 15 min.

Instead of wrapping tortillas around seasoned meat, the tortillas are torn into pieces and combined with traditional enchilada fillings for this easy Tex-Mex skillet supper.

1 pound ground sirloin
½ cup refrigerated prechopped onion
1 cup refrigerated fresh salsa
6 ounces reduced-fat shredded sharp cheddar cheese (about 1½ cups), divided
½ cup light sour cream
2 tablespoons 25%-less-sodium taco seasoning
1 (10.75-ounce) can 30% reduced-sodium 98% fat-free cream of mushroom soup
8 (6-inch) corn tortillas, torn into 1-inch pieces
2 cups shredded iceberg lettuce
Additional fresh salsa (optional)

1. Heat a large nonstick skillet over medium-high heat. Add beef and onion to pan; cook 4 minutes or until beef is browned, stirring to crumble. Drain and return beef mixture to pan.
2. Combine salsa, 2 ounces cheese, sour cream, taco seasoning, and soup, stirring well. Add to beef mixture in pan; stir in tortilla pieces. Bring to a boil, stirring frequently; reduce heat, and simmer 6 minutes, stirring occasionally. Top with 4 ounces cheese; cook 2 minutes or until cheese melts. Top each serving with lettuce and additional salsa, if desired. YIELD: 6 SERVINGS (SERVING SIZE: ABOUT 1 CUP MEAT MIXTURE AND ⅓ CUP LETTUCE).

PER SERVING: Calories 347; Fat 15g (sat 6.8g, mono 4.5g, poly 1.8g); Protein 24.3g; Carb 26g; Fiber 2.3g; Chol 66mg; Iron 1.9mg; Sodium 701mg; Calc 495mg

LINGUINE WITH SPICY BEEF AND OLIVES

PointsPlus value per serving: 8 *(pictured on page 13)*

HANDS-ON TIME: 15 min. ▪ **TOTAL TIME:** 15 min.

Any leftover dry red wine will work in this dish, and it adds an extra depth of Italian-inspired flavor. Decrease the crushed red pepper if you'd like less heat.

8 ounces uncooked linguine
1 tablespoon olive oil
1½ cups refrigerated prechopped onion
3 garlic cloves, minced
1 teaspoon dried oregano
½ teaspoon crushed red pepper
¼ teaspoon salt
8 ounces ground sirloin
1⅔ cups lower-sodium marinara sauce
⅓ cup pimiento-stuffed olives, sliced
¼ cup dry red wine
1 tablespoon capers, drained
Chopped fresh parsley (optional)

1. Cook pasta according to package directions, omitting salt and fat; drain.
2. While pasta cooks, heat a large skillet over medium-high heat. Add oil to pan; swirl to coat. Add onion to pan; sauté 2 minutes or until tender. Add garlic, and sauté 1 minute. Stir in oregano, pepper, and salt. Add beef; cook 5 minutes or until beef is browned, stirring to crumble. Stir in marinara sauce and next 3 ingredients (through capers); bring to a boil. Reduce heat; simmer 4 to 5 minutes, stirring occasionally.
3. Add hot linguine to sauce mixture; toss to coat. Sprinkle with parsley, if desired. YIELD: 6 SERVINGS (SERVING SIZE: ABOUT ¾ CUP).

PER SERVING: Calories 298; Fat 9.4g (sat 1.8g, mono 5.2g, poly 1.6g); Protein 13.5g; Carb 38.5g; Fiber 3.2g; Chol 18mg; Iron 3.2mg; Sodium 485mg; Calc 34mg

PORK MEDALLIONS WITH CHILE-PLUM SAUCE

PointsPlus value per serving: 5

HANDS-ON TIME: 15 min. ▪ **TOTAL TIME:** 15 min.

Good-quality plum preserves produce the best results. Pair these medallions with steamed asparagus and a side of fresh fruit.

⅓ cup plum preserves
2 tablespoons fresh lime juice
2 teaspoons lower-sodium soy sauce
1½ teaspoons Thai chili garlic paste
1 (1 pound) pork tenderloin, trimmed
¼ teaspoon salt
Cooking spray
2 tablespoons chopped fresh cilantro (optional)

1. Combine first 4 ingredients in a small bowl. Cut pork crosswise into 12 equal slices. Flatten pork slices slightly with palm of hand. Sprinkle evenly with salt.
2. Heat a large nonstick skillet over medium-high heat. Coat pan with cooking spray. Place pork slices in pan. Cook 2 to 3 minutes on each side or until lightly browned. Pour preserves mixture over pork slices. Cook 1 minute, turning pork to glaze. Remove from heat. Serve sauce over pork. Garnish with cilantro, if desired. **YIELD: 4 SERVINGS (SERVING SIZE: 3 PORK SLICES AND ¼ CUP SAUCE).**

PER SERVING: Calories 206; Fat 4g (sat 1.3g, mono 1.5g, poly 0.6g); Protein 23.6g; Carb 18.2g; Fiber 0g; Chol 74mg; Iron 1.1mg; Sodium 351mg; Calc 8mg

LEAN PORK CUTS

Skinless chicken breasts are often considered the leanest option when choosing meat and poultry cuts. But what many don't know is that some cuts of pork are as lean—or leaner—than chicken. Pork tenderloin is the leanest pork option, with a total calorie and fat content that is essentially the same as that of a skinless chicken breast. Other lean pork cuts are loin chops, loin roast, and Canadian bacon. For quick cooking on the stove top, select small thin cuts, or cut tenderloins into medallions. Larger cuts like roasts or whole tenderloins take longer and are best baked or grilled. Fresh pork can be kept in the refrigerator for two to four days. It can also be frozen for up to six months when wrapped well.

PORK MEDALLIONS WITH ROSEMARY PAN SAUCE

PointsPlus value per serving: 5

HANDS-ON TIME: 14 min. ▪ **TOTAL TIME:** 14 min.

White wine and fresh rosemary dress up ordinary pan gravy. Serve with roasted potato wedges and steamed broccoli.

1 (1-pound) pork tenderloin, trimmed
¾ teaspoon freshly ground black pepper, divided
¼ teaspoon salt, divided
1 teaspoon canola oil
1 tablespoon butter
2 garlic cloves, minced
1 tablespoon all-purpose flour
½ cup fat-free, lower-sodium chicken broth
½ cup dry white wine
1 teaspoon chopped fresh rosemary

1. Cut pork crosswise into 12 equal slices. Flatten pork slices slightly with palm of hand; sprinkle with ¼ teaspoon pepper and ⅛ teaspoon salt.
2. Heat a large nonstick skillet over medium-high heat. Add oil to pan; swirl to coat. Add pork slices; cook 3 minutes on each side or until pork is done. Remove pork from pan; set aside, and keep warm.
3. Melt butter in pan over medium heat. Add garlic; sauté 30 seconds. Add flour; cook 30 seconds, stirring constantly. Gradually add chicken broth and wine, stirring constantly with a whisk. Bring to a boil; reduce heat, and cook 2 minutes or until slightly thickened, stirring constantly. Remove from heat. Stir in ½ teaspoon pepper, ⅛ teaspoon salt, and rosemary. Serve sauce over pork. **YIELD: 4 SERVINGS (SERVING SIZE: 3 PORK SLICES AND 2 TABLESPOONS SAUCE).**

PER SERVING: Calories 204; Fat 8.1g (sat 3.3g, mono 3g, poly 1.1g); Protein 24.2g; Carb 3.1g; Fiber 0.2g; Chol 81mg; Iron 1.3mg; Sodium 305mg; Calc 15mg

CUBAN PORK TENDERLOIN WITH BLACK BEAN SALSA

PointsPlus value per serving: 9

HANDS-ON TIME: 12 min. ■ **TOTAL TIME:** 12 min.

To complete the meal, pair with yellow saffron rice, and serve with a green salad with lemony vinaigrette.

1 (1-pound) pork tenderloin, trimmed
2½ teaspoons ground cumin, divided
1 teaspoon freshly ground black pepper, divided
1 teaspoon dried oregano, divided
½ teaspoon salt, divided
2 tablespoons canola oil
1 cup diced peeled avocado
1 cup orange sections
¼ cup chopped fresh cilantro
2 tablespoons fresh orange juice
1 (15-ounce) can reduced-sodium black beans, rinsed and drained
1 garlic clove, minced
Cilantro leaves (optional)

1. Cut pork crosswise into 8 pieces. Combine 2 teaspoons cumin, ½ teaspoon pepper, ½ teaspoon oregano, and ¼ teaspoon salt; sprinkle over pork slices.
2. Heat a large nonstick skillet over medium-high heat. Add oil to pan; swirl to coat. Add pork to pan; cook 3 minutes on each side or until pork is done.
3. While pork cooks, combine avocado and next 5 ingredients (through garlic) in a medium bowl. Add ½ teaspoon cumin, ½ teaspoon pepper, ½ teaspoon oregano, and ¼ teaspoon salt; toss well. Serve pork with salsa; sprinkle with cilantro leaves, if desired. **YIELD: 4 SERVINGS (SERVING SIZE: 2 PORK SLICES AND ¾ CUP SALSA).**

PER SERVING: Calories 349; Fat 17g (sat 2.6g, mono 9.6g, poly 3.3g); Protein 28.9g; Carb 23.4g; Fiber 7.6g; Chol 74mg; Iron 3.4mg; Sodium 441mg; Calc 81mg

ASIAN PORK MEDALLIONS WITH SPICY BROCCOLI SLAW

PointsPlus value per serving: 6 *(pictured on page 60)*

HANDS-ON TIME: 11 min. ■ **TOTAL TIME:** 11 min.

This is an easy weeknight dinner that's ideal for lunch the next day. If you'd like an extra layer of flavor in the slaw, add a generous sprinkling of chopped fresh cilantro. Serve with brown rice to round out the meal.

1 (1-pound) pork tenderloin, trimmed
½ teaspoon garlic powder
½ teaspoon ground ginger
¼ teaspoon freshly ground black pepper
4 teaspoons dark sesame oil, divided
2 tablespoons fresh lime juice
1 tablespoon bottled ground fresh ginger
1 tablespoon lower-sodium soy sauce
1 tablespoon honey
2 teaspoons Sriracha (hot chile sauce)
1 (12-ounce) package broccoli coleslaw
Cilantro leaves (optional)

1. Cut pork crosswise into 12 (½-inch-thick) slices. Combine garlic powder, ½ teaspoon ginger, and pepper in a small bowl; sprinkle pork with spice mixture.
2. Heat a medium skillet over medium-high heat. Add 2 teaspoons sesame oil to pan; swirl to coat. Add pork to pan; cook 3 minutes on each side or until pork is done.
3. While pork cooks, combine 2 teaspoons sesame oil, lime juice, and next 4 ingredients (through Sriracha), stirring well with a whisk. Add broccoli coleslaw; toss well. Top pork with slaw; sprinkle with cilantro, if desired. **YIELD: 4 SERVINGS (SERVING SIZE: 3 PORK SLICES AND 1 CUP SLAW).**

PER SERVING: Calories 228; Fat 8.7g (sat 2g, mono 3.5g, poly 2.7g); Protein 25.8g; Carb 11.2g; Fiber 2.1g; Chol 74mg; Iron 1.9mg; Sodium 279mg; Calc 49mg

SRIRACHA

Native to Thailand, Sriracha is a thick hot sauce made from chile peppers, vinegar, garlic, sugar, and salt. Sriracha is different from other hot sauces in that it adds heat as well as flavor, which makes it a popular ingredient, condiment, and dipping sauce in cuisines around the world. If you're new to Sriracha, start small and add more as needed.

PARMESAN PORK CHOPS

PointsPlus value per serving: 7 *(pictured on page 56)*

HANDS-ON TIME: 14 min. ■ **TOTAL TIME:** 14 min.

A crisp seasoned coating, marinara sauce, and pork chops make for a quick, skillet-friendly take on chicken Parmesan. Serve with steamed green beans.

8 (2-ounce) boneless center-cut loin pork chops (about ¼ inch thick)
¼ teaspoon freshly ground black pepper
¾ cup whole-wheat panko (Japanese breadcrumbs)
1 ounce grated fresh Parmesan cheese (about ¼ cup)
1 tablespoon self-rising yellow cornmeal mix
¼ teaspoon dried Italian seasoning
1 large egg, lightly beaten
2 teaspoons Dijon mustard
Cooking spray
4 teaspoons canola oil, divided
½ cup lower-sodium marinara sauce
Chopped fresh flat-leaf parsley (optional)

1. Sprinkle both sides of pork with pepper. Combine panko and next 3 ingredients (through Italian seasoning) in a shallow dish. Combine egg and mustard in another shallow dish, stirring well with a whisk. Dip pork in egg mixture; dredge in panko mixture, pressing to adhere. Discard remaining panko mixture. Coat pork with cooking spray.
2. Heat a large nonstick skillet over medium-high heat. Add 2 teaspoons oil to pan; swirl to coat. Add half of pork to pan; cook 2 to 3 minutes on each side or until browned. Repeat procedure with remaining oil and pork.
3. While pork cooks, place marinara sauce in a 2-cup glass measure. Cover with heavy-duty plastic wrap, and microwave at HIGH 2 minutes or until thoroughly heated. Spoon marinara sauce over pork, and sprinkle with parsley, if desired. **YIELD: 4 SERVINGS (SERVING SIZE: 2 PORK CHOPS AND 2 TABLESPOONS MARINARA SAUCE).**

PER SERVING: Calories 277; Fat 13.9g (sat 3.1g, mono 6.5g, poly 2.3g); Protein 24.7g; Carb 12.6g; Fiber 1.9g; Chol 108mg; Iron 1.6mg; Sodium 327mg; Calc 115mg

PORK CUTLETS WITH ALMOND BUTTER SAUCE

PointsPlus value per serving: 7

HANDS-ON TIME: 15 min. ■ **TOTAL TIME:** 15 min.

Look for boneless pork loin chops that are labeled "thin sliced" for this recipe. If you can't find them, thicker chops will work but be sure to check for doneness before removing them from the heat.

⅓ cup sliced almonds
Butter-flavored cooking spray
8 (2-ounce) boneless center-cut loin pork chops
¼ teaspoon salt
¼ teaspoon freshly ground black pepper
3 tablespoons all-purpose flour
1 tablespoon canola oil, divided
½ cup fat-free, lower-sodium chicken broth
3 tablespoons low-sugar orange marmalade
¼ teaspoon dried thyme
1 tablespoon butter

1. Place almonds in a small skillet; coat nuts with cooking spray. Cook over medium heat 3 minutes or until lightly browned. Remove from pan; set aside.
2. Sprinkle both sides of pork with salt and pepper; dredge in flour. Heat a large nonstick skillet over medium-high heat. Add 1½ teaspoons oil to pan; swirl to coat. Add half of pork; cook 2 minutes on each side or until lightly browned. Remove from pan; keep warm. Repeat procedure with remaining oil and pork.
3. Add chicken broth to pan, scraping pan to loosen browned bits. Add orange marmalade and thyme; cook 1 minute or until marmalade melts and mixture is slightly thick, stirring constantly. Stir in butter and almonds. Spoon sauce over pork. **YIELD: 4 SERVINGS (SERVING SIZE: 2 PORK CHOPS AND 2 TABLESPOONS SAUCE).**

PER SERVING: Calories 258; Fat 15.2g (sat 3.8g, mono 7.1g, poly 2.6g); Protein 20.7g; Carb 9.4g; Fiber 1.1g; Chol 65mg; Iron 1.1mg; Sodium 283mg; Calc 39mg

HERBED PORK CHOPS

PointsPlus value per serving: 5

HANDS-ON TIME: 20 min. ■ **TOTAL TIME:** 20 min.

We used 2 teaspoons each of fresh rosemary, thyme, and oregano, but feel free to use any combination of fresh herbs that you have on hand.

4 (6-ounce) bone-in center-cut pork chops (about ½ inch thick)
Cooking spray
1 tablespoon olive oil
2 tablespoons chopped fresh herbs (such as rosemary, thyme, and oregano)
¼ teaspoon salt
¼ teaspoon freshly ground black pepper
2 garlic cloves, minced
1½ teaspoons cornstarch
½ cup water

1. Coat pork with cooking spray. Combine oil and next 4 ingredients (through garlic), and rub over pork.
2. Heat a large nonstick skillet over medium-high heat. Coat pan with cooking spray. Add pork to pan; cook 2 minutes on each side. Remove pork from pan, reserving drippings in pan.
3. Combine cornstarch and ½ cup water in a small bowl, stirring until smooth. Stir cornstarch mixture into drippings in pan, scraping pan to loosen browned bits. Cook 1 minute, stirring constantly. Return pork chops to pan. Cover and cook over medium heat 3 to 5 minutes or until pork is done. Serve sauce over pork. **YIELD: 4 SERVINGS (SERVING SIZE: 1 PORK CHOP AND 1 TABLESPOON SAUCE).**

PER SERVING: Calories 188; Fat 9.6g (sat 2.3g, mono 4.7g, poly 1.1g); Protein 22.7g; Carb 1.5g; Fiber 0.2g; Chol 71mg; Iron 0.8mg; Sodium 195mg; Calc 28mg

HERBED LAMB CHOPS

PointsPlus value per serving: 6

HANDS-ON TIME: 15 min. ■ **TOTAL TIME:** 15 min.

Toasting whole spices in a dry skillet brings out their essential oils and adds a depth of fragrance to the dish. Once toasted, the spices are crushed and mixed with herbs and olive oil to form a wet rub.

2 teaspoons coriander seeds
2 teaspoons fennel seeds
1 teaspoon mustard seeds
2 teaspoons grated fresh lemon rind
2 teaspoons chopped fresh thyme leaves
1 teaspoon kosher salt
1 teaspoon coarsely ground black pepper
5 teaspoons olive oil
5 garlic cloves, minced
8 (4-ounce) lamb loin chops, trimmed
Cooking spray

1. Preheat broiler.
2. Cook coriander, fennel, and mustard seeds in a medium saucepan over medium heat 1 minute or until toasted. Let cool slightly, and place in a small heavy-duty zip-top plastic bag; coarsely crush seeds (using a meat mallet or small heavy skillet).
3. Combine crushed seeds, lemon rind, and next 5 ingredients (through garlic) in a bowl. Rub spice mixture evenly over both sides of lamb. Arrange lamb in a single layer on a broiler pan coated with cooking spray; broil 4 minutes on each side or until desired degree of doneness. **YIELD: 4 SERVINGS (SERVING SIZE: 2 LAMB CHOPS).**

PER SERVING: Calories 253; Fat 14.5g (sat 3.8g, mono 8.1g, poly 1.2g); Protein 26.6g; Carb 3.1g; Fiber 1.2g; Chol 82mg; Iron 2.3mg; Sodium 555mg; Calc 49mg

OVENPROOF SKILLETS

Oven-Fried Chicken has a crisp flaky coating because it is cooked on the stove top and then the skillet is placed in the oven to continue cooking at high heat. Only skillets that are oven-safe or ovenproof should be used in conventional ovens. If you aren't sure if your skillet is oven-safe, see this list to help you decide.

- Does the skillet have a plastic handle or other plastic on it? If so, the skillet is not oven-safe because the plastic will melt at high temperatures.
- What is the skillet made of? Cast iron, stainless steel, aluminum, and ceramic are all safe materials. Enamel is not an oven-safe material.
- Does the skillet have a nonstick coating? If so, it is not oven-safe. These coatings can melt at high temperatures.
- Does the skillet have a marking on the bottom indicating it is oven-safe? Most skillets manufactured today will indicate that they are safe to go in the oven.

OVEN-FRIED CHICKEN

PointsPlus value per serving: 7

HANDS-ON TIME: 10 min. ■ **TOTAL TIME:** 35 min.

Cornflake crumbs baked at a high temperature yield a crunchy coating for this classic family favorite.

1 cup nonfat buttermilk
4 (8-ounce) skinless, bone-in chicken breast halves
½ cup cornflake crumbs
½ cup all-purpose flour
½ teaspoon salt
¼ teaspoon ground red pepper
1 tablespoon canola oil

1. Preheat oven to 425°.
2. Place buttermilk in a large heavy-duty zip-top plastic bag. Add chicken to bag. Seal bag, turning to coat chicken. Combine cornflake crumbs and next 3 ingredients (through red pepper) in a second large heavy-duty zip-top plastic bag. Remove chicken from buttermilk, 1 piece at a time; drain excess, and add, 1 piece at a time, to flour mixture, shaking bag to coat chicken. Remove chicken from bag, shaking off excess flour mixture.
3. Heat a 12-inch ovenproof skillet over medium-high heat. Add oil to pan; swirl to coat. Add chicken to pan, meaty side down. Cook 4 minutes or until golden brown. Turn chicken over. Place pan in oven. Bake at 425° for 25 minutes or until done. **YIELD: 4 SERVINGS (SERVING SIZE: 1 CHICKEN BREAST HALF).**

PER SERVING: Calories 307; Fat 8.3g (sat 1.3g, mono 3.6g, poly 1.8g); Protein 42g; Carb 13.4g; Fiber 0.4g; Chol 116mg; Iron 1.8mg; Sodium 482mg; Calc 11mg

GRILLED CIDER CHICKEN

PointsPlus value per serving: 6

HANDS-ON TIME: 18 min. ■ **TOTAL TIME:** 38 min.

Chicken breast halves will cook more quickly and evenly if they're a uniform thickness. You can pound the chicken while the cider simmers.

1½ cups apple cider
1 tablespoon butter
2 teaspoons cider vinegar
4 (6-ounce) skinless, boneless chicken breast halves
½ teaspoon salt
¼ teaspoon freshly ground black pepper
Cooking spray
1½ teaspoons chopped fresh rosemary

1. Preheat grill to medium-high heat.
2. Place apple cider in a small saucepan; bring to a boil. Reduce heat, and simmer 25 minutes or until reduced to ⅓ cup. Stir in butter and cider vinegar.
3. Sprinkle chicken with salt and pepper. Brush chicken with cider mixture. Place chicken on grill rack coated with cooking spray; grill 5 minutes on each side or until done, basting frequently with cider mixture. Sprinkle with rosemary. **YIELD: 4 SERVINGS (SERVING SIZE: 1 CHICKEN BREAST HALF).**

PER SERVING: Calories 265; Fat 7.3g (sat 2.8g, mono 2g, poly 0.8g); Protein 36.2g; Carb 11.4g; Fiber 0.1g; Chol 117mg; Iron 0.7mg; Sodium 527mg; Calc 11mg

POUNDING CHICKEN BREASTS

Place chicken breast halves between two sheets of heavy-duty plastic wrap, and pound with a meat mallet or small heavy skillet to an even thickness.

COCONUT-CURRY CHICKEN

PointsPlus value per serving: 8

HANDS-ON TIME: 12 min. ■ **TOTAL TIME:** 37 min.

Substitute unsweetened coconut if you prefer less sweetness in this Thai-inspired entrée.

¾ cup flaked sweetened coconut
2 teaspoons curry powder
¼ cup apricot spreadable fruit, melted
⅛ teaspoon ground red pepper
4 (6-ounce) skinless, boneless chicken breast halves
¼ teaspoon salt
Cooking spray

1. Preheat oven to 350°.
2. Place coconut in a shallow dish. Sprinkle with curry powder, tossing to coat. Combine spreadable fruit and ground red pepper; brush evenly over chicken. Sprinkle chicken evenly with salt. Dredge chicken in coconut mixture. Place chicken breast halves, 2 inches apart, in a 13 x 9–inch glass or ceramic baking dish coated with cooking spray. Bake at 350° for 25 minutes or until done. **YIELD: 4 SERVINGS (SERVING SIZE: 1 CHICKEN BREAST HALF).**

PER SERVING: Calories 310; Fat 9g (sat 5.2g, mono 1.6g, poly 0.7g); Protein 36.7g; Carb 18.9g; Fiber 1.9g; Chol 109mg; Iron 1.2mg; Sodium 391mg; Calc 15mg

CHICKEN WITH TOMATOES AND OLIVES

PointsPlus value per serving: 7

HANDS-ON TIME: 16 min. ■ **TOTAL TIME:** 16 min.

Canned tomatoes can be quite high in sodium, so opt for no-salt-added tomatoes, particularly when you're adding them to a dish with other flavorful ingredients.

2 tablespoons olive oil
6 (6-ounce) skinless, boneless chicken breast halves
¼ cup dry white wine
½ cup chopped pitted kalamata olives (29 olives)
1 teaspoon chopped fresh oregano
1 (14.5-ounce) can no-salt-added diced tomatoes, undrained

1. Heat a large skillet over medium-high heat. Add olive oil to pan; swirl to coat. Add chicken to pan; cook 3 minutes on each side or until browned. Add white wine to pan; cook 30 seconds. Cover and cook 2 minutes. Add olives, oregano, and tomatoes. Cover and cook 2 minutes. Uncover and cook 5 minutes or until chicken is done and mixture is slightly thick. **YIELD: 6 SERVINGS (SERVING SIZE: 1 CHICKEN BREAST HALF AND ABOUT ¼ CUP SAUCE).**

PER SERVING: Calories 305; Fat 13.7g (sat 2.2g, mono 8.2g, poly 1.7g); Protein 37g; Carb 5.1g; Fiber 0.7g; Chol 109mg; Iron 1.2mg; Sodium 501mg; Calc 29mg

PITTING OLIVES

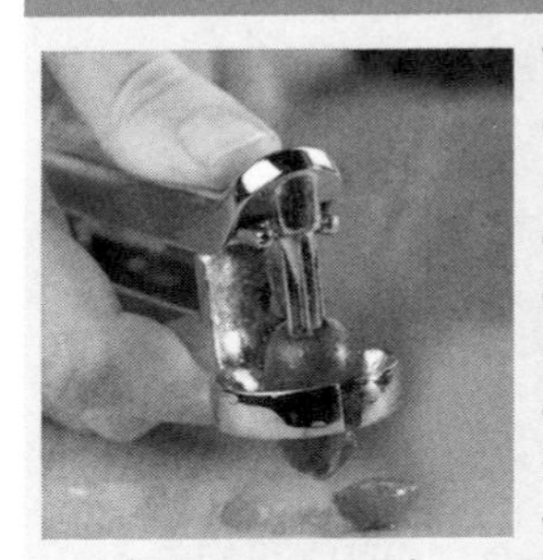

To make easy work of pitting olives (or cherries), you can use a pitter. If you don't have one, place the olives on a cutting board. Place the flat side of a chef's knife on top, and press down using the heel of your hand. The olives will pop open, exposing the pits for easy removal. To pit a large number of olives, wrap them in a dish towel, and smack them with a rolling pin or heavy skillet.

LEMON-ZA'ATAR–RUBBED CHICKEN BREASTS

PointsPlus value per serving: 6 *(pictured on page 53)*

HANDS-ON TIME: 23 min. ■ **TOTAL TIME:** 23 min.

Za'atar is a Middle Eastern spice blend made from sesame seeds, thyme, sumac, and other herbs. You can usually find it in the spice section of the grocery store. Garnish with fresh grated lemon rind, if you'd like. Serve with Chopped Vegetable Salad (page 86) for a colorful side.

3 tablespoons za'atar seasoning
2 tablespoons olive oil
2 teaspoons fresh lemon juice
¾ teaspoon grated fresh lemon rind
3 garlic cloves, minced
6 (6-ounce) skinless, boneless chicken breast halves
Cooking spray

1. Combine first 5 ingredients in a small bowl, stirring until a paste forms.
2. Place chicken between 2 sheets of heavy-duty plastic wrap; pound to ½-inch thickness using a meat mallet or small heavy skillet. Rub chicken on all sides with za'atar mixture.
3. Heat a grill pan over medium-high heat. Coat pan with cooking spray. Add half of chicken to pan; cook 4 to 5 minutes on each side or until done. Remove from pan; keep warm. Repeat procedure with remaining chicken. **YIELD: 6 SERVINGS (SERVING SIZE: 1 CHICKEN BREAST HALF).**

PER SERVING: Calories 236; Fat 8.9g (sat 1.6g, mono 4.6g, poly 1.2g); Protein 36.2g; Carb 0.7g; Fiber 0.1g; Chol 109mg; Iron 0.7mg; Sodium 354mg; Calc 12mg

BRUSCHETTA CHICKEN

PointsPlus value per serving: 7

HANDS-ON TIME: 20 min. ■ **TOTAL TIME:** 20 min.

Pair this Italian-flavored chicken with a side of ½ cup cooked angel hair pasta per serving for a complete meal with a ***PointsPlus*** value of 10.

4 (6-ounce) skinless, boneless chicken breast halves
¼ teaspoon salt
¼ teaspoon freshly ground black pepper
2 teaspoons olive oil, divided
¼ cup tomato bruschetta topping
2 tablespoons chopped pitted kalamata olives (about 6 olives)
1 teaspoon julienne-cut fresh basil
2 ounces crumbled feta cheese (about ½ cup)

1. Place chicken between 2 sheets of heavy-duty plastic wrap; pound to ¼-inch thickness using a meat mallet or small heavy skillet. Sprinkle chicken with salt and pepper.
2. Heat a large nonstick skillet over medium-high heat. Add 1 teaspoon oil to pan; swirl to coat. Add half of chicken to pan; cook 3 minutes on each side or until done. Remove chicken from pan. Repeat procedure with remaining oil and chicken.
3. Combine bruschetta topping, olives, and basil. Spoon topping mixture over chicken, and sprinkle with cheese. **YIELD: 4 SERVINGS (SERVING SIZE: 1 CHICKEN BREAST HALF, ABOUT 1 TABLESPOON TOPPING, AND ABOUT 2 TABLESPOONS CHEESE).**

PER SERVING: Calories 280; Fat 12.1g (sat 3.1g, mono 5.2g, poly 1.7g); Protein 39.1g; Carb 2g; Fiber 0.6g; Chol 119mg; Iron 1.4mg; Sodium 699mg; Calc 63mg

CHEESY SUN-DRIED TOMATO CHICKEN

PointsPlus value per serving: 10

HANDS-ON TIME: 13 minutes ■ **TOTAL TIME:** 13 minutes

Accompany this super quick supper with a simple green salad—undressed veggies have a ***PointsPlus*** value of 0.

- 2 teaspoons olive oil
- 4 (6-ounce) skinless, boneless chicken breast halves
- ½ teaspoon dried Italian seasoning
- ¼ teaspoon freshly ground black pepper
- ½ cup sun-dried tomato pesto
- 2 ounces preshredded 6-cheese Italian blend cheese (about ½ cup)
- 2 tablespoons finely chopped pitted kalamata olives (about 6 olives)

1. Heat a large nonstick skillet over medium-high heat. Add oil to pan; swirl to coat. Sprinkle chicken with Italian seasoning and pepper. Add chicken to pan; cook 4 minutes on each side or until browned. Spread 2 tablespoons pesto over top of each chicken breast. Top chicken with cheese and olives. Cover and cook 1 to 2 minutes or until chicken is done and cheese melts. YIELD: 4 SERVINGS (SERVING SIZE: 1 CHICKEN BREAST HALF).

PER SERVING: Calories 390; Fat 21.5g (sat 5.1g, mono 12.2g, poly 2.2g); Protein 41.8g; Carb 5.9g; Fiber 1.1g; Chol 122mg; Iron 1.1mg; Sodium 623mg; Calc 164mg

CURRIED CITRUS CHICKEN

PointsPlus value per serving: 7

HANDS-ON TIME: 15 min. ■ **TOTAL TIME:** 15 min.

It takes about 1½ lemons to yield 3 tablespoons of fresh lemon juice. Store the remaining lemon half in a zip-top plastic bag in the refrigerator for another use.

- 1 teaspoon curry powder
- ¼ teaspoon salt
- ¼ teaspoon freshly ground black pepper
- 4 (6-ounce) skinless, boneless chicken breast halves
- 2 teaspoons olive oil
- ⅓ cup low-sugar orange marmalade
- 3 tablespoons fresh lemon juice
- 1 tablespoon water
- 2 tablespoons slivered almonds, toasted

1. Combine first 3 ingredients in a small bowl; rub mixture over chicken.
2. Heat a large nonstick skillet over medium-high heat. Add oil to pan; swirl to coat. Add chicken to pan; cover and cook 5 to 6 minutes on each side or until done. Remove chicken from pan, and keep warm.
3. Add marmalade, lemon juice, and 1 tablespoon water to pan, scraping pan to loosen browned bits. Cook over medium heat 1 minute. Spoon sauce over chicken; sprinkle with almonds. YIELD: 4 SERVINGS (SERVING SIZE: 1 CHICKEN BREAST HALF, 1 TABLESPOON SAUCE, AND 1½ TEASPOONS ALMONDS).

PER SERVING: Calories 271; Fat 8.4g (sat 1.4g, mono 4g, poly 1.3g); Protein 36.9g; Carb 9.8g; Fiber 0.6g; Chol 109mg; Iron 0.9mg; Sodium 345mg; Calc 21mg

HOW TO JUICE CITRUS

To get the most juice out of fresh lemons, limes, and other citrus, bring it to room temperature, and then use the palm of your hand to roll the fruit on a countertop a few times, applying a bit of pressure. Cut the fruit in half, and then squeeze. Or, for easier work, use a handheld press to release the most juice while safely trapping the seeds. Place the citrus half, cut side down, in the press, and lower the handle.

FARMER'S CHICKEN

PointsPlus value per serving: 6

HANDS-ON TIME: 10 min. ■ **TOTAL TIME:** 18 min.

This dish is inspired by the classic Chicken à la Paysanne—a simple dish prepared in a rustic style that brings out the natural flavors of the chicken and mushrooms.

4 (6-ounce) skinless, boneless chicken breast halves
4 teaspoons whole-grain Dijon mustard
2 teaspoons herbes de Provence
¼ teaspoon salt
¼ teaspoon freshly ground black pepper
1 tablespoon olive oil
1 (8-ounce) package sliced cremini mushrooms
1 tablespoon fresh lemon juice
Chopped fresh parsley (optional)

1. Preheat oven to 400°.
2. Brush chicken with mustard; sprinkle with herbes de Provence, salt, and pepper. Heat a large ovenproof skillet over medium-high heat. Add oil to pan; swirl to coat. Add chicken; cook 2 minutes on each side or until browned.
3. Add mushrooms and lemon juice to pan. Place pan in oven. Bake, uncovered, at 400° for 8 minutes or until chicken is done and mushrooms are tender. Sprinkle with parsley, if desired. **YIELD: 4 SERVINGS (SERVING SIZE: 1 CHICKEN BREAST HALF AND ABOUT 3 TABLESPOONS MUSHROOMS).**

PER SERVING: Calories 243; Fat 7.8g (sat 1.4g, mono 3.8g, poly 1.1g); Protein 37.6g; Carb 3.8g; Fiber 0.4g; Chol 109mg; Iron 0.9mg; Sodium 468mg; Calc 20mg

TOMATO-BASIL CHICKEN

PointsPlus value per serving: 5

HANDS-ON TIME: 17 min. ■ **TOTAL TIME:** 17 min.

We recommend serving this Italian-inspired dish over cheesy polenta instead of traditional pasta. Try it with a serving of Parmesan Polenta with Garlic (page 156) for a complete meal with a *PointsPlus* value per serving of 9.

4 (6-ounce) skinless, boneless chicken breast halves
Cooking spray
½ teaspoon salt, divided
¼ teaspoon freshly ground black pepper
3 garlic cloves, minced
2 cups grape tomatoes, halved
1 teaspoon balsamic vinegar
¼ cup torn basil leaves

1. Place chicken breast halves between 2 sheets of heavy-duty plastic wrap; pound to ¼-inch thickness using a meat mallet or small heavy skillet.
2. Heat a large nonstick skillet over medium-high heat. Coat pan with cooking spray. Sprinkle chicken evenly with ¼ teaspoon salt and pepper. Add chicken to pan. Cook 5 minutes on each side or until done. Remove chicken from pan; cover and keep warm.
3. Heat pan over medium-high heat; recoat pan with cooking spray. Add garlic to pan; sauté 30 seconds. Stir in grape tomatoes, and cook 4 minutes, stirring occasionally. Remove pan from heat. Stir in vinegar and ¼ teaspoon salt. Spoon tomato mixture over chicken; sprinkle with basil. **YIELD: 4 SERVINGS (1 CHICKEN BREAST HALF AND ABOUT ¼ CUP TOMATO MIXTURE).**

PER SERVING: Calories 213; Fat 4.6g (sat 1g, mono 1.3g, poly 0.8g); Protein 37g; Carb 4g; Fiber 1g; Chol 109mg; Iron 1mg; Sodium 497mg; Calc 26mg

CHICKEN PUTTANESCA

PointsPlus value per serving: 7

HANDS-ON TIME: 8 min. ▪ **TOTAL TIME:** 15 min.

Spicy, salty puttanesca sauce is usually prepared with chicken breasts and served over pasta, but you could also use chicken thighs.

1 tablespoon olive oil
4 (6-ounce) skinless, boneless chicken breast halves
¼ cup chopped pitted kalamata olives
2 tablespoons capers, drained
1 teaspoon anchovy paste
¼ teaspoon crushed red pepper
¼ teaspoon freshly ground black pepper
1 (14.5-ounce) can unsalted diced tomatoes with basil, garlic, and oregano, undrained
Chopped fresh parsley (optional)

1. Heat a large nonstick skillet over medium-high heat. Add oil to pan; swirl to coat. Add chicken to pan; cook 1 to 2 minutes on each side or until browned. Stir in olives and next 5 ingredients (through diced tomatoes); bring to a boil. Cover, reduce heat, and simmer 7 minutes. Uncover and simmer 3 minutes or until sauce is slightly thick. Place chicken on individual plates; top evenly with sauce, and sprinkle with parsley, if desired. **YIELD: 4 SERVINGS (SERVING SIZE: 1 CHICKEN BREAST HALF AND ABOUT ⅓ CUP SAUCE).**

PER SERVING: Calories 295; Fat 10.3g (sat 1.7g, mono 5.6g, poly 1.3g); Protein 38.2g; Carb 9.6g; Fiber 1.1g; Chol 113mg; Iron 0.8mg; Sodium 581mg; Calc 14mg

TOMATILLO CHICKEN

PointsPlus value per serving: 6

HANDS-ON TIME: 15 min. ▪ **TOTAL TIME:** 15 min.

Tomatillos cook up quickly for a fresh take on tomato sauce. The small round fruit imparts a tart, lemony flavor. Be sure to remove the papery husks from the tomatillos, and wash them well to remove the sticky residue.

2 teaspoons ground cumin
½ teaspoon salt
½ teaspoon freshly ground black pepper
4 (6-ounce) skinless, boneless chicken breast halves
Cooking spray
1 tablespoon olive oil
1½ cups chopped tomatillos (about 4 tomatillos)
2 tablespoons minced seeded jalapeño pepper (about 1 pepper)
Lime wedges (optional)

1. Combine first 3 ingredients in a small bowl; rub mixture over chicken.
2. Heat a large nonstick skillet over medium-high heat. Coat pan with cooking spray. Add chicken; cook 5 to 6 minutes on each side or until done. Remove chicken from pan, and keep warm.
3. Add oil to pan; swirl to coat. Stir in tomatillos and jalapeño pepper. Cook, stirring constantly, 3 minutes or until tender and saucy. Place a chicken breast half on each of 4 plates. Spoon sauce over chicken. Serve with lime wedges, if desired. **YIELD: 4 SERVINGS (SERVING SIZE: 1 CHICKEN BREAST HALF AND ¼ CUP SAUCE).**

PER SERVING: Calories 235; Fat 8.1g (sat 1.9g, mono 4.4g, poly 1.7g); Protein 35g; Carb 3.7g; Fiber 1.5g; Chol 94mg; Iron 1.9mg; Sodium 375mg; Calc 30mg

TOMATILLOS

Tomatillos, the key ingredient in green salsas and Latin American sauces, look like small green tomatoes. In fact, they are sometimes even referred to as "Mexican tomatoes." A cousin of the tomato, tomatillos are technically a fruit that grows surrounded by a papery husk. Ripe tomatillos are green or purple in color and have a slightly more sour taste than a ripe tomato. Choose firm, but not hard, tomatillos and store them in an airtight bag in the refrigerator. If they need more ripening, store in a paper bag at room temperature. Tomatillos are typically harvested in late summer and early fall but should be available year-round at Latin and ethnic markets.

Cashew Chicken Pot Stickers, *page 22*

Black-Eyed Pea and Tomato Salsa,
page 18

Cranberry-Apple-Orange Cider, *page 26*

Curried Chicken Lettuce Wraps, *page 25*

Feta Shrimp, *page 33*

Lemon-Za'atar–Rubbed Chicken Breasts, *page 45*

Grilled Chicken with Peach Chutney, *page 67*

Chicken Tostadas,
page 77

Thai Beef in Brown Sauce,
page 37

Beef Chow Mein, *page 36*

Parmesan Pork Chops, *page 41*

Black Bean and Kale Quesadillas, *page 28*

Spinach Chicken Roulades, *page 68*

Spice-Rubbed Salmon with Cucumber-Yogurt Sauce, *page 32*

Asian Pork Medallions
with Spicy Broccoli Slaw,
page 40

Spinach and Chicken Sausage Pizza, *page 78*

Layered Cobb Salad, *page 100*

Strawberry Spinach Salad, *page 84*

White Bean Salad,
page 87

Warm Quinoa and Rice Caprese Salad, *page 88*

GREEK CHICKEN POCKETS

PointsPlus value per serving: 6

HANDS-ON TIME: 15 min. ▪ **TOTAL TIME:** 35 min.

Serving this chicken with a side of 1 cup cooked orzo tossed with fresh oregano and lemon juice results in a satisfying weeknight meal with a *PointsPlus* value per serving of 11.

- **½ cup part-skim ricotta cheese**
- **½ cup julienne-cut sun-dried tomatoes, packed without oil**
- **1 tablespoon chopped fresh oregano**
- **2 teaspoons salt-free Greek seasoning, divided**
- **½ teaspoon freshly ground black pepper, divided**
- **4 (6-ounce) skinless, boneless chicken breast halves**
- **Cooking spray**

1. Preheat oven to 400°.
2. Combine ricotta cheese, tomatoes, oregano, 1 teaspoon Greek seasoning, and ¼ teaspoon pepper in a small bowl.
3. Cut a horizontal slit through thickest portion of each chicken breast half to form a pocket. Stuff ¼ cup ricotta mixture into each pocket; close openings with wooden picks. Sprinkle chicken with 1 teaspoon Greek seasoning and ¼ teaspoon pepper.
4. Heat a large nonstick skillet over medium-high heat. Coat pan with cooking spray. Add chicken to pan. Cook 2 minutes on each side or until browned.
5. Place chicken in an 11 x 7–inch glass or ceramic baking dish coated with cooking spray. Bake, uncovered, at 400° for 20 minutes or until done. Remove and discard wooden picks. Serve immediately. **YIELD: 4 SERVINGS (SERVING SIZE: 1 STUFFED CHICKEN BREAST HALF).**

PER SERVING: Calories 256; Fat 7.1g (sat 2.5g, mono 2.1g, poly 0.8g); Protein 41g; Carb 5.7g; Fiber 0.9g; Chol 119mg; Iron 1.4mg; Sodium 253mg; Calc 106mg

CREAM CHEESE AND PEPPER JELLY CHICKEN

PointsPlus value per serving: 9

HANDS-ON TIME: 20 min. ▪ **TOTAL TIME:** 40 min.

Use a cast-iron or other ovenproof skillet for browning the chicken on the stove top, so you won't need to dirty another pan to bake the chicken.

- **½ cup jalapeño pepper jelly**
- **2 large garlic cloves, minced**
- **4 ounces ⅓-less-fat tub-style cream cheese, softened (about ½ cup)**
- **2 tablespoons minced fresh cilantro**
- **4 (6-ounce) skinless, boneless chicken breast halves**
- **¼ teaspoon freshly ground black pepper**
- **⅛ teaspoon salt**
- **Cooking spray**
- **2 tablespoons water**

1. Preheat oven to 400°.
2. Place jelly and garlic in a small microwave-safe bowl. Microwave at HIGH 45 seconds or until jelly melts, stirring after 30 seconds.
3. Combine cream cheese and cilantro in another small bowl. Cut a horizontal slit through thickest portion of each chicken breast half to form a pocket. Stuff about 2 tablespoons cheese mixture into each pocket; close openings with wooden picks. Sprinkle chicken with pepper and salt.
4. Heat a 12-inch cast-iron skillet over medium-high heat. Coat pan with cooking spray. Add chicken to pan, meaty sides down; cook 4 minutes. Turn chicken over; brush with jelly mixture.
5. Place pan in oven. Bake at 400° for 15 minutes or until chicken is done, basting with remaining jelly mixture after 7 minutes. Remove pan from oven, and remove chicken from pan. Add 2 tablespoons water to pan, stirring with a whisk to loosen browned bits. Let stand 5 minutes.
6. Remove and discard wooden picks; place chicken on serving plates. Spoon pan sauce over chicken. **YIELD: 4 SERVINGS (SERVING SIZE: 1 CHICKEN BREAST HALF AND ABOUT 1 TABLESPOON SAUCE).**

PER SERVING: Calories 357; Fat 11.7g (sat 5g, mono 3.1g, poly 1g); Protein 39.1g; Carb 21.7g; Fiber 0.1g; Chol 133mg; Iron 0.7mg; Sodium 468mg; Calc 49mg

PISTACHIO-CRUSTED CHICKEN

PointsPlus value per serving: 8

HANDS-ON TIME: 11 min. ■ **TOTAL TIME:** 25 min.

Pistachios are a great source of B_6, potassium, and magnesium. You can substitute unsalted almonds, pine nuts, cashews, or peanuts for the pistachios.

¾ cup unsalted shelled dry-roasted pistachios
2 large egg whites, lightly beaten
4 (6-ounce) skinless, boneless chicken breast halves
¼ teaspoon salt
¼ teaspoon freshly ground black pepper
Cooking spray

1. Preheat oven to 400°.
2. Place pistachios in a food processor. Process until finely chopped; transfer to a shallow bowl. Place egg whites in a shallow bowl. Sprinkle chicken with salt and pepper. Dip chicken into egg whites; dredge in pistachios, pressing lightly to adhere.
3. Heat a large ovenproof skillet over medium-high heat. Coat pan with cooking spray. Add chicken to pan; cook 4 minutes. Coat chicken with cooking spray. Turn chicken over; cook 4 minutes. Place pan in oven. Bake, uncovered, at 400° for 14 minutes or until done.
YIELD: 4 SERVINGS (SERVING SIZE: 1 CHICKEN BREAST HALF).

PER SERVING: Calories 329; Fat 13g (sat 1.9g, mono 6.2g, poly 3.7g); Protein 46g; Carb 6.6g; Fiber 2.4g; Chol 99mg; Iron 2.3mg; Sodium 286mg; Calc 46mg

PISTACHIOS

Almonds and walnuts are common snack choices, but don't forget about pistachios! This little green nut is one of the healthiest nuts around. A 1-ounce serving of pistachios is about 49 nuts. When 1-ounce servings of nuts are compared, pistachios tie with cashews for being lowest in calories and fat (160 calories and 13 grams fat), and they're highest in protein content (6 grams) along with almonds. Pistachios are good sources of B_6, potassium, thiamin, beta-carotene, and fiber. They're also high in plant sterols which have been shown to help reduce blood cholesterol levels and possibly reduce risk of heart disease. Pistachios come shelled and unshelled, roasted and raw, salted and unsalted. If you choose a roasted, make sure it's dry-roasted rather than roasted in oil.

SOUTHWESTERN SMOTHERED CHICKEN

PointsPlus value per serving: 7

HANDS-ON TIME: 13 min. ■ **TOTAL TIME:** 13 min.

Accompany this Tex-Mex–style chicken with super nutritious chopped fresh mango. A 1-cup serving is full of vitamin C and has a *PointsPlus* value of 0.

½ cup canned lower-sodium black beans, rinsed and drained
½ cup canned lower-sodium whole-kernel corn, rinsed and drained
½ cup fresh salsa
4 (6-ounce) skinless, boneless chicken breast halves
¼ teaspoon freshly ground black pepper
⅛ teaspoon salt
2 teaspoons canola oil
1 ounce grated reduced-fat Monterey Jack cheese with jalapeño peppers (about ¼ cup)
Chopped fresh cilantro (optional)

1. Combine first 3 ingredients in a medium bowl. Set aside.
2. Sprinkle chicken with pepper and salt. Heat a large nonstick skillet over medium-high heat. Add canola oil to pan; swirl to coat. Add chicken to pan; cover and cook 5 to 6 minutes on each side or until done.
3. Add bean mixture to pan. Top chicken with cheese. Cover and cook 1 minute or until cheese melts. Sprinkle with cilantro, if desired. **YIELD: 4 SERVINGS (SERVING SIZE: 1 CHICKEN BREAST HALF AND ABOUT ¼ CUP BEAN MIXTURE).**

PER SERVING: Calories 294; Fat 8.5g (sat 2.1g, mono 3.2g, poly 1.3g); Protein 40.2g; Carb 11.3g; Fiber 1.8g; Chol 113mg; Iron 1.3mg; Sodium 501mg; Calc 80mg

FIG-STUFFED CHICKEN BREASTS

PointsPlus value per serving: 8

HANDS-ON TIME: 23 min. ▪ **TOTAL TIME:** 45 min.

Sweet dried figs and tangy goat cheese are the perfect pair in these elegant stuffed chicken breasts. We used twine to secure the cheese-stuffed chicken breasts but you could use wooden picks instead.

⅓ cup chopped dried Black Mission figs
1 (4-ounce) package herbed goat cheese
4 (6-ounce) skinless, boneless chicken breast halves
¼ teaspoon salt
¼ teaspoon freshly ground black pepper
Cooking spray
2 tablespoons balsamic vinegar
2 tablespoons fig preserves

1. Preheat oven to 400°.
2. Combine figs and cheese in a small bowl. Cut a horizontal slit through thickest portion of each chicken breast half to form a pocket. Stuff about 3 tablespoons cheese mixture into each pocket; secure at 1½-inch intervals with twine. Sprinkle chicken with salt and pepper.
3. Heat a 12-inch cast-iron skillet over medium-high heat. Coat pan with cooking spray. Add chicken to pan; cook 2 minutes. Turn chicken over; place pan in oven. Bake at 400° for 15 minutes or until done. Remove from oven; let stand 2 minutes. Stir together vinegar and preserves; add to pan. Let stand 5 minutes. Remove and discard twine. Cut chicken diagonally across grain into ½-inch-thick slices. Drizzle with sauce. **YIELD: 4 SERVINGS (SERVING SIZE: 1 CHICKEN BREAST HALF AND 2 TEASPOONS PAN JUICES).**

PER SERVING: Calories 328; Fat 10.6g (sat 5g, mono 2.7g, poly 0.8g); Protein 40.6g; Carb 16.8g; Fiber 1.2g; Chol 119mg; Iron 0.9mg; Sodium 480mg; Calc 51mg

GRILLED CHICKEN WITH PEACH CHUTNEY

PointsPlus value per serving: 7 *(pictured on page 53)*

HANDS-ON TIME: 30 min. ▪ **TOTAL TIME:** 30 min.

Cooking the peach mixture while you prep and grill the chicken allows you to get this company-worthy dish on the table in only 30 minutes. Pair with Green Beans with Pancetta (page 148), which have a *PointsPlus* value per serving of 2.

5 cups diced peeled peaches (about 8 peaches)
⅓ cup packed brown sugar
3 tablespoons minced crystallized ginger
2 tablespoons fresh orange juice
¾ teaspoon salt, divided
8 (6-ounce) skinless, boneless chicken breast halves
½ teaspoon freshly ground black pepper
Cooking spray
Thinly sliced green onions (optional)

1. Preheat grill to medium-high heat.
2. Combine first 4 ingredients and ¼ teaspoon salt in a medium saucepan. Bring to a boil; reduce heat, and simmer, uncovered, 20 minutes, stirring occasionally. Remove from heat.
3. While peach mixture cooks, sprinkle chicken evenly with ½ teaspoon salt and pepper. Place chicken on grill rack coated with cooking spray. Grill 5 minutes on each side or until done. Remove chicken from grill. Place chicken on serving plates; top with chutney. Garnish with green onions, if desired. **YIELD: 8 SERVINGS (SERVING SIZE: 1 CHICKEN BREAST HALF AND ABOUT ¼ CUP CHUTNEY).**

PER SERVING: Calories 283; Fat 4.7g (sat 1g, mono 1.4g, poly 0.8g); Protein 37.1g; Carb 22.3g; Fiber 1.4g; Chol 109mg; Iron 1.8mg; Sodium 424mg; Calc 33mg

SPINACH CHICKEN ROULADES

PointsPlus value per serving: 5 *(pictured on page 58)*

HANDS-ON TIME: 13 min. ■ **TOTAL TIME:** 22 min.

Roll up flattened chicken breast halves with a lemony spinach filling to create this elegant entrée worthy of a dinner party.

- **1 (10-ounce) package frozen chopped spinach, thawed and drained**
- **1 teaspoon grated fresh lemon rind**
- **2 garlic cloves, minced**
- **4 (6-ounce) skinless, boneless chicken breast halves**
- **¼ teaspoon salt**
- **¼ teaspoon freshly ground black pepper**
- **2 teaspoons olive oil**
- **½ cup white wine and herb–flavored chicken broth**

1. Combine first 3 ingredients in a small bowl.
2. Place chicken between 2 sheets of heavy-duty plastic wrap; pound to ¼-inch thickness using a meat mallet or small heavy skillet. Spread spinach mixture evenly on chicken breast halves, leaving a ¼-inch border. Tuck in sides; roll up jelly-roll fashion, and secure with wooden picks. Sprinkle rolls evenly with salt and pepper.
3. Heat a large nonstick skillet over medium-high heat. Add oil to pan; swirl to coat. Add chicken to pan; cook 6 minutes, turning to brown all sides. Add broth to pan. Cover; reduce heat, and cook 9 minutes or until chicken is done. Remove chicken from pan. YIELD: 4 SERVINGS (SERVING SIZE: 1 ROULADE).

PER SERVING: Calories 235; Fat 6.7g (sat 1.3g, mono 2.9g, poly 0.9g); Protein 37.7g; Carb 2.9g; Fiber 0.9g; Chol 109mg; Iron 1.3mg; Sodium 596mg; Calc 57mg

CHICKEN ALFREDO

PointsPlus value per serving: 10 *(pictured on cover)*

HANDS-ON TIME: 15 min. ■ **TOTAL TIME:** 15 min.

Thanks to refrigerated fresh pasta and Alfredo sauce, you can get this family favorite on the table in only 15 minutes. Steam some broccoli for a quick side with a *PointsPlus* value per serving of 0.

- **1 (9-ounce) package fresh fettuccine**
- **2 teaspoons olive oil**
- **1½ pounds skinless, boneless chicken breast, cut into 1½-inch pieces**
- **½ cup chopped onion**
- **1 cup grape tomatoes, halved**
- **1 cup frozen green peas, thawed**
- **1 (10-ounce) container refrigerated light Alfredo sauce**
- **¼ teaspoon freshly ground black pepper**
- **1 ounce grated fresh Parmesan cheese (about ¼ cup)**

1. Cook pasta according to package directions, omitting salt and fat. Drain, reserving ¼ cup cooking liquid.
2. While pasta cooks, heat a large nonstick skillet over medium-high heat. Add oil to pan; swirl to coat. Add chicken and onion to pan; sauté 6 minutes or until chicken is done and onion is tender.
3. Add tomatoes and peas to pan. Cook 1 minute, stirring constantly. Stir in Alfredo sauce, pepper, and reserved cooking liquid. Cook 1 minute or until thoroughly heated. Stir in pasta. Sprinkle with cheese, and serve immediately. YIELD: 6 SERVINGS (SERVING SIZE: ABOUT 1⅓ CUPS).

PER SERVING: Calories 382; Fat 11.6g (sat 4.4g, mono 3.9g, poly 1.3g); Protein 35.6g; Carb 32.5g; Fiber 3.3g; Chol 119mg; Iron 2.3mg; Sodium 524mg; Calc 168mg

ROTINI WITH CHICKEN, ASPARAGUS, AND TOMATOES

PointsPlus value per serving: 8

HANDS-ON TIME: 15 min. ■ **TOTAL TIME:** 15 min.

Reminiscent of pasta salad, this recipe calls for mixing pasta with tender, garden-fresh vegetables and a basil-flecked balsamic vinaigrette. This dish is delicious served warm or chilled, which makes it a great option for lunch boxes.

8 ounces uncooked rotini (corkscrew pasta)
Cooking spray
1 pound skinless, boneless chicken breast, cut into ¼-inch strips
½ teaspoon kosher salt
½ teaspoon freshly ground black pepper
1 cup (1-inch) slices asparagus
2 cups cherry tomatoes, halved
2 garlic cloves, minced
2 tablespoons chopped fresh basil
2 tablespoons balsamic vinegar
1 tablespoon extra-virgin olive oil
1 ounce crumbled goat cheese (about ¼ cup)

1. Cook pasta according to package directions, omitting salt and fat.
2. While pasta cooks, heat a large nonstick skillet over medium-high heat. Coat pan with cooking spray. Sprinkle chicken with salt and pepper. Add chicken and asparagus to pan; sauté 5 minutes. Add tomatoes and garlic to pan; sauté 1 minute. Remove from heat. Stir in pasta, basil, vinegar, and oil; sprinkle with cheese. **YIELD: 5 SERVINGS (SERVING SIZE: ABOUT 1½ CUPS CHICKEN MIXTURE AND ABOUT 1 TABLESPOON CHEESE).**

PER SERVING: Calories 336g; Fat 7.5g (sat 2.3g, mono 3.1g, poly 0.9g); Protein 27.7g; Carb 38.5g; Fiber 2.6g; Chol 63mg; Iron 2.2mg; Sodium 333mg; Calc 45mg

CHICKEN-BROCCOLI STIR-FRY

PointsPlus value per serving: 6

HANDS-ON TIME: 15 min. ■ **TOTAL TIME:** 15 min.

This Asian-inspired dish combines chicken and broccoli with meaty shiitake mushrooms and a savory sauce, all served over cooked rice. To keep prep time to a minimum, purchase a pouch of microwaveable precooked rice.

Cooking spray
12 ounces chicken breast tenders, cubed
4½ cups large broccoli florets
2 (3.5-ounce) packages shiitake mushrooms, sliced
1½ cups fat-free, lower-sodium beef broth
2 tablespoons cornstarch
2 tablespoons oyster sauce
1 teaspoon sugar
2 teaspoons lower-sodium soy sauce
⅛ teaspoon salt
2 cups hot cooked brown rice

1. Heat a large nonstick skillet over medium-high heat. Coat pan with cooking spray. Add chicken; cook 4 minutes, stirring frequently. Add broccoli and mushrooms; cook 3 minutes, stirring frequently.
2. Combine broth and next 5 ingredients (through salt) in a small bowl; add to chicken mixture. Cook 3 minutes or until sauce thickens, stirring constantly. Serve immediately over rice. **YIELD: 4 SERVINGS (SERVING SIZE: ABOUT 1⅔ CUPS CHICKEN MIXTURE AND ½ CUP RICE).**

PER SERVING: Calories 266; Fat 2.5g (sat 0.5g, mono 0.6g, poly 0.7g); Protein 26.4g; Carb 34.2g; Fiber 4.3g; Chol 49mg; Iron 2mg; Sodium 659mg; Calc 63mg

CHICKEN FINGERS WITH DIJON-BARBECUE SAUCE

PointsPlus value per serving: 5

HANDS-ON TIME: 6 min. ▪ **TOTAL TIME:** 16 min.

The best way to get an even coating on the tenders is to start with 1 cup panko and discard what doesn't stick to the egg-coated chicken. Cut larger tenders in half, if necessary, so that you have eight tenders that weigh about 2 ounces each.

1 egg white, lightly beaten
¼ teaspoon salt
¼ teaspoon freshly ground black pepper
1 cup panko (Japanese breadcrumbs)
1 pound chicken breast tenders (8 tenders)
Olive oil–flavored cooking spray
4 teaspoons canola oil
3 tablespoons barbecue sauce
1 tablespoon honey Dijon mustard

1. Preheat oven to 450°.
2. Combine first 3 ingredients in a shallow dish. Place panko in another shallow dish. Dip chicken in egg mixture; dredge in panko. Discard remaining egg mixture and panko. Coat chicken with cooking spray.
3. Heat a large nonstick skillet over medium heat. Add oil to pan; swirl to coat. Add chicken; cook 1 minute on each side. Place chicken on an ovenproof rack coated with cooking spray; place rack in sheet pan. Bake at 450° for 10 minutes.
4. While chicken cooks, combine barbecue sauce and mustard in a small bowl. Serve chicken fingers with sauce. **YIELD: 4 SERVINGS (SERVING SIZE: 2 CHICKEN FINGERS AND 1 TABLESPOON SAUCE).**

PER SERVING: Calories 214; Fat 7.6g (sat 1g, mono 3.8g, poly 1.8g); Protein 25.7g; Carb 7.7g; Fiber 0.2g; Chol 73mg; Iron 0.6mg; Sodium 461mg; Calc 7mg

SCHNITZEL CHICKEN

PointsPlus value per serving: 7

HANDS-ON TIME: 17 min. ▪ **TOTAL TIME:** 17 min.

Schnitzel refers to a thin slice of meat that is breaded and fried. In this recipe, we pan-fry the chicken to keep calories and fat low but still get a satisfyingly crisp coating.

¼ cup all-purpose flour
1 large egg, lightly beaten
1 cup whole-wheat panko (Japanese breadcrumbs)
4 (4-ounce) chicken cutlets
⅜ teaspoon salt
¼ teaspoon freshly ground black pepper
2 teaspoons olive oil, divided
Cooking spray
4 lemon wedges

1. Place flour, egg, and panko in separate shallow dishes. Sprinkle chicken cutlets evenly with salt and pepper. Dredge each chicken cutlet in flour. Dip in egg; dredge in panko.
2. Heat a large nonstick skillet over medium-high heat. Add 1 teaspoon oil to pan; swirl to coat. Add 2 cutlets to pan. Cook 3 minutes or until golden; remove pan from heat, and coat chicken with cooking spray. Turn chicken over. Cook 3 minutes or until chicken is done. Transfer to a plate; cover and keep warm. Repeat procedure with 1 teaspoon oil, remaining 2 cutlets, and cooking spray. Serve with lemon wedges. **YIELD: 4 SERVINGS (SERVING SIZE: 1 CHICKEN CUTLET AND 1 LEMON WEDGE).**

PER SERVING: Calories 268; Fat 7g (sat 1.4g, mono 3.1g, poly 1.2g); Protein 29.5g; Carb 20.8g; Fiber 2.4g; Chol 119mg; Iron 1.8mg; Sodium 394mg; Calc 16mg

CUTLETS

Cutlets are thin, tenderized cuts taken from pork loins or chicken breasts that allow for quick, even cooking. Use pork or chicken cutlets in place of pork loin chops or chicken breasts to save time when needed. If you substitute cutlets for chops or breasts, simply cut back 2 to 3 minutes from the total cook time.

CHICKEN WITH CREAMY MUSHROOM SAUCE

PointsPlus value per serving: 5

HANDS-ON TIME: 17 min. ▪ **TOTAL TIME:** 17 min.

You can substitute ordinary white mushrooms for the cremini mushrooms (also known as baby bellas), but creminis have a stronger earthy flavor.

- **Cooking spray**
- **6 (4-ounce) chicken cutlets**
- **1 teaspoon freshly ground black pepper, divided**
- **¼ teaspoon salt**
- **2 tablespoons olive oil**
- **1 (8-ounce) package sliced cremini mushrooms**
- **2 tablespoons dry vermouth**
- **¼ cup fat-free, lower-sodium chicken broth**
- **2 tablespoons whipping cream**

1. Heat a large nonstick skillet over medium-high heat. Coat pan with cooking spray. Sprinkle chicken with ½ teaspoon pepper and salt; coat with cooking spray, and add to pan. Cook chicken 3 to 4 minutes on each side or until done. Remove from pan; keep warm.

2. Add oil to pan; swirl to coat. Add mushrooms, and sauté 4 to 6 minutes or until tender. Stir in vermouth; cook 1 minute or until liquid almost evaporates. Stir in broth; cook 1 minute or until liquid is reduced by half. Stir in cream and ½ teaspoon pepper; bring to a simmer. Return chicken to pan, turning to coat. Cook 1 minute or until thoroughly heated. **YIELD: 6 SERVINGS (SERVING SIZE: 1 CHICKEN CUTLET AND ABOUT 3 TABLESPOONS MUSHROOM SAUCE).**

PER SERVING: Calories 200; Fat 9.2g (sat 2.3g, mono 4.6g, poly 1g); Protein 25.2g; Carb 2.4g; Fiber 0.3g; Chol 79mg; Iron 0.6mg; Sodium 256mg; Calc 14mg

CREMINI MUSHROOMS

Cremini mushrooms are simply a slightly darker and more mature form of the common white button mushrooms, and they have a slightly deeper flavor. If left to grow and mature, cremini eventually become portobello mushrooms, which are the larger mushrooms with dark gills, dense texture, and a "meaty" flavor.

CHICKEN CUTLETS WITH CAPERS, GRAPES, AND ONIONS

PointsPlus value per serving: 5

HANDS-ON TIME: 15 min. ▪ **TOTAL TIME:** 15 min.

Capers and grapes offer a sweet and tangy flavor combination. Round out your meal with mashed potatoes or pasta.

- **4 (4-ounce) chicken cutlets**
- **Cooking spray**
- **½ teaspoon freshly ground black pepper**
- **¼ teaspoon salt**
- **½ cup fat-free, lower-sodium chicken broth**
- **½ cup dry white wine**
- **1 onion, vertically sliced**
- **1 cup seedless red grapes, halved**
- **1 tablespoon capers, drained**
- **1½ teaspoons butter**
- **1 teaspoon grated fresh lemon rind**
- **1 teaspoon chopped fresh thyme**

1. Heat a large nonstick skillet over medium-high heat. Coat chicken with cooking spray; sprinkle chicken with pepper and salt. Add chicken to pan; cook 4 minutes on each side or until done. Transfer to a plate; keep warm. Add broth and wine to pan, scraping pan to loosen browned bits.

2. While chicken cooks, heat a medium nonstick skillet over medium heat. Add onion to pan; coat onion with cooking spray. Cook 8 minutes or until golden, stirring occasionally.

3. Add cooked onions, grapes, and remaining ingredients to broth mixture; cook 2 minutes. Return chicken to pan; cook 1 minute or until thoroughly heated. **YIELD: 4 SERVINGS (SERVING SIZE: 1 CUTLET AND ABOUT ⅓ CUP ONION MIXTURE).**

PER SERVING: Calories 201; Fat 4.5g (sat 1.6g, mono 1.2g, poly 0.5g); Protein 25.1g; Carb 11g; Fiber 1.3g; Chol 76mg; Iron 0.9mg; Sodium 426mg; Calc 25mg

CHICKEN CUTLETS WITH WARM LEMON-ARTICHOKE RELISH

PointsPlus value per serving: 4

HANDS-ON TIME: 10 min. ▪ **TOTAL TIME:** 10 min.

Artichokes and lemon are a natural flavor combination that brightens up boneless chicken. Using thinner cutlets shortens cook time. Serve with steamed green beans—1 cup has a *PointsPlus* value per serving of 0.

4 (4-ounce) chicken cutlets
¼ teaspoon freshly ground black pepper
⅛ teaspoon salt
Cooking spray
1 teaspoon minced fresh garlic
1 (14-ounce) can artichoke hearts, drained and chopped
2 tablespoons water
1½ teaspoons grated fresh lemon rind
2 teaspoons fresh lemon juice
1 tablespoon chopped fresh parsley
1 ounce shredded fresh Parmesan cheese (about ¼ cup; optional)

1. Sprinkle chicken with pepper and salt. Heat a large nonstick skillet over medium-high heat. Coat pan with cooking spray. Add chicken; cook 3 minutes on each side or until done. Remove chicken from pan; keep warm.
2. Recoat pan with cooking spray; add garlic. Cook 1 minute. Add artichokes and next 3 ingredients (through lemon juice); cook 2 minutes or until thoroughly heated. Stir in parsley. Spoon artichoke relish over chicken, and sprinkle with Parmesan cheese, if desired. **YIELD: 4 SERVINGS (SERVING SIZE: 1 CHICKEN CUTLET AND ¼ CUP RELISH).**

PER SERVING: Calories 164; Fat 1.8g (sat 0.4g, mono 0.5g, poly 0.4g); Protein 28.4g; Carb 7.2g; Fiber 2.3g; Chol 66mg; Iron 0.9mg; Sodium 514mg; Calc 16mg

APPLE-SAGE CHICKEN THIGHS

PointsPlus value per serving: 7

HANDS-ON TIME: 23 min. ▪ **TOTAL TIME:** 35 min.

Apple cider is the base for this simple sauce and adds a slight sweetness to the dish. For a variation, try using fresh thyme to flavor the sauce instead of sage.

8 (5-ounce) bone-in chicken thighs, skinned
½ teaspoon freshly ground black pepper, divided
¼ teaspoon salt, divided
Cooking spray
¾ cup apple cider, divided
¾ cup fat-free, lower-sodium chicken broth
3 tablespoons all-purpose flour
1 tablespoon chopped fresh sage
Sage leaves (optional)

1. Sprinkle chicken with ¼ teaspoon pepper and ⅛ teaspoon salt. Heat a large nonstick skillet over medium-high heat. Coat pan with cooking spray. Add chicken to pan; cook 5 minutes on each side or until browned. Remove chicken from pan. Drain fat from pan.
2. Add ½ cup apple cider and chicken broth to pan, scraping pan to loosen browned bits. Return chicken to pan. Bring to a boil; cover, reduce heat, and simmer 12 minutes or until chicken is done. Remove chicken from pan, reserving broth mixture in pan.
3. Combine ¼ cup apple cider and flour in a small bowl, stirring with a whisk until smooth; gradually stir in ¼ cup hot broth mixture. Gradually add flour mixture to broth mixture in pan, stirring with a whisk until smooth. Bring to a boil; cook 4 minutes or until mixture thickens slightly, stirring constantly with a whisk. Remove from heat. Stir in ¼ teaspoon pepper, ⅛ teaspoon salt, and chopped sage. Serve sauce over chicken. Garnish with sage leaves, if desired. **YIELD: 4 SERVINGS (SERVING SIZE: 2 CHICKEN THIGHS AND ¼ CUP SAUCE).**

PER SERVING: Calories 300; Fat 13.9g (sat 3.9g, mono 5.3g, poly 3.2g); Protein 33.8g; Carb 7.6g; Fiber 0.1g; Chol 121mg; Iron 1.8mg; Sodium 371mg; Calc 20mg

APRICOT-GLAZED CHICKEN THIGHS

PointsPlus value per serving: 10

HANDS-ON TIME: 12 min. ■ **TOTAL TIME:** 22 min.

A single thigh (with 3 tablespoons of the flavorful sauce) has a *PointsPlus* value per serving of 5.

4 (5-ounce) skinless, bone-in chicken thighs
Cooking spray
¼ teaspoon salt
¼ teaspoon freshly ground black pepper
½ cup low-sugar apricot preserves
2 tablespoons cider vinegar
½ teaspoon crushed red pepper
1 garlic clove, crushed
⅓ cup water

1. Preheat oven to 400°.
2. Heat a large cast-iron skillet over medium-high heat. Coat chicken with cooking spray, and sprinkle with salt and pepper. Add chicken to pan. Cook 4 minutes on each side or until lightly browned.
3. Combine preserves and next 3 ingredients (through garlic). Brush chicken with preserves mixture. Place pan in oven. Bake, uncovered, at 400° for 10 minutes or until done. Remove chicken from pan. Add ⅓ cup water to pan, stirring with a whisk to deglaze pan. Spoon sauce over thighs. YIELD: 2 SERVINGS (SERVING SIZE: 2 CHICKEN THIGHS AND 6 TABLESPOONS SAUCE).

PER SERVING: Calories 392; Fat 13.5g (sat 3.7g, mono 5.5g, poly 2.7g); Protein 39.1g; Carb 24.9g; Fiber 0.2g; Chol 219mg; Iron 1.8mg; Sodium 437mg; Calc 21mg

ROASTED CHICKEN WITH SHALLOTS, GRAPES, AND THYME

PointsPlus value per serving: 7

HANDS-ON TIME: 10 min. ■ **TOTAL TIME:** 32 min.

We recommend serving the chicken and grape mixture over a side of brown rice—1 cup cooked brown rice has a *PointsPlus* value per serving of 5.

2 teaspoons olive oil, divided
4 (8-ounce) skinless, bone-in chicken leg quarters
½ teaspoon freshly ground black pepper
¼ teaspoon salt
2 cups seedless red grapes
1 tablespoon fresh thyme leaves
4 large shallots, peeled and quartered
Thyme sprigs (optional)

1. Preheat oven to 425°.
2. Heat a 12-inch cast-iron skillet or other ovenproof skillet over medium-high heat. Add 1 teaspoon oil to pan; swirl to coat. Sprinkle chicken with pepper and salt. Add chicken to pan; cook 4 minutes on each side or until browned. Remove pan from heat.
3. While chicken cooks, combine 1 teaspoon oil, grapes, thyme leaves, and shallots. Spoon grape mixture around chicken in pan. Place pan in oven. Bake, uncovered, at 425° for 22 to 25 minutes or until chicken is done. Garnish with thyme sprigs, if desired. YIELD: 4 SERVINGS (SERVING SIZE: 1 CHICKEN LEG QUARTER AND ABOUT ½ CUP GRAPE MIXTURE).

PER SERVING: Calories 293; Fat 8.7g (sat 2.3g, mono 4.1g, poly 2.2g); Protein 35.4g; Carb 17.5g; Fiber 1.2g; Chol 136mg; Iron 2.4mg; Sodium 297mg; Calc 37mg

CREOLE CHICKEN THIGHS

PointsPlus value per serving: 6

HANDS-ON TIME: 8 min. ■ **TOTAL TIME:** 18 min.

To make chopping the tomatoes easier, try snipping them with kitchen shears while they are still in the can. Serve with Dirty Rice (page 158) for a complete Louisiana-inspired meal with a *PointsPlus* value per serving of 10.

½ teaspoon Creole seasoning
8 (3-ounce) skinless, boneless chicken thighs
2 teaspoons canola oil
½ cup frozen cut okra
½ teaspoon chopped fresh thyme
1 (14.5-ounce) can stewed tomatoes, undrained and chopped

1. Rub Creole seasoning evenly over chicken.
2. Heat a large nonstick skillet over medium-high heat. Add oil to pan; swirl to coat. Add chicken; cook 2 minutes. Turn chicken over. Stir in okra, thyme, and tomatoes. Bring to a boil; cover, reduce heat, and simmer 10 minutes. Uncover and cook 2 minutes or until liquid is reduced by half. YIELD: 4 SERVINGS (SERVING SIZE: 2 CHICKEN THIGHS AND ⅓ CUP TOMATO MIXTURE).

PER SERVING: Calories 258; Fat 12g (sat 2.8g, mono 5.4g, poly 2.6g); Protein 29.1g; Carb 5.8g; Fiber 1.2g; Chol 158mg; Iron 1.6mg; Sodium 413mg; Calc 38mg

APPLE BUTTER–GLAZED CHICKEN THIGHS

PointsPlus value per serving: 7

HANDS-ON TIME: 14 min. ■ **TOTAL TIME:** 14 min.

Serve this easy dish with mashed potatoes (½ cup per serving) for a family-friendly meal with a *PointsPlus* value per serving of 10.

½ cup apple butter
1 tablespoon spicy brown mustard
1½ teaspoons Worcestershire sauce
1½ teaspoons honey
8 (3-ounce) skinless, boneless chicken thighs
¼ teaspoon salt
¼ teaspoon freshly ground black pepper
Cooking spray

1. Preheat grill to medium-high heat.
2. Combine first 4 ingredients in a small bowl. Sprinkle chicken with salt and pepper. Brush half of apple butter mixture evenly over chicken. Place chicken on grill rack coated with cooking spray. Grill 3 to 4 minutes; turn chicken over, and brush with remaining apple butter mixture. Grill 3 to 4 minutes or until done. YIELD: 4 SERVINGS (SERVING SIZE: 2 CHICKEN THIGHS).

PER SERVING: Calories 278; Fat 6.7g (sat 1.7g, mono 2.1g, poly 1.7g); Protein 33.6g; Carb 18.1g; Fiber 0.6g; Chol 141mg; Iron 2mg; Sodium 355mg; Calc 25mg

APPLE BUTTER

Apple butter can be a little misleading if you aren't familiar with this fruit spread because it actually has no butter (or fat) in it at all. Rather, apple butter is made by cooking apples and cider for a long time until the apples turn brown and caramelize. The end result is a thick, applesauce-like "butter" commonly used as a spread in place of real butter or jelly, but with no saturated fat and fewer calories. Look for it near the jellies and jams in your local market.

BRAISED CHICKEN WITH SAFFRON AND OLIVES

PointsPlus value per serving: 8

HANDS-ON TIME: 15 min. ■ **TOTAL TIME:** 15 min.

A colorful medley of bell peppers and yellow-orange saffron adds flavor and brightness to meaty chicken thighs. The chicken simmers in a broth-based stew and is ready to enjoy in only 15 minutes.

8 (3-ounce) skinless, boneless chicken thighs
Cooking spray
¾ teaspoon paprika
½ teaspoon freshly ground black pepper
¼ teaspoon salt
2 teaspoons olive oil
2 cups refrigerated prechopped tricolor bell pepper
¾ cup fat-free, lower-sodium chicken broth
1 tablespoon fresh thyme leaves
¾ teaspoon saffron threads
3 garlic cloves, minced
⅓ cup halved small green olives

1. Coat chicken with cooking spray. Combine paprika, black pepper, and salt; sprinkle over chicken.
2. Heat a large nonstick skillet over medium-high heat. Add oil to pan; swirl to coat. Add chicken; cook 3 minutes on each side or until lightly browned. Remove from pan; keep warm.
3. Add bell pepper to pan. Stir in broth and next 3 ingredients (through garlic), scraping pan to loosen browned bits. Bring to a boil, and return chicken to pan. Cover, reduce heat to medium, and cook 3 minutes or until chicken is done and sauce is slightly thick. Stir in olives; cook 1 minute. **YIELD: 4 SERVINGS (SERVING SIZE: 2 CHICKEN THIGHS AND ⅓ CUP VEGETABLE MIXTURE).**

PER SERVING: Calories 309; Fat 16.5g (sat 4.2g, mono 8.2g, poly 4g); Protein 32.6g; Carb 5g; Fiber 1g; Chol 113mg; Iron 2.3mg; Sodium 543mg; Calc 22mg

CURRIED CHICKEN THIGHS

PointsPlus value per serving: 7

HANDS-ON TIME: 15 min. ■ **TOTAL TIME:** 15 min.

Madras curry powder contains a bit of heat, so if you prefer less spice use regular curry powder.

1 tablespoon Madras curry powder
1 tablespoon all-purpose flour
¼ teaspoon freshly ground black pepper
⅛ teaspoon salt
6 (3-ounce) skinless, boneless chicken thighs
Olive oil–flavored cooking spray
1 cup julienne-cut red bell pepper
1 cup sliced onion
⅓ cup plain 2% reduced-fat Greek yogurt

1. Place curry powder in a large nonstick skillet; cook over medium-high heat 1 minute or until toasted. Remove from pan, and set aside.
2. Place flour, black pepper, and salt in a large zip-top plastic bag. Coat chicken with cooking spray; add to flour mixture. Seal bag, and shake to coat. Remove chicken from bag, shaking off excess flour mixture. Discard flour mixture. Add chicken to pan; cook over medium-high heat 7 minutes or until golden brown, turning after 4 minutes. Remove chicken from pan; keep warm.
3. Coat bell pepper and onion with cooking spray; add to pan. Cook 3 minutes or until almost crisp-tender. Stir in curry powder; add chicken, and cook 2 minutes. Remove from heat, and add yogurt just before serving, tossing to coat vegetables. **YIELD: 3 SERVINGS (SERVING SIZE: 2 CHICKEN THIGHS AND ½ CUP VEGETABLE MIXTURE).**

PER SERVING: Calories 274; Fat 10.9g (sat 3.1g, mono 4.2g, poly 2g); Protein 31.7g; Carb 10.8g; Fiber 2.4g; Chol 160mg; Iron 2.3mg; Sodium 213mg; Calc 51mg

PLUM-SAUCED CHICKEN THIGHS

PointsPlus value per serving: 8 *(pictured on page 10)*

HANDS-ON TIME: 9 min. ■ **TOTAL TIME:** 15 min.

8 (3-ounce) skinless, boneless chicken thighs
½ teaspoon five-spice powder
Olive oil–flavored cooking spray
1 cup red bell pepper strips
2 green onions, cut into 2-inch pieces
1 (15.5-ounce) can purple plums in heavy syrup
¼ cup water
2 tablespoons lower-sodium soy sauce

1. Sprinkle chicken evenly with five-spice powder; coat chicken with cooking spray. Heat a large nonstick skillet over medium-high heat. Add chicken to pan; cook 2 to 3 minutes on each side or until golden brown. Add bell pepper and onion to pan; cook 1 minute.
2. While chicken cooks, drain plums, reserving ¼ cup syrup; discard pits. Place plums, reserved syrup, ¼ cup water, and soy sauce in a blender; process until smooth. Add plum mixture to pan; bring to a boil. Cover, reduce heat, and simmer 6 minutes or until chicken is done. YIELD: 4 SERVINGS (SERVING SIZE: 2 CHICKEN THIGHS AND ABOUT ½ CUP SAUCE).

PER SERVING: Calories 309; Fat 10.2g (sat 2.7g, mono 4g, poly 2g); Protein 29.5g; Carb 24.3g; Fiber 1.6g; Chol 158mg; Iron 2.5mg; Sodium 409mg; Calc 31mg

BELL PEPPERS

Delicious raw, sautéed, stir-fried, or stuffed, bell peppers are one of the most commonly used vegetables. Often used to add a dash of color and a bit of crunch, bell peppers may seem kind of ordinary especially when compared to their hot pepper cousins. But these colorful beauties—they range from green to yellow to orange to red—have a wealth of nutritional perks. First, bell peppers are packed full of vitamin A and vitamin C—one bell pepper provides almost 300% of the recommended daily amount of vitamin A and 100% of the recommended daily amount of vitamin C. Second, compounds called carotenoids are partly responsible for bell peppers' vibrant colors, and these carotenoids have been shown to have possible antioxidant effects when it comes to reducing cancer risk. Lastly, these vegetables are full of fiber and very low in calories. In fact, one medium-sized pepper has just 40 or so calories, making it a great way to bulk up stir-fries and sautés. Choose firm, blemish-free peppers, and store them in the refrigerator until ready to use.

CHICKEN SUPREME CALZONE

PointsPlus value per serving: 8

HANDS-ON TIME: 6 min. ■ **TOTAL TIME:** 29 min.

There's no need to go out for dinner when you can make this tasty calzone at home. Ground chicken is a healthier option than the usual ground beef and just as tasty.

Cooking spray
½ cup refrigerated prechopped celery, onion, and bell pepper mix
¾ pound ground chicken
1 (13.8-ounce) can refrigerated pizza crust dough
½ cup spicy red pepper pasta sauce
3 ounces shredded part-skim mozzarella cheese (about ¾ cup)

1. Preheat oven to 450°.
2. Heat a large nonstick skillet over medium-high heat. Coat pan with cooking spray. Add celery mixture and chicken to pan. Cook 5 minutes or until chicken is browned and celery mixture is tender; stir to crumble chicken.
3. While chicken cooks, place dough on a lightly floured surface; roll into a 15-inch circle. Spread pasta sauce over dough, leaving a ¼-inch border. Sprinkle chicken mixture over half of circle; top with cheese. Fold half of dough over filling; press edges together with a fork to seal.
4. Place calzone on a baking sheet coated with cooking spray. Coat calzone with cooking spray.
5. Bake at 450° for 18 minutes or until golden brown. Remove from oven. Let stand 5 minutes; cut into wedges. YIELD: 6 SERVINGS (SERVING SIZE: 1 WEDGE).

PER SERVING: Calories 289; Fat 9.3g (sat 3.5g, mono 3.1g, poly 2.1g); Protein 18g; Carb 33.4g; Fiber 1.5g; Chol 45mg; Iron 2.1mg; Sodium 658mg; Calc 120mg

CHICKEN TOSTADAS

PointsPlus value per serving: 7 *(pictured on page 54)*

HANDS-ON TIME: 10 min. ▪ **TOTAL TIME:** 10 min.

Make your own flour tostada shells if you prefer flour tortillas over corn. Simply coat flour tortillas with cooking spray, place on a baking sheet, and place under the broiler until lightly browned.

Cooking spray
1 pound ground chicken breast
1 teaspoon salt-free Southwest chipotle seasoning
½ cup refrigerated guacamole
½ cup fat-free sour cream
8 (6-inch) corn tostada shells
2 cups shredded iceberg lettuce
1 cup chopped tomato
2 ounces crumbled queso fresco (about ½ cup)
Lime wedges (optional)

1. Heat a large skillet over medium-high heat. Coat pan with cooking spray. Add chicken to pan; sprinkle with seasoning, and cook 5 minutes or until done, stirring to crumble. Drain.
2. Combine guacamole and sour cream in a small bowl. Spread guacamole mixture evenly over tostada shells. Top evenly with lettuce, chicken, tomato, and cheese. Serve with lime wedges, if desired. YIELD: 4 SERVINGS (SERVING SIZE: 2 TOSTADAS).

PER SERVING: Calories 277; Fat 10.6g (sat 3.3g, mono 4.8g, poly 1.2g); Protein 31.5g; Carb 12.5g; Fiber 3g; Chol 88mg; Iron 0.8mg; Sodium 293mg; Calc 166mg

TURKEY PILAF–STUFFED PEPPERS

PointsPlus value per serving: 8

HANDS-ON TIME: 15 min. ▪ **TOTAL TIME:** 15 min.

Try this lighter, protein-packed version of your mom's stuffed peppers. Look for peppers weighing 6 to 8 ounces each to ensure that all the stuffing fits.

1 (8.5-ounce) pouch microwaveable precooked seven whole grains mix
1 tablespoon olive oil
1 pound ground turkey
1 (8-ounce) package refrigerated prechopped celery, onion, and bell pepper mix
1 teaspoon smoked paprika
1 teaspoon dried oregano
6 red bell peppers
⅔ cup water
5 ounces crumbled feta cheese (about 1¼ cups), divided
1 cup roasted garlic pasta sauce

1. Heat grain mix according to package directions; keep warm.
2. Heat a large nonstick skillet over medium-high heat. Add oil to pan; swirl to coat. Add turkey to pan, and cook 6 minutes. Add bell pepper mix, and cook 2 minutes, stirring occasionally. Stir in paprika and oregano; cook 1 minute.
3. While turkey mixture cooks, cut tops off bell peppers; discard tops, seeds, and membranes. Place peppers and ⅔ cup water in an 11 x 7–inch glass or ceramic baking dish. Cover tightly with plastic wrap. Microwave at HIGH 6 minutes. Drain peppers, and return to baking dish.
4. Combine grain mix, turkey mixture, 4 ounces feta, and pasta sauce in a large bowl; divide mixture evenly among peppers. Cover with plastic wrap; microwave at HIGH 2 minutes. Top each pepper with 2 teaspoons feta, and serve immediately. YIELD: 6 SERVINGS (SERVING SIZE: 1 STUFFED PEPPER).

PER SERVING: Calories 329; Fat 14.4g (sat 4.7g, mono 5.1g, poly 2.4g); Protein 23.6g; Carb 28g; Fiber 5.5g; Chol 70mg; Iron 3mg; Sodium 552mg; Calc 117mg

KUNG PAO CHICKEN WITH NOODLES

PointsPlus value per serving: 7

HANDS-ON TIME: 15 min. ■ **TOTAL TIME:** 15 min.

"Kung Pao" refers to a spicy Szechuan stir-fry dish usually made with chicken. Control the heat by going up or down on the amount of crushed red pepper.

1 (8-ounce) package uncooked Chinese curly noodles
Cooking spray
1 pound ground chicken breast
2 teaspoons minced garlic
6 tablespoons stir-fry sauce
¼ teaspoon crushed red pepper
¼ cup unsalted, dry-roasted peanuts, coarsely chopped
¼ cup sliced green onions
Lime wedges (optional)

1. Cook noodles according to package directions, omitting salt and fat.
2. While noodles cook, heat a large nonstick skillet over medium-high heat. Coat pan with cooking spray. Add chicken to pan. Cook 5 minutes or until done; stir to crumble. Add garlic; sauté 1 minute. Stir in stir-fry sauce and crushed red pepper.
3. Divide noodles among 6 plates. Spoon chicken mixture evenly over noodles; sprinkle with peanuts and green onions. Garnish with lime wedges, if desired. **YIELD: 6 SERVINGS (SERVING SIZE: ⅔ CUP NOODLES, ABOUT ⅓ CUP CHICKEN MIXTURE, 2 TEASPOONS GREEN ONIONS, AND 2 TEASPOONS PEANUTS).**

PER SERVING: Calories 276; Fat 5.3g (sat 0.9g, mono 2.2g, poly 1.4g); Protein 24.1g; Carb 34.2g; Fiber 2.1g; Chol 48mg; Iron 1.2mg; Sodium 648mg; Calc 12mg

SPINACH AND CHICKEN SAUSAGE PIZZA

PointsPlus value per serving: 8 *(pictured on page 61)*

HANDS-ON TIME: 10 min. ■ **TOTAL TIME:** 25 min.

You'll find refrigerated pizza crust dough in the bakery of many supermarkets—it's a great timesaver for the busy cook.

1 (5-ounce) package fresh baby spinach
1 pound refrigerated pizza crust dough
¾ cup lower-sodium marinara sauce
2 (3-ounce) links sun-dried tomato chicken sausage, cut into ¼-inch slices
3 ounces crumbled goat cheese (about ¾ cup)

1. Preheat oven to 500°.
2. Heat a large nonstick skillet over medium heat. Add spinach to pan; cook 1½ minutes or until spinach wilts, stirring constantly. Place spinach in a colander, pressing until barely moist.
3. Press dough into a 15 x 10–inch rectangle on a large ungreased baking sheet. Spread marinara sauce over dough, leaving a 1-inch border. Place spinach and sausage over sauce. Sprinkle with cheese. Bake at 500° for 15 minutes or until crust and cheese are browned. Cut into 12 rectangles. **YIELD: 6 SERVINGS (SERVING SIZE: 2 PIECES).**

PER SERVING: Calories 271; Fat 8.7g (sat 4.1g, mono 1.8g, poly 1.5g); Protein 13.2g; Carb 44.6g; Fiber 2.1g; Chol 30mg; Iron 3.2mg; Sodium 548mg; Calc 57mg

CREAMY SPINACH-CHICKEN PIZZA

PointsPlus value per serving: 9

HANDS-ON TIME: 4 min. ▪ **TOTAL TIME:** 14 min.

This hearty pizza with a creamy cheese sauce is worth the points! Serve with mixed greens drizzled with balsamic vinegar.

1 (10-ounce) package whole-wheat Italian cheese-flavored thin pizza crust
⅓ cup lower-sodium marinara sauce
1½ cups chopped cooked chicken breast
1½ cups chopped fresh baby spinach
3 ounces light garlic-and-herb spreadable cheese (about ⅓ cup)
1 ounce grated fresh Parmesan cheese (about ¼ cup)
¼ teaspoon freshly ground black pepper

1. Preheat oven to 450°.
2. Place crust on a baking sheet. Spread marinara sauce over crust, leaving a ½-inch border. Combine chicken, spinach, and spreadable cheese in a large bowl; spread chicken mixture over marinara. Sprinkle pizza with Parmesan cheese and pepper. Bake at 450° for 10 minutes or until cheese melts and crust is lightly browned. Cut pizza into 8 slices. **YIELD: 4 SERVINGS (SERVING SIZE: 2 SLICES).**

PER SERVING: Calories 358; Fat 11.5g (sat 5.4g, mono 3.9g, poly 0.6g); Protein 30.2g; Carb 37.1g; Fiber 6.8g; Chol 61mg; Iron 2.7mg; Sodium 710mg; Calc 198mg

COOKED CHICKEN

Keeping cooked chicken on hand makes it easy to throw meals together. Skinless, rotisserie chickens are an easy way to get cooked chicken for a recipe, but you can also quickly cook your own in about 20 minutes. For a yield of about 3 cups chopped cooked chicken, place 3 (6-ounce) skinless, boneless chicken breast halves in a large skillet, and add about 1½ cups water. Bring to a boil; cover, reduce heat, and simmer 14 minutes or until the chicken is no longer pink. Drain the chicken, and then slice, chop, or shred as directed for the recipe.

BALSAMIC CHICKEN AND WHITE BEANS

PointsPlus value per serving: 6

HANDS-ON TIME: 11 min. ▪ **TOTAL TIME:** 11 min.

This Tuscan-inspired meal is full of flavor and color, and it's a great choice served chilled on hot summer days.

1½ teaspoons olive oil
2 cups shredded skinless, boneless rotisserie chicken breast
1 tablespoon bottled minced garlic
4 teaspoons balsamic vinegar
1 (15-ounce) can unsalted cannellini beans or other white beans, rinsed and drained
1 (14.5-ounce) can diced tomatoes with basil, garlic, and oregano, drained
2 cups fresh baby spinach
2 tablespoons thinly sliced fresh basil
2 tablespoons grated fresh Parmesan cheese

1. Heat a large nonstick skillet over medium-high heat. Add oil to pan; swirl to coat. Add chicken and garlic to pan. Cook 1 minute, stirring constantly. Add vinegar, beans, and tomatoes; cook 5 minutes or until thoroughly heated, stirring frequently.
2. Divide spinach among 4 plates. Top evenly with chicken mixture, basil, and cheese. **YIELD: 4 SERVINGS (SERVING SIZE: ½ CUP SPINACH, ABOUT ¾ CUP CHICKEN MIXTURE, 1½ TEASPOONS BASIL, AND 1½ TEASPOONS CHEESE).**

PER SERVING: Calories 249; Fat 6.1g (sat 1.4g, mono 2.7g, poly 0.8g); Protein 28g; Carb 17.9g; Fiber 3.9g; Chol 62mg; Iron 2.9mg; Sodium 449mg; Calc 105mg

CHICKEN-BROCCOLI CASSEROLE

PointsPlus value per serving: 6

HANDS-ON TIME: 8 min. ▪ **TOTAL TIME:** 33 min.

Use lightened versions of condensed soup, sour cream, and potato chips to keep saturated fat and sodium in check in this potluck dinner favorite.

1 (12-ounce) package fresh broccoli florets
1 (10.75-ounce) can condensed reduced-fat, reduced-sodium cream of chicken soup, undiluted
1 (8-ounce) carton light sour cream
½ teaspoon freshly ground black pepper
¼ teaspoon salt
2 cups chopped cooked chicken breast
Cooking spray
3 cups baked cheddar and sour cream–flavored potato crisps, coarsely crushed (about 3 ounces)

1. Preheat oven to 350°.
2. Cook broccoli according to package directions. Drain and coarsely chop.
3. Combine soup and next 3 ingredients (through salt) in a large bowl. Add chicken and broccoli. Spoon mixture into an 11 x 7–inch glass or ceramic baking dish coated with cooking spray. Sprinkle top with crisps. Coat crisps with cooking spray. Bake, uncovered, at 350° for 25 minutes or until bubbly. **YIELD: 6 SERVINGS (SERVING SIZE: ABOUT 1 CUP).**

PER SERVING: Calories 236; Fat 7.1g (sat 3.1g, mono 2.2g, poly 1.6g); Protein 19.5g; Carb 20.6g; Fiber 2.6g; Chol 55mg; Iron 0.8mg; Sodium 457mg; Calc 110mg

MEDITERRANEAN CHICKEN WITH ZUCCHINI

PointsPlus value per serving: 5

HANDS-ON TIME: 15 min. ▪ **TOTAL TIME:** 15 min.

Using zucchini "noodles" instead of pasta gives this dish a nutritional boost and helps keep the *PointsPlus* value per serving low.

2 medium zucchini, trimmed
1 tablespoon olive oil
¾ cup refrigerated prechopped tricolor bell pepper
⅔ cup refrigerated prechopped onion
1 tablespoon bottled minced garlic
3 tablespoons chopped pitted kalamata olives
¼ teaspoon freshly ground black pepper
1 (14.5-ounce) can unsalted diced tomatoes, undrained
1 (8-ounce) package grilled chicken breast strips
1 ounce grated fresh Parmesan cheese (about ¼ cup)

1. Using a vegetable peeler, thinly slice zucchini into ribbons. Cook zucchini in boiling water 8 minutes or until crisp-tender. Remove from heat; do not drain. Set aside, and keep warm.
2. While zucchini cooks, heat a large nonstick skillet over medium-high heat. Add oil to pan; swirl to coat. Add bell pepper, onion, and garlic to pan; sauté 5 minutes. Add olives and next 3 ingredients (through grilled chicken); sauté 6 minutes or until thoroughly heated.
3. Drain zucchini, and divide among 4 bowls. Top evenly with chicken mixture and cheese. **YIELD: 4 SERVINGS (SERVING SIZE: ¼ OF ZUCCHINI, 1 CUP CHICKEN MIXTURE, AND 1 TABLESPOON CHEESE).**

PER SERVING: Calories 208; Fat 9g (sat 2.2g, mono 5.2g, poly 0.8g); Protein 20g; Carb 13.7g; Fiber 2.7g; Chol 39mg; Iron 1.7mg; Sodium 581mg; Calc 149mg

ZUCCHINI

Part of the squash family, zucchini is a staple summer vegetable. It is tasty steamed, grilled, or sautéed, takes just a few minutes to prepare, and requires little seasoning. Having approximately 25 calories per cup when cooked, zucchini is low in calories yet filling thanks to the fiber content. It's also a good source of vitamin C, beta-carotene, and potassium. Keep the skin on this vegetable if possible because it's thought that this is where most of the nutrients are stored. When shopping, look for zucchini that are firm and heavy with smooth, unblemished skin. Store them in the refrigerator in a plastic bag until ready to use.

SALSA VERDE CHICKEN ENCHILADAS

PointsPlus value per serving: 7 *(pictured on page 12)*

HANDS-ON TIME: 11 min. ■ **TOTAL TIME:** 11 min.

Microwaving the chicken filling makes these enchiladas a quick and easy weeknight meal. Substitute your favorite salsa or picante sauce for the salsa verde.

4 cups shredded cooked chicken breast
4 ounces shredded Monterey Jack cheese (about 1 cup), divided
1 (16-ounce) jar salsa verde, divided
½ cup light sour cream
¼ cup chopped fresh cilantro, divided
8 (6-inch) flour tortillas
Cooking spray

1. Preheat broiler.
2. Combine chicken, 2 ounces cheese, ½ cup salsa, sour cream, and 2 tablespoons cilantro in a medium microwave-safe bowl. Microwave at HIGH 2 minutes or until thoroughly heated.
3. Warm tortillas according to package directions.
4. Spread 1 cup salsa in bottom of a 13 x 9–inch glass or ceramic baking dish coated with cooking spray. Spoon about ½ cup chicken mixture down center of each tortilla; roll up. Place, seam sides down, in prepared dish. Top with remaining salsa; sprinkle with 2 ounces cheese.
5. Broil 3 minutes or until cheese melts. Sprinkle with 2 tablespoons cilantro. **YIELD: 8 SERVINGS (SERVING SIZE: 1 ENCHILADA).**

PER SERVING: Calories 289; Fat 10.3g (sat 4.5g, mono 3.5g, poly 1.1g); Protein 28.7g; Carb 19.1g; Fiber 1.4g; Chol 80mg; Iron 1.7mg; Sodium 656mg; Calc 174mg

BARBECUED CHICKEN–STUFFED POTATOES

PointsPlus value per serving: 8

HANDS-ON TIME: 4 min. ■ **TOTAL TIME:** 14 min.

Feel free to top these potatoes with chopped green onions or even crumbled cooked bacon. An average slice of bacon will add a *PointsPlus* value of 1.

4 (6-ounce) baking potatoes, scrubbed
1⅓ cups shredded cooked chicken breast
⅓ cup barbecue sauce
½ cup reduced-fat sour cream
2 ounces reduced-fat shredded extra-sharp cheddar cheese (about ½ cup)

1. Pierce potatoes with a fork; arrange in a circle on a paper towel in a microwave oven. Microwave at HIGH 10 minutes or until done, rearranging potatoes after 5 minutes.
2. Combine chicken and barbecue sauce in a microwave-safe bowl. Cover with plastic wrap (do not allow plastic wrap to touch food); vent. Microwave at HIGH 2 minutes or until thoroughly heated, stirring after 1 minute.
3. Cut potatoes lengthwise, cutting to, but not through, other side. Spoon 2 tablespoons sour cream into center of each potato; fluff with a fork. Top each potato with about ⅓ cup chicken mixture and 2 tablespoons cheese.
YIELD: 4 SERVINGS (SERVING SIZE: 1 STUFFED POTATO).

PER SERVING: Calories 309; Fat 8.4g (sat 4.9g, mono 2.5g, poly 0.6g); Protein 22.8g; Carb 35.7g; Fiber 2.3g; Chol 65mg; Iron 2mg; Sodium 399mg; Calc 181mg

POTATOES

Because most of their calories come from carbohydrates, potatoes have become a vegetable that people feel like they need to avoid if trying to lose or maintain weight. The truth is that a medium-sized potato offers just as much fiber, protein, vitamins, and minerals as a ½-cup serving of brown rice or oatmeal and for around the same calories. In addition, potatoes are higher in potassium than most all other vegetables and fruits, and they are a surprisingly good source of vitamin C with a medium potato providing 45% of one's daily needs. Two keys to getting the most out of this nutrient-rich vegetable are to eat the skin and to be mindful of how you prepare it. The skin is full of fiber and many of the nutrients are located just under the skin, so try to resist the urge to lose the peel. Also, look for new ways to prepare potatoes other than baking and loading with butter and sour cream. It's these toppings, along with other preparation techniques like frying, that can turn this healthy vegetable into a high-calorie disaster.

LOADED CHICKEN NACHOS

PointsPlus value per serving: 8

HANDS-ON TIME: 4 min. ▪ **TOTAL TIME:** 9 min.

A pub favorite, these nachos are perfect when having a few people over to watch a big game. Serve as an entrée or as an appetizer. Pick up a rotisserie chicken at the grocery store and you can put this crowd-pleaser together in a snap.

4 cups baked tortilla chips
2 cups shredded skinless, boneless rotisserie chicken breast
2 tablespoons chopped fresh cilantro
3 tablespoons fresh lime juice
6 ounces reduced-fat shredded white cheddar cheese with jalapeño peppers (about 1½ cups)
1 cup shredded lettuce
1 cup fresh salsa
½ cup fat-free sour cream
½ cup diced peeled avocado (optional)
Chopped fresh cilantro (optional)

1. Preheat oven to 425°.
2. Spread tortilla chips in a single layer on a large foil-lined jelly-roll pan. Combine chicken, 2 tablespoons cilantro, and lime juice. Spread chicken mixture over chips; top with cheese.
3. Bake, uncovered, at 425° for 5 minutes or until cheese melts. Top with lettuce, salsa, and sour cream. Garnish with avocado and cilantro, if desired. Serve immediately. **YIELD: 5 SERVINGS (SERVING SIZE: ⅕ OF NACHOS).**

PER SERVING: Calories 326; Fat 11.2g (sat 5g, mono 3.1g, poly 1.7g); Protein 30.3g; Carb 24.5g; Fiber 1.5g; Chol 69mg; Iron 1mg; Sodium 613mg; Calc 324mg

SMOKED CHICKEN CHIPOTLE QUESADILLAS

PointsPlus value per serving: 6

HANDS-ON TIME: 17 min. ▪ **TOTAL TIME:** 17 min.

If you want to decrease the heat in these fiery quesadillas, use a smaller amount of the chiles. Serve with fruit, such as seedless grapes and cubed pineapple, for an easy side with a *PointsPlus* value per serving of 0.

4 ounces ⅓-less-fat cream cheese (about ½ cup), softened
2 tablespoons chopped chipotle chiles, canned in adobo sauce
4 (6-inch) whole-wheat tortillas
2 cups shredded smoked cooked chicken
¼ cup chopped green onions
Cooking spray
¼ cup chipotle salsa (optional)
¼ cup light sour cream (optional)

1. Combine cream cheese and chiles in a small bowl. Spread cream cheese mixture over tortillas. Sprinkle chicken and green onions over half of each tortilla. Fold tortillas in half.
2. Heat a large nonstick skillet over medium heat. Coat pan with cooking spray. Place 2 tortillas, folded sides together, in pan. Cook 2 to 3 minutes or until lightly browned; turn quesadillas over, keeping folded sides in center of pan. Cook 2 to 3 minutes or until lightly browned. Remove from pan, and keep warm. Repeat procedure with remaining quesadillas. Cut each quesadilla into 4 wedges. Serve with salsa and sour cream, if desired. **YIELD: 4 SERVINGS (SERVING SIZE: 4 WEDGES).**

PER SERVING: Calories 274; Fat 10.9g (sat 5.8g, mono 2.3g, poly 0.7g); Protein 26.9g; Carb 15.3g; Fiber 8.8g; Chol 80mg; Iron 1.3mg; Sodium 466mg; Calc 95mg

salads

Greek Chicken Salad, *page 99*

GINGERED TROPICAL FRUIT SALAD

PointsPlus value per serving: 2

HANDS-ON TIME: 12 min. ▪ **TOTAL TIME:** 12 min.

Section the orange over a bowl, and reserve the juice to use for making the dressing.

2 tablespoons fresh orange juice
2 tablespoons fresh lime juice
1 tablespoon honey
1 teaspoon grated peeled fresh ginger
2 cups cubed fresh pineapple
¾ cup sliced peeled kiwifruit (about 2 kiwifruit)
1 large navel orange, peeled and sectioned
¼ cup flaked sweetened coconut, toasted

1. Combine first 4 ingredients in a large bowl. Add pineapple, kiwifruit, and orange; toss gently to coat. Sprinkle with coconut. Cover and chill until ready to serve. **YIELD: 6 SERVINGS (SERVING SIZE: ABOUT ½ CUP).**

PER SERVING: Calories 85; Fat 1.3g (sat 0.9g, mono 0.1g, poly 0g); Protein 0.9g; Carb 19.2g; Fiber 2.3g; Chol 0mg; Iron 0.3mg; Sodium 11mg; Calc 26mg

SECTIONING CITRUS FRUIT

The acidic juices in fresh citrus fruits help heighten and brighten the flavors of a variety of dishes. Be sure to wash citrus thoroughly under warm water to remove dirt and wax before you begin.

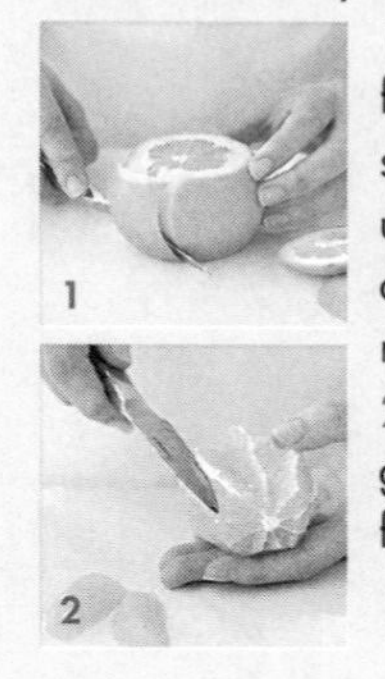

1. Cut the top and bottom portions from the fruit to create a stable cutting surface. Stand the fruit upright, and use a small paring knife to slice downward in a long, slow curve to remove the rind and the white pith.
2. Hold the fruit in your palm, and gently follow the natural sections of the fruit with the knife to cut out wedges.

STRAWBERRY SPINACH SALAD

PointsPlus value per serving: 3 *(pictured on page 62)*

HANDS-ON TIME: 5 min. ▪ **TOTAL TIME:** 5 min.

Toss fresh spinach with naturally sweet strawberries and tangy goat cheese for a delightful hurry-up salad.

1 (6-ounce) package fresh baby spinach
1½ cups quartered strawberries
¼ cup thinly sliced red onion
3 tablespoons blush wine vinaigrette
¼ teaspoon freshly ground black pepper
1 tablespoon chopped fresh mint (optional)
2 ounces crumbled goat cheese (about ½ cup)

1. Combine first 5 ingredients and, if desired, mint in a large bowl; toss. Sprinkle with cheese. **YIELD: 4 SERVINGS (SERVING SIZE: ABOUT 1⅔ CUPS SALAD AND 2 TABLESPOONS CHEESE).**

PER SERVING: Calories 124; Fat 5.8g (sat 2.3g, mono 1.7g, poly 0.6g); Protein 4.1g; Carb 15.4g; Fiber 3.4g; Chol 7mg; Iron 1.9mg; Sodium 278mg; Calc 62mg

BROCCOLI SLAW WITH MUSTARD VINAIGRETTE

PointsPlus value per serving: 2

HANDS-ON TIME: 4 min. ▪ **TOTAL TIME:** 4 min.

This seven-ingredient slaw is a light and refreshing side dish that is almost effortless.

3 tablespoons cider vinegar
1 tablespoon olive oil
1 tablespoon honey Dijon mustard
1 teaspoon sugar
¼ teaspoon freshly ground black pepper
⅛ teaspoon salt
1 (12-ounce) package broccoli slaw
Additional freshly ground black pepper (optional)

1. Combine first 6 ingredients in a large bowl, stirring with a whisk. Microwave at HIGH 30 seconds. Add broccoli slaw, tossing to coat. Sprinkle with pepper, if desired. **YIELD: 4 SERVINGS (SERVING SIZE: 1¼ CUPS).**

PER SERVING: Calories 67; Fat 3.4g (sat 0.5g, mono 2.5g, poly 0.4g); Protein 2g; Carb 6.9g; Fiber 2g; Chol 0mg; Iron 0.8mg; Sodium 129mg; Calc 41mg

WARM BRUSSELS SPROUTS AND APPLE SLAW

PointsPlus value per serving: 3

HANDS-ON TIME: 16 min. ■ **TOTAL TIME:** 16 min.

Granny Smith apples, cider vinegar, and sweetened dried cranberries provide a pleasant sweet-and-sour combination in this warm slaw.

4 teaspoons canola oil, divided
1 tablespoon cider vinegar
¼ teaspoon salt
¼ teaspoon freshly ground black pepper
2 cups thinly sliced Brussels sprouts (½ pound)
¾ cup chopped Granny Smith apple (1 small)
⅓ cup sweetened dried cranberries

1. Combine 1 tablespoon oil, vinegar, salt, and pepper in a large bowl, stirring with a whisk.
2. Heat a large skillet over medium-high heat. Add 1 teaspoon oil to pan; swirl to coat. Add Brussels sprouts and apple to pan; sauté 5 minutes or until crisp-tender. Stir in cranberries. Add Brussels sprouts mixture to vinegar mixture, tossing to coat. YIELD: 4 SERVINGS (SERVING SIZE: ABOUT ⅔ CUP).

PER SERVING: Calories 105; Fat 4.8g (sat 0.4g, mono 3g, poly 1.4g); Protein 1.6g; Carb 15.5g; Fiber 2.8g; Chol 0mg; Iron 0.7mg; Sodium 159mg; Calc 20mg

BRUSSELS SPROUTS

These tiny green vegetables resemble mini-cabbages. It makes sense: They're part of the cruciferous vegetable family, which includes cabbages, broccoli, turnip greens, mustard greens, and kale. Although tiny in size, Brussels sprouts pack a powerful nutritional punch of fiber, vitamin C, vitamin K, and chemical compounds called phytochemicals. Phytochemicals have antioxidant properties, and the phytochemicals in these cruciferous vegetables have been linked to reducing the risk of several types of cancer. Brussels sprouts like cool weather, so they're most commonly found in markets from fall until early spring although you can find frozen varieties year-round. Choose Brussels sprouts that are firm with dark green leaves. Store them in the refrigerator in a plastic bag for up to a week. When you're ready to eat, wash and trim the leaves. Two popular and quick ways to prepare Brussels sprouts are to steam them on the stove top (or in the microwave) for 5 to 6 minutes or roast them in the oven at 400° for 30 to 35 minutes. Season simply with olive oil, salt, and freshly ground black pepper.

ASIAN SLAW

PointsPlus value per serving: 2 *(pictured on page 9)*

HANDS-ON TIME: 10 min. ■ **TOTAL TIME:** 10 min.

This slaw is an ideal make-ahead dish. Preparing it and chilling until you're ready to serve allows the slaw time to marinate in the dressing. This side pairs well with grilled fish.

¼ cup light mayonnaise
2 tablespoons fresh lime juice
1½ teaspoons wasabi paste
1 teaspoon sugar
¼ teaspoon salt
1 (16-ounce) package 3-color coleslaw
½ cup thinly sliced snow peas
¼ cup chopped fresh cilantro
3 green onions, chopped
¼ cup chopped unsalted, dry-roasted peanuts

1. Combine first 5 ingredients in a medium bowl, stirring with a whisk. Add coleslaw and next 3 ingredients (through green onions), tossing well to coat. Sprinkle with peanuts just before serving. YIELD: 8 SERVINGS (SERVING SIZE: ABOUT ⅔ CUP SLAW AND 1½ TEASPOONS PEANUTS).

PER SERVING: Calories 74; Fat 5g (sat 0.7g, mono 1.7g, poly 2.1g); Protein 2g; Carb 6.5g; Fiber 1.9g; Chol 3mg; Iron 0.6mg; Sodium 154mg; Calc 35mg

HARICOTS VERTS AND RADISHES WITH SHALLOT VINAIGRETTE

PointsPlus value per serving: 2

HANDS-ON TIME: 10 min. ■ **TOTAL TIME:** 10 min.

Haricots verts **is French for "green beans" and usually refers to a longer, thinner green bean variety. While fresh thyme is preferable, you can substitute 1 teaspoon dried thyme.**

1 (8-ounce) package microwaveable haricots verts (French green beans)
2 tablespoons finely chopped shallots
1 tablespoon minced fresh thyme
2 tablespoons canola oil
2 tablespoons water
1 tablespoon sherry vinegar
1 tablespoon honey Dijon mustard
½ teaspoon freshly ground black pepper
¼ teaspoon salt
1 (6-ounce) bag radishes, grated

1. Microwave haricots verts according to package directions. Plunge beans into ice water; drain.
2. Place shallots and next 7 ingredients (through salt) in a blender; process until smooth. Place radishes and 2 tablespoons vinaigrette in a medium bowl; toss to coat.
3. Divide beans among 4 plates. Top evenly with radishes, and drizzle with vinaigrette. **YIELD: 4 SERVINGS (SERVING SIZE: ¼ OF HARICOTS VERTS, ABOUT ⅓ CUP RADISHES, AND 1½ TABLESPOONS VINAIGRETTE).**

PER SERVING: Calories 105; Fat 7.1g (sat 0.5g, mono 4.4g, poly 2g); Protein 1.2g; Carb 6.7g; Fiber 2.3g; Chol 0mg; Iron 0.6mg; Sodium 195mg; Calc 43mg

CHOPPED VEGETABLE SALAD

PointsPlus value per serving: 1

HANDS-ON TIME: 9 min. ■ **TOTAL TIME:** 9 min.

This simple raw salad lets the flavors of the vegetables shine through and develops more flavor the longer it chills. It's also a good way to use up end-of-summer produce.

3 cups chopped zucchini (about 2 medium)
2 cups cherry tomatoes, halved
1¼ cups chopped orange bell pepper (about 1 medium)
¾ cup chopped yellow squash (about 1 medium)
2 garlic cloves, minced
3 tablespoons white balsamic vinegar
1 tablespoon olive oil
2 teaspoons Dijon mustard
½ teaspoon salt
¼ teaspoon freshly ground black pepper

1. Combine first 5 ingredients in a large bowl; set aside.
2. Combine vinegar and remaining ingredients in a small bowl, stirring with a whisk. Drizzle dressing over vegetables, tossing to coat. Serve immediately, or cover and chill 2 hours. **YIELD: 6 SERVINGS (SERVING SIZE: ABOUT ¾ CUP).**

PER SERVING: Calories 54; Fat 2.6g (sat 0.4g, mono 1.7g, poly 0.4g); Protein 1.7g; Carb 7.5g; Fiber 1.9g; Chol 0mg; Iron 0.6mg; Sodium 248mg; Calc 22mg

VINEGAR TYPES

Vinegar is an essential ingredient in many recipes but particularly salads. Often too harsh by itself, vinegar can be combined with milder ingredients such as oils and juice to create delicious salads, dressings, marinades, and condiments. Vinegar is made when alcohol ferments and creates an acidic liquid which is then watered down and bottled. The alcohol and seasonings that were involved in the fermentation process determine the flavor of the vinegar. Today there are dozens of different vinegars available, so it can get a little confusing as to which to use. Here's a quick list of the most common vinegars and the best uses for each.

White Distilled Vinegar: Possibly the strongest in flavor, this vinegar can easily overpower milder flavors, so it's most often used in pickling and as an all-natural cleaning product.
Red Wine Vinegar: Made when red wine is allowed to ferment, this vinegar is commonly used to make salad dressings and vinaigrettes.
Balsamic Vinegar: This aged dark brown vinegar is originally from Italy. Its thickness, sweetness, and price will vary based on how long it has aged. Popular as a condiment for fresh vegetables such as tomatoes, it is also commonly used to deepen the flavor of vinaigrettes.
Apple Cider Vinegar: Made from pressed apples that have fermented into alcohol, it has a mild tartness with a fruit flavor. It's good in a wide variety of dishes due to its mellow, sweet flavor.
Rice Vinegar: Common in Asian dishes such as stir-fries and sushi, this vinegar is made from rice wine. It's milder in flavor than distilled vinegar but not as fruity as other wine vinegars.

WHITE BEAN SALAD

PointsPlus value per serving: 3 *(pictured on page 63)*

HANDS-ON TIME: 8 min. ▪ **TOTAL TIME:** 8 min.

Serve this hearty salad alongside grilled chicken breasts or tuna steaks.

1 tablespoon olive oil
2 teaspoons white balsamic vinegar
½ teaspoon grated fresh lemon rind
¼ teaspoon freshly ground black pepper
½ cup chopped bottled roasted red bell peppers
¼ cup finely chopped red onion
2 tablespoons chopped fresh parsley
2 (15.5-ounce) cans cannellini beans, rinsed and drained

1. Combine first 4 ingredients in a medium bowl, stirring with a whisk. Add bell pepper and remaining ingredients; toss to coat. Cover and chill until ready to serve. YIELD: 7 SERVINGS (SERVING SIZE: ABOUT ½ CUP).

PER SERVING: Calories 108; Fat 2.3g (sat 0.3g, mono 1.7g, poly 0.3g); Protein 6.1g; Carb 16.2g; Fiber 4.6g; Chol 0mg; Iron 1.5mg; Sodium 195mg; Calc 49mg

SODIUM AND CANNED BEANS

While dried beans are nice, the soaking and prep time required for them is not, making canned beans an essential pantry staple for anyone who needs to prepare healthy meals quickly. Not only are canned beans inexpensive, but they are an immediate source of complex carbohydrates, fat-free protein, and fiber. The only downside to canned beans may be their sodium content. Sodium levels are higher in canned beans because the liquid they are preserved in enables them to remain shelf-stable, but there are some ways you can quickly and easily reduce the sodium content. First, when available, choose a no-salt-added variety. Then, pour the canned beans in a colander to drain the canning liquid off and rinse the beans thoroughly with running water. Studies have shown that rinsing and draining canned beans can eliminate up to 40 percent of the sodium.

WARM CHIPOTLE SWEET POTATO SALAD

PointsPlus value per serving: 2

HANDS-ON TIME: 10 min. ▪ **TOTAL TIME:** 15 min.

Microwaving the sweet potatoes before browning them in the skillet is the key to getting this salad on the table in only 15 minutes. Add a double dose of flavor with both a teaspoon of the chopped chipotle chiles (canned in adobo sauce) and a half teaspoon of the adobo sauce itself.

1 pound sweet potatoes, peeled and cut into ½-inch pieces
Cooking spray
1 tablespoon chopped green onions
1 teaspoon olive oil
1 teaspoon chopped chipotle chiles, canned in adobo sauce
½ teaspoon adobo sauce
⅛ teaspoon salt
⅛ teaspoon freshly ground black pepper
⅛ teaspoon chili powder
⅛ teaspoon ground cumin

1. Place potatoes in an 8-inch square glass or ceramic baking dish. Cover with plastic wrap; vent. Microwave at HIGH 5 minutes or until almost tender.
2. Heat large nonstick skillet over medium-high heat; add potatoes. Coat potatoes with cooking spray, and cook 5 minutes or until browned, stirring occasionally.
3. Remove pan from heat. Add green onions and remaining ingredients, tossing gently to coat. YIELD: 4 SERVINGS (SERVING SIZE: ½ CUP).

PER SERVING: Calories 102; Fat 1.2g (sat 0.2g, mono 0.8g, poly 0.1g); Protein 1.8g; Carb 20.9g; Fiber 4.1g; Chol 0mg; Iron 0.8mg; Sodium 198mg; Calc 20mg

WARM ISRAELI COUSCOUS TABBOULEH

PointsPlus value per serving: 3

HANDS-ON TIME: 5 min. ▪ **TOTAL TIME:** 15 min.

Tabbouleh is a traditional Mediterranean salad made with bulgur wheat, which can require a lengthy cooking time. Instead, this variation uses quick-cooking Israeli couscous instead.

2 cups fat-free, lower-sodium chicken broth
1 cup Israeli couscous
¼ teaspoon freshly ground black pepper
1 cup chopped fresh parsley
1 cup diced cucumber
1 cup diced tomato
¼ cup chopped fresh mint
¼ cup fresh lemon juice (about 2 lemons)
1 tablespoon olive oil

1. Bring chicken broth to a boil in a medium saucepan. Stir in couscous and pepper; cover, reduce heat, and simmer 10 minutes or until couscous is tender and liquid is absorbed.
2. Remove from heat; stir in parsley and remaining ingredients. **YIELD: 6 SERVINGS (SERVING SIZE: ⅔ CUP).**

PER SERVING: Calories 126; Fat 2.4g (sat 0.3g, mono 1.7g, poly 0.3g); Protein 4.3g; Carb 21.9g; Fiber 1.9g; Chol 0mg; Iron 1.4mg; Sodium 198mg; Calc 23mg

WARM QUINOA AND RICE CAPRESE SALAD

PointsPlus value per serving: 9 *(pictured on page 64)*

HANDS-ON TIME: 6 min. ▪ **TOTAL TIME:** 6 min.

Quinoa is a nutritional powerhouse, high in protein, fiber, iron, and calcium. This main dish salad can also be served as a side. Eight (¾-cup) servings each have a *PointsPlus* value of 4.

2 (8.5-ounce) pouches microwaveable precooked quinoa and brown rice with garlic
2 cups grape tomatoes, halved
2 teaspoons extra-virgin olive oil
½ teaspoon kosher salt
½ teaspoon freshly ground black pepper
12 basil leaves, torn into pieces
½ (8-ounce) container fresh mozzarella pearls
6 cups arugula or baby spinach

1. Heat quinoa according to package directions, and keep warm.
2. Combine tomatoes and next 5 ingredients (through mozzarella); toss well. Stir in quinoa. Divide arugula evenly among 4 plates. Top with quinoa mixture. **YIELD: 4 SERVINGS (SERVING SIZE: 1½ CUPS ARUGULA AND ABOUT 1½ CUPS QUINOA MIXTURE).**

PER SERVING: Calories 335; Fat 12.8g (sat 4.7g, mono 5.4g, poly 1.9g); Protein 10.9g; Carb 44.4g; Fiber 4.6g; Chol 23mg; Iron 5mg; Sodium 568mg; Calc 75mg

QUINOA

Classified as a whole grain, quinoa (pronounced "KEEN-wah") is actually a tiny seed. It's a common substitute for grains like rice, barley, and couscous because of its stellar nutritional content. Quinoa is gluten-free and full of both fiber and protein. In fact, unlike many other grains, the protein in quinoa provides all of the essential amino acids. It's also a good source of iron, magnesium, and phosphrous. All of these qualities make quinoa a great option if you're a vegetarian, avoiding gluten, or simply trying to eat healthier. Quinoa has a mild, slightly nutty flavor that's good when served by itself or as part of a salad or pilaf. The only special treatment quinoa needs is that it must be rinsed prior to cooking to remove the natural outer coating that can be bitter. After that, preparation is similar to cooking rice —bring water to a boil, add quinoa, and then cover and cook. Each 1 cup of quinoa requires 2 cups of liquid for cooking, and it usually takes just 15 to 20 minutes to cook.

SEVEN-GRAIN ASIAN SLAW

PointsPlus value per serving: 6

HANDS-ON TIME: 10 min. ▪ **TOTAL TIME:** 10 min.

This filling salad offers lots of delicious flavor, texture, and crunch. You can enhance it even more with a squeeze of lime juice, a dash of Sriracha sauce, a pinch of bean sprouts, or a sprinkle of chopped peanuts. This makes a great main-dish salad, but you can also serve it as a side. A ½-cup serving has a *PointsPlus* value of 2.

1 (8.5-ounce) package quick-cooking seven whole grains mix
2 cups frozen shelled edamame (green soybeans), thawed
½ cup low-fat sesame-ginger dressing
1 tablespoon natural-style creamy peanut butter
1 cup chopped English cucumber
¾ cup refrigerated prechopped tricolor bell pepper
½ cup chopped fresh cilantro
1 (10-ounce) package angel hair slaw

1. Cook grain mix according to package directions. Spread in a single layer on a rimmed baking sheet; cool.
2. Place edamame in a microwave-safe bowl; microwave at HIGH 2 minutes. Rinse with cold running water until cool.
3. Place dressing and peanut butter in a blender; process until smooth.
4. Combine cooled grain mix, edamame, cucumber, and remaining ingredients in a large bowl. Pour dressing over mixture, tossing gently to coat. **YIELD: 4 SERVINGS (SERVING SIZE: 1¾ CUPS).**

PER SERVING: Calories 255; Fat 7.6g (sat 0.7g, mono 2.6g, poly 2.6g); Protein 11.3g; Carb 36.4g; Fiber 7.3g; Chol 0mg; Iron 2.6mg; Sodium 567mg; Calc 83mg

EDAMAME

Edamame are immature soybeans served either in their pods or shelled. They are most often sold frozen, but more markets are now offering fresh edamame as well. Steaming and boiling are the most common ways to prepare them when in the shell, and you often see them served as an appetizer either seasoned or with a dipping sauce. Shelled edamame are often blanched or roasted and stirred into salads, grain pilafs, or pastas or eaten as a snack. Because edamame are baby soybeans, they're a great vegetarian protein source, and they're also full of folate and essential fatty acids.

SALMON COBB SALAD

PointsPlus value per serving: 8

HANDS-ON TIME: 13 min. ▪ **TOTAL TIME:** 13 min.

With an overload of bacon and creamy dressing, traditional Cobb salads can be nutritional bombs, but this quick-and-easy take packs a ton of flavor with only a fraction of the calories, saturated fat, and sodium.

1 (12-ounce) salmon fillet
Cooking spray
1 tablespoon sweet and smoky grilling rub with cinnamon and chipotle
6 cups chopped romaine lettuce
1½ cups chopped tomato
½ diced peeled avocado
3 center-cut bacon slices, cooked and crumbled
½ cup refrigerated light blue cheese dressing
Freshly ground black pepper (optional)

1. Preheat broiler.
2. Place fish on a broiler pan coated with cooking spray. Rub fish with grilling rub. Broil 9 to 11 minutes or until fish flakes easily when tested with a fork or until desired degree of doneness. Remove fish from oven; break into large chunks.
3. Divide lettuce among 4 plates; top with tomato, avocado, bacon, and fish. Drizzle dressing evenly over salads. Sprinkle with pepper, if desired. **YIELD: 4 SERVINGS (SERVING SIZE: 2 CUPS SALAD AND 2 TABLESPOONS DRESSING).**

PER SERVING: Calories 313; Fat 21g (sat 5.2g, mono 6.5g, poly 7.1g); Protein 23.4g; Carb 8.5g; Fiber 3.4g; Chol 59mg; Iron 1.3mg; Sodium 499mg; Calc 42mg

TUNA, WHITE BEAN, AND ARUGULA SALAD

PointsPlus value per serving: 7

HANDS-ON TIME: 5 min. ■ **TOTAL TIME:** 5 min.

Make the tuna mixture ahead of time and allow it to chill until ready to serve. Add the arugula just before serving so it doesn't wilt and get soggy.

- **3 tablespoons red wine vinegar**
- **2 tablespoons olive oil**
- **½ teaspoon freshly ground black pepper**
- **¼ teaspoon kosher salt**
- **½ cup vertically sliced red onion**
- **½ cup sliced celery**
- **⅓ cup pitted kalamata olives, cut in half**
- **1 (15-ounce) can cannellini beans, rinsed and drained**
- **3 (2.6-ounce) packages low-sodium albacore tuna in water, flaked**
- **2 cups arugula**
- **2 ounces crumbled goat cheese (about ½ cup)**

1. Combine first 4 ingredients in a medium bowl, stirring with a whisk. Add onion and next 4 ingredients (through tuna); toss well. Add arugula; toss gently. Sprinkle with goat cheese, and serve immediately. **YIELD: 4 SERVINGS (SERVING SIZE: 1¼ CUPS TUNA MIXTURE AND ABOUT 2 TABLESPOONS CHEESE).**

PER SERVING: Calories 266; Fat 13.2g (sat 3.7g, mono 7.6g, poly 1.5g); Protein 23.5g; Carb 14.6g; Fiber 4.1g; Chol 29mg; Iron 1.9mg; Sodium 515mg; Calc 83mg

TIPS FOR SLICING ONIONS

Onions contain sulfuric compounds that are released when they are peeled or sliced. Those compounds irritate the eyes and produce tears. More of these compounds are found in the root, so it's best to cut that last. Slice the top off the onion, leaving the root end intact. Remove the papery skin, and slice the onion in half vertically. Continue cutting the onion vertically into thin slices.

SHRIMP AND SUN-DRIED TOMATO PASTA SALAD

PointsPlus value per serving: 8

HANDS-ON TIME: 13 min. ■ **TOTAL TIME:** 13 min.

Prepare this hearty pasta salad for a light weeknight meal, and pack any leftovers for lunch the next day. Just be sure to keep the salad chilled until lunchtime. You can use your favorite type of pasta in place of the rotini, if desired.

- **6 ounces uncooked rotini (corkscrew pasta)**
- **4 teaspoons olive oil, divided**
- **1 pound peeled and deveined medium shrimp**
- **2 tablespoons white balsamic vinegar**
- **1 teaspoon Dijon mustard**
- **¼ teaspoon salt**
- **¼ teaspoon freshly ground black pepper**
- **¼ cup chopped celery**
- **¼ cup chopped red onion**
- **¼ cup julienne-cut sun-dried tomatoes**
- **¼ cup chopped fresh basil**
- **1 ounce crumbled feta cheese (about ¼ cup)**

1. Cook pasta according to package directions, omitting salt and fat. Drain and set aside.

2. While pasta cooks, heat a medium skillet over medium-high heat. Add 1 teaspoon oil to pan; swirl to coat. Add shrimp to pan, and sauté 3 to 4 minutes or until done.

3. Combine 1 tablespoon oil, vinegar, and next 3 ingredients (through black pepper) in a large bowl, stirring with a whisk. Add pasta, shrimp, celery, and next 3 ingredients (through basil); toss to coat. Sprinkle with cheese. Cover and chill until ready to serve. **YIELD: 4 SERVINGS (SERVING SIZE: ABOUT 1 CUP PASTA MIXTURE AND 1 TABLESPOON CHEESE).**

PER SERVING: Calories 317; Fat 7.8g (sat 1.8g, mono 3.9g, poly 0.9g); Protein 23.4g; Carb 37.9g; Fiber 2.3g; Chol 148mg; Iron 2.3mg; Sodium 444mg; Calc 106mg

GRILLED CALAMARI SALAD

PointsPlus value per serving: 8

HANDS-ON TIME: 15 min. ▪ **TOTAL TIME:** 15 min.

Use frozen calamari (squid) to keep the total preparation time to only 15 minutes in this unique main-dish salad. Smoked paprika, a staple in Spanish kitchens, provides a deep smoky flavor to the vinaigrette that doubles as a marinade.

1 large navel orange
2 tablespoons chopped fresh parsley
½ teaspoon smoked paprika
3 garlic cloves, minced
1 pound frozen cleaned calamari (tubes and tentacles), thawed, rinsed, and sliced
2 pounds multi-colored baby fingerling potatoes
¼ cup olive oil, divided
⅓ cup pitted kalamata olives, quartered lengthwise
½ teaspoon coarse sea salt
¼ teaspoon ground red pepper
4 cups arugula

1. Grate 2 teaspoons rind and squeeze ½ cup juice from only 1 orange over a bowl. Combine rind, juice, parsley, paprika, and garlic in a small bowl; set aside ⅓ cup juice mixture. Place calamari in a large bowl. Pour remaining juice mixture over calamari. Cover calamari, and let stand 5 minutes. Remove calamari from marinade, discarding marinade.
2. While calamari stands, cut any large potatoes in half. Place potatoes in a large microwave-safe bowl. Cover with plastic wrap; cut a 1-inch slit in center of plastic wrap. Microwave at HIGH 6 minutes or until tender. Let stand 2 minutes.
3. Heat a large skillet over medium-high heat. Add 2 tablespoons oil to pan; swirl to coat. Add calamari to pan, and sauté 2 to 3 minutes or until opaque.
4. Combine potatoes, calamari, ⅓ cup juice mixture, 2 tablespoons oil, and olives in a large bowl. Sprinkle with salt and red pepper, tossing to coat. Add arugula; toss to coat. **YIELD: 6 SERVINGS (SERVING SIZE: 1⅓ CUPS).**

PER SERVING: Calories 298; Fat 12.9g (sat 1.9g, mono 8.6g, poly 1.8g); Protein 15.5g; Carb 30.8g; Fiber 3.1g; Chol 176mg; Iron 2.1mg; Sodium 376mg; Calc 73mg

ROAST BEEF SALAD

PointsPlus value per serving: 4

HANDS-ON TIME: 10 min. ▪ **TOTAL TIME:** 10 min.

Use a bottled red wine vinaigrette if you don't have time to make your own, but be sure to check the label for sodium.

4 ounces thinly sliced low-sodium deli roast beef
1 tablespoon chopped fresh flat-leaf parsley
2 tablespoons olive oil
2 tablespoons red wine vinegar
1 teaspoon stone-ground mustard
¼ teaspoon freshly ground black pepper
⅛ teaspoon salt
1 garlic clove, minced
6 cups mixed salad greens
1⅓ cups mini bell pepper slices
1 ounce shredded mozzarella and provolone artisan blend cheese (about ¼ cup)

1. Stack roast beef slices; roll up. Cut into 8 (1-inch) pieces.
2. Combine parsley and next 6 ingredients (through garlic) in a small bowl, stirring with a whisk.
3. Divide greens among 4 plates. Top with roast beef, bell pepper slices, and cheese. Drizzle dressing over salad. **YIELD: 4 SERVINGS (SERVING SIZE: 1½ CUPS GREENS, 1 OUNCE ROAST BEEF, ⅓ CUP BELL PEPPER SLICES, 1 TABLESPOON CHEESE, AND 4 TEASPOONS DRESSING).**

PER SERVING: Calories 150; Fat 9.9g (sat 2.6g, mono 5.9g, poly 0.8g); Protein 10.6g; Carb 6.7g; Fiber 2.9g; Chol 20mg; Iron 1.8mg; Sodium 206mg; Calc 59mg

SPICY PORK CHOPPED SALAD

PointsPlus value per serving: 7 *(pictured on page 11)*

HANDS-ON TIME: 14 min. ■ **TOTAL TIME:** 14 min.

Sesame dressing pairs well with mandarin oranges, smoky pork, and fresh cilantro in this Asian-inspired main dish.

1 (1 pound) pork tenderloin, trimmed and cut into 1-inch pieces
½ teaspoon ground red pepper
¼ teaspoon salt
2 teaspoons olive oil
6 cups coarsely chopped napa (Chinese) cabbage (about ¾ pound)
1 (11-ounce) can mandarin oranges in light syrup, drained
1 red bell pepper, cut into ¼-inch-thick strips
4 green onions, sliced
¼ cup wasabi and soy sauce–flavored almonds
6 tablespoons light sesame-ginger dressing
¼ cup fresh cilantro leaves

1. Sprinkle pork evenly with ground red pepper and salt, and toss well.
2. Heat a large nonstick skillet over medium-high heat. Add oil to pan; swirl to coat. Add pork; sauté 6 minutes or until done.
3. Place napa cabbage and next 3 ingredients (through green onions) in a large bowl. Add pork and almonds, and drizzle with dressing; toss well. Sprinkle with cilantro leaves. **YIELD: 4 SERVINGS (SERVING SIZE: 2¼ CUPS).**

PER SERVING: Calories 291; Fat 11.4g (sat 1.9g, mono 5.8g, poly 2.3g); Protein 27.3g; Carb 18.8g; Fiber 3.7g; Chol 74mg; Iron 2.2mg; Sodium 550mg; Calc 104mg

SLICING APPLES

Look for vibrantly colored apples that are firm to the touch and free of bruises. The skins should be tight and smooth.

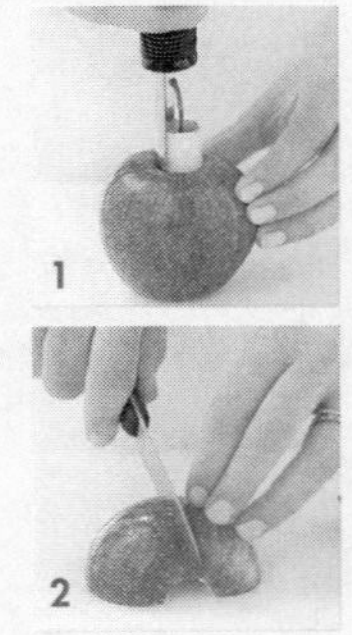

1. Pierce the center of the fruit with an apple corer, and rotate the apple to remove the core.
2. Use a paring knife to slice the apples in half vertically. Place the apple halves, cut sides down, on a cutting board. Cut into wedges or thinner slices. After slicing, sprinkle the flesh with lemon juice to prevent it from browning.

PORK SALAD WITH CIDER VINAIGRETTE

PointsPlus value per serving: 6

HANDS-ON TIME: 13 min. ■ **TOTAL TIME:** 13 min.

Cider, vinegar, and mustard create a sweet and tangy dressing that complements the sautéed pork and fresh sliced apple perfectly. Use a Granny Smith if you would like a slightly less sweet apple.

1 (1-pound) pork tenderloin, trimmed and cut into 12 slices
½ teaspoon freshly ground black pepper, divided
¼ teaspoon salt, divided
Cooking spray
¼ cup apple cider
2 tablespoons olive oil
1 tablespoon cider vinegar
1 teaspoon chopped fresh rosemary
1 teaspoon stone-ground mustard
1 garlic clove, minced
1 (6-ounce) package fresh baby spinach
1 Fuji apple, sliced

1. Place pork slices between 2 sheets of heavy-duty plastic wrap; pound each to ¼-inch thickness using a meat mallet or small heavy skillet. Sprinkle pork evenly with ¼ teaspoon pepper and ⅛ teaspoon salt.
2. Heat a large skillet over medium heat. Coat pan with cooking spray. Add pork to pan; cook 3 minutes on each side or until done.
3. Combine cider, oil, vinegar, rosemary, mustard, garlic, ¼ teaspoon pepper, and ⅛ teaspoon salt in a small bowl, stirring with a whisk.
4. Divide spinach among 4 plates. Top evenly with apple and pork. Drizzle dressing evenly over salads. **YIELD: 4 SERVINGS (SERVING SIZE: ABOUT 1⅓ CUPS SPINACH, ¼ OF APPLE, 3 SLICES PORK, AND 2 TABLESPOONS DRESSING).**

PER SERVING: Calories 247; Fat 10.9g (sat 2.3g, mono 6.5g, poly 1.4g); Protein 24.6g; Carb 13.1g; Fiber 3.2g; Chol 74mg; Iron 2.6mg; Sodium 293mg; Calc 43mg

CHICKEN TENDER SALAD

PointsPlus value per serving: 6

HANDS-ON TIME: 8 min. ■ **TOTAL TIME:** 38 min.

Dredging chicken tenders in flavored panko produces a coating so crunchy you won't miss the traditional fried batter that's common in most fried-chicken salads.

- **1 pound chicken breast tenders (8 tenders)**
- **Cooking spray**
- **½ teaspoon freshly ground black pepper**
- **⅛ teaspoon salt**
- **¾ cup Italian-seasoned panko (Japanese breadcrumbs)**
- **8 cups mixed salad greens**
- **1 cup cherry tomatoes, halved**
- **¼ cup light honey mustard dressing**

1. Preheat oven to 450°.
2. Coat both sides of chicken with cooking spray; sprinkle with pepper and salt. Dredge chicken in breadcrumbs, pressing to adhere. Place chicken on a baking sheet coated with cooking spray; coat chicken with cooking spray.
3. Bake at 450° for 15 minutes. Turn chicken over; cook 15 minutes or until lightly browned and crisp.
4. Divide salad greens among 4 plates. Top with chicken and tomatoes, and drizzle with dressing. YIELD: 4 SERVINGS (SERVING SIZE: 2 CUPS GREENS, 2 CHICKEN TENDERS, ¼ CUP TOMATOES, AND 1 TABLESPOON DRESSING).

PER SERVING: Calories 231; Fat 5.3g (sat 0.9g, mono 2.4g, poly 1.1g); Protein 26.9g; Carb 18.9g; Fiber 4.3g; Chol 73mg; Iron 1.9mg; Sodium 464mg; Calc 31mg

LETTUCE UPKEEP

Nothing is worse than finding your salad greens have gone bad before you've had time to use them. Whether you buy your greens in a bag, by the head, or by the bunch, follow these tips to keep them in good condition.

- Lettuces should appear crisp and fresh when you buy them. Avoid wilted, blemished, discolored, or slimy ones.
- Wait to wash lettuce leaves until you are ready to prepare your salad. The added moisture can make them go bad more quickly. If they appear damp from store misters, dry them before storing.
- To store, place in plastic storage bags. If you think the lettuces may have some moisture, wrap in dry paper towels before placing in storage bags. They'll keep well for 2 to 3 days in the refrigerator's crisper drawer.

GRILLED CHICKEN CAESAR SALAD

PointsPlus value per serving: 8

HANDS-ON TIME: 15 min. ■ **TOTAL TIME:** 15 min.

Grilling romaine hearts yields an intense smoky flavor without additional fat or sodium.

- **4 (4-ounce) chicken cutlets**
- **½ teaspoon freshly ground black pepper, divided**
- **2 romaine hearts, halved lengthwise**
- **Cooking spray**
- **2 large garlic cloves, divided**
- **8 (½-inch-thick) French bread baguette slices**
- **⅓ cup canola mayonnaise**
- **2 tablespoons white wine vinegar**
- **2 tablespoons water**
- **1 teaspoon anchovy paste**
- **1 ounce shaved Parmesan cheese (about ¼ cup)**

1. Preheat grill to medium-high heat.
2. Sprinkle chicken with ¼ teaspoon pepper. Coat romaine heart halves with cooking spray. Cut 1 garlic clove in half. Rub garlic halves on both sides of bread slices. Coat both sides of bread slices with cooking spray.
3. Place romaine on grill rack coated with cooking spray. Grill romaine 4 to 5 minutes on each side or until done. Add chicken to grill after 2 minutes; grill 2 to 3 minutes on each side or until done. Add bread to grill for the last 2 minutes of cook time. Grill 1 to 2 minutes on each side or until toasted. Remove chicken, romaine, and bread from grill.
4. Mince 1 garlic clove. Combine minced garlic, ¼ teaspoon pepper, mayonnaise, and next 3 ingredients (through anchovy paste) in a bowl, stirring with a whisk.
5. Cut chicken diagonally across grain into thin slices; arrange slices from 1 chicken cutlet over each romaine heart half. Drizzle dressing over chicken and romaine; top with cheese. Serve with toast slices. YIELD: 4 SERVINGS (SERVING SIZE: 1 ROMAINE HEART HALF, 1 CHICKEN CUTLET, ABOUT 3 TABLESPOONS DRESSING, ABOUT 1 TABLESPOON CHEESE, AND 2 TOAST SLICES).

PER SERVING: Calories 332; Fat 11.7g (sat 2.1g, mono 4.3g, poly 3.2g); Protein 33.4g; Carb 23.2g; Fiber 7.2g; Chol 82mg; Iron 4.3mg; Sodium 616mg; Calc 211mg

LUAU CHICKEN SALAD

PointsPlus value per serving: 9

HANDS-ON TIME: 15 min. ▪ **TOTAL TIME:** 15 min.

To save prep time, opt for precut pineapple from the produce section of the supermarket instead of buying and cutting a whole pineapple.

4 (6-ounce) skinless, boneless chicken breast halves
½ teaspoon freshly ground black pepper
¼ teaspoon salt
Cooking spray
8 cups gourmet salad greens
1 cup thinly sliced English cucumber
1 cup shredded carrot
1 cup red bell pepper strips
1 cup (1-inch) cubed fresh pineapple
¼ cup thinly sliced green onions
½ cup papaya–poppy seed dressing

1. Preheat grill to medium-high heat.
2. Sprinkle chicken with pepper and salt. Place chicken on grill rack coated with cooking spray. Grill 5 minutes on each side or until done; shred chicken.
3. While chicken cooks, divide salad greens among 4 plates. Top with cucumber and next 4 ingredients (through green onions). Top with chicken, and drizzle with dressing. YIELD: 4 SERVINGS (SERVING SIZE: 2 CUPS GREENS, ¼ CUP CUCUMBER, ¼ CUP CARROT, ¼ CUP BELL PEPPER, ¼ CUP PINEAPPLE, 1 TABLESPOON GREEN ONIONS, 1 CHICKEN BREAST HALF, AND 2 TABLESPOONS DRESSING).

PER SERVING: Calories 353; Fat 12.6g (sat 2g, mono 6g, poly 3.2g); Protein 38.5g; Carb 22.2g; Fiber 5.2g; Chol 109mg; Iron 2.1mg; Sodium 592mg; Calc 38mg

HOW TO PEEL & CHOP FRESH PINEAPPLE

Don't let this fruit's prickly exterior deter you. Lay the pineapple horizontally on a cutting board, and cut off the leafy top (the plume) and the base. Stand the pineapple upright, and cut down the sides to remove the rind. Try to remove as little of the flesh as possible. While the pineapple is upright, cut it into thirds by carefully slicing downward as shown to remove the fibrous core. You can then slice it into cubes.

SANTA FE CHICKEN SALAD

PointsPlus value per serving: 8

HANDS-ON TIME: 11 min. ▪ **TOTAL TIME:** 11 min.

Serve this salad warm, or make it ahead and chill for a healthy lunch at work; just pack the dressing separately, and keep the salad cold until lunchtime.

2 teaspoons canola oil
1 pound ground chicken breast
¾ teaspoon salt-free Southwest chipotle seasoning, divided
2 cups frozen seasoned corn and black beans
6 cups shredded romaine lettuce
½ cup fresh salsa
2 ounces preshredded reduced-fat 4-cheese Mexican blend cheese (about ½ cup)
8 baked tortilla chips, coarsely crushed
¼ cup light ranch dressing

1. Heat a large nonstick skillet over medium-high heat. Add oil to pan; swirl to coat. Add chicken and ½ teaspoon seasoning to pan, and cook 4 minutes or until browned, stirring to crumble. Add frozen vegetables; cook 4 minutes or until vegetables are tender and chicken is done, stirring often.
2. Divide lettuce among 4 plates. Top with chicken mixture, salsa, cheese, and tortilla chips.
3. Combine dressing and ¼ teaspoon seasoning in a small bowl. Drizzle over salads. Serve immediately. YIELD: 4 SERVINGS (SERVING SIZE: 1½ CUPS LETTUCE, ¾ CUP CHICKEN, 2 TABLESPOONS SALSA, 2 TABLESPOONS CHEESE, 1 TABLESPOON TORTILLA CHIPS, AND 1 TABLESPOON DRESSING).

PER SERVING: Calories 333; Fat 11.1g (sat 2.7g, mono 4.2g, poly 2.2g); Protein 32g; Carb 22.8g; Fiber 3.2g; Chol 85mg; Iron 1.2mg; Sodium 661mg; Calc 169mg

CHICKEN BULGUR SALAD

PointsPlus value per serving: 6

HANDS-ON TIME: 14 min. ■ **TOTAL TIME:** 14 min.

Incorporate more fiber into your diet with this bulgur-based dish. Serve the salad with warmed whole-wheat pita bread—a small 1-ounce pita has a *PointsPlus* value of 2.

1 cup water
½ cup uncooked quick-cooking bulgur
1½ cups cubed cooked chicken breast
1 cup finely chopped fresh parsley
1 cup grape tomatoes, halved
⅓ cup light Northern Italian salad dressing with basil and Romano
2 tablespoons fresh lemon juice
1 (14-ounce) can quartered artichoke hearts, drained and coarsely chopped

1. Bring 1 cup water to a boil in a medium saucepan; stir in bulgur. Return to a boil; cover, reduce heat, and simmer 8 minutes or until liquid is absorbed. Drain bulgur, and rinse with cold water; drain well.
2. Combine chicken and remaining ingredients in a large bowl, tossing to coat. Add bulgur; toss gently to coat. **YIELD: 4 SERVINGS (SERVING SIZE: 1¼ CUPS).**

PER SERVING: Calories 228; Fat 6g (sat 1g, mono 1.5g, poly 2.1g); Protein 21.2g; Carb 22.8g; Fiber 4.5g; Chol 45mg; Iron 3mg; Sodium 435mg; Calc 56mg

BULGUR

Common in Middle Eastern cuisines, bulgur is one of the lesser-known forms of wheat in the United States. It's made by steaming and drying whole-wheat grain, and then grinding them into a coarse meal. The smaller the grains are ground, the less time the bulgur needs to cook. Use bulgur as a nutritious substitute for rice and pastas—one cooked cup has about 150 calories, 8 grams of fiber, and 6 grams of protein—or as a hot cereal in the morning. Look for it in the rice and pasta section of your grocery store.

CHICKEN TABBOULEH SALAD

PointsPlus value per serving: 6

HANDS-ON TIME: 7 min. ■ **TOTAL TIME:** 7 min.

We use a convenient quick-cooking blend of seven grains that's a speedy alternative to traditional bulgur wheat. It also offers more flavor and contrasting texture.

3 tablespoons red wine vinegar
2 tablespoons olive oil
1 teaspoon sugar
½ teaspoon freshly ground black pepper
1 (8.5-ounce) pouch microwaveable precooked seven whole grains mix
2 cups shredded skinless, boneless rotisserie chicken breast
1 cup grape tomatoes, halved
¼ cup chopped red onion
¼ cup chopped fresh flat-leaf parsley
¼ cup chopped fresh mint
1 English cucumber, chopped
2 ounces crumbled feta cheese (about ½ cup)

1. Combine first 4 ingredients in a large bowl, stirring with a whisk. Add grains mix; toss well. Add chicken and remaining ingredients; toss gently to coat. Cover and chill until ready to serve. **YIELD: 6 SERVINGS (SERVING SIZE: 1 CUP).**

PER SERVING: Calories 225; Fat 9g (sat 2.2g, mono 4.7g, poly 1.3g); Protein 19g; Carb 17.2g; Fiber 2.4g; Chol 47mg; Iron 1.5mg; Sodium 379mg; Calc 51mg

CURRIED CHICKEN-RICE SALAD

PointsPlus value per serving: 8

HANDS-ON TIME: 15 min. ■ **TOTAL TIME:** 15 min.

There's no need to thaw the peas before adding them to the pan—they'll cook thoroughly in only a minute or so.

Cooking spray
2¼ cups chopped onion (1 large)
1 cup frozen petite green peas
2½ teaspoons curry powder
½ teaspoon salt
¼ teaspoon freshly ground black pepper
2 (8.8-ounce) pouches microwaveable precooked whole-grain brown rice
3 cups chopped cooked chicken
1 cup grape tomatoes, halved
½ cup golden raisins
¼ cup chopped fresh cilantro

1. Heat a large nonstick skillet over medium-high heat. Coat pan with cooking spray. Add onion to pan; sauté 5 minutes or until tender. Stir in peas and next 3 ingredients (through black pepper); cook 1 minute or until peas are thoroughly heated.
2. While pea mixture cooks, microwave rice according to package directions.
3. Combine pea mixture, rice, chicken, and remaining ingredients in a large bowl. Serve immediately, or cover and chill until ready to serve. **YIELD: 6 SERVINGS (SERVING SIZE: 1⅓ CUPS).**

PER SERVING: Calories 350; Fat 4.5g (sat 0.8g, mono 2g, poly 1.1g); Protein 27g; Carb 43.6g; Fiber 4.5g; Chol 60mg; Iron 2.4mg; Sodium 315mg; Calc 38mg

BASMATI CHICKEN SALAD

PointsPlus value per serving: 8

HANDS-ON TIME: 13 min. ■ **TOTAL TIME:** 43 min.

Oil-packed sun-dried tomatoes and artichokes give this salad richness, as well as a nice tang.

1½ cups water
1 cup uncooked basmati rice
3 garlic cloves, minced
2 cups shredded skinless, boneless rotisserie chicken breast
½ cup thinly sliced green onions
¼ cup chopped drained oil-packed sun-dried tomato halves
1 teaspoon grated fresh lemon rind
1 (15½-ounce) can chickpeas (garbanzo beans), drained
1 (14-ounce) can artichoke hearts, drained and coarsely chopped
¼ cup fat-free, lower-sodium chicken broth
3 tablespoons fresh lemon juice
3 tablespoons extra-virgin olive oil
1 teaspoon Dijon mustard
¾ teaspoon salt
½ teaspoon freshly ground black pepper
¼ teaspoon dried oregano

1. Bring 1½ cups water to a boil in a 3-quart saucepan; add rice and garlic. Cover; reduce heat, and simmer 20 minutes or until liquid is absorbed. Remove from heat, and let stand 5 minutes. Place in a large bowl. Add chicken, onions, tomato, rind, chickpeas, and artichokes to rice; stir gently to combine.
2. Combine broth and remaining ingredients, stirring with a whisk. Drizzle over salad, tossing gently to coat. **YIELD: 8 SERVINGS (SERVING SIZE: ¾ CUP).**

PER SERVING: Calories 298; Fat 7.6g (sat 1.2g, mono 4.7g, poly 1.1g); Protein 17.1g; Carb 43.1g; Fiber 6.4g; Chol 30mg; Iron 2.7mg; Sodium 572mg; Calc 52mg

CHICKEN SALAD WITH ROASTED PEPPERS

PointsPlus value per serving: 7

HANDS-ON TIME: 10 min. ■ **TOTAL TIME:** 10 min.

It's a snap to stir together this tasty salad when you use prechopped bell pepper, celery, and onion, which are available in most produce departments.

2 cups chopped cooked chicken breast
½ cup refrigerated prechopped green bell pepper
½ cup refrigerated prediced celery
½ cup dried cranberries
½ cup chopped bottled roasted red bell peppers
¼ cup refrigerated prechopped red onion
¼ cup chopped pecans, toasted
¼ cup light mayonnaise
2 teaspoons lower-sodium soy sauce
¼ teaspoon crushed red pepper

1. Combine all ingredients in a medium bowl; toss well. Cover and chill until ready to serve. YIELD: 4 SERVINGS (SERVING SIZE: 1 CUP).

PER SERVING: Calories 280; Fat 13g (sat 2.2g, mono 4.9g, poly 4.9g); Protein 23g; Carb 17.5g; Fiber 2.3g; Chol 65mg; Iron 1.1mg; Sodium 333mg; Calc 26mg

PESTO CHICKEN SALAD

PointsPlus value per serving: 7

HANDS-ON TIME: 10 min. ■ **TOTAL TIME:** 10 min.

If you use leftover baked or poached chicken in place of the rotisserie chicken, you'll save about 200mg of sodium per serving.

½ cup plain 2% reduced-fat Greek yogurt
⅓ cup commercial pesto
¼ teaspoon freshly ground black pepper
1 tablespoon fresh lemon juice
2 cups chopped skinless, boneless rotisserie chicken breast
1 cup drained canned quartered artichoke hearts
6 cups arugula
1 cup quartered cherry tomatoes (about 6 ounces)

1. Combine first 4 ingredients in a medium bowl, stirring with a whisk. Add chicken and artichokes, tossing to coat. Divide arugula among 4 plates. Top with chicken mixture and cherry tomatoes. YIELD: 4 SERVINGS (SERVING SIZE: 1½ CUPS ARUGULA, ⅔ CUP CHICKEN MIXTURE, AND ¼ CUP TOMATOES).

PER SERVING: Calories 268; Fat 12.6g (sat 2.8g, mono 7.5g, poly 1.6g); Protein 28.8g; Carb 9.1g; Fiber 1.6g; Chol 68mg; Iron 2.5mg; Sodium 582mg; Calc 131mg

TARRAGON-GRAPE CHICKEN SALAD

PointsPlus value per serving: 7

HANDS-ON TIME: 10 min. ■ **TOTAL TIME:** 10 min.

This chicken salad is perfect for those who prefer a savory and tangy salad instead of a sweet version. Pair it with crunchy melba toast or breadsticks; one ounce of either has a *PointsPlus* value per serving of 3.

½ cup canola mayonnaise
1 tablespoon chopped fresh tarragon
1 tablespoon white wine vinegar
2 teaspoons country-style Dijon mustard
¼ teaspoon salt
¼ teaspoon freshly ground black pepper
3 cups shredded cooked chicken breast
¾ cup seedless red grapes, halved
4 Boston lettuce leaves

1. Combine first 6 ingredients in a large bowl. Stir in chicken and grapes. Serve immediately, or cover and chill. Spoon onto lettuce leaves just before serving. YIELD: 4 SERVINGS (SERVING SIZE: ¾ CUP CHICKEN SALAD AND 1 LETTUCE LEAF).

PER SERVING: Calories 279; Fat 11.8g (sat 1.1g, mono 5.3g, poly 3.8g); Protein 33g; Carb 6.2g; Fiber 0.5g; Chol 89mg; Iron 1.4mg; Sodium 517mg; Calc 27mg

CHICKEN PANZANELLA SALAD

PointsPlus value per serving: 6

HANDS-ON TIME: 14 min. ▪ **TOTAL TIME:** 14 min.

Panzanella is a classic Tuscan salad created as a way to use stale bread. This version is a tasty way to use up leftover bakery bread and chicken.

4 ounces day-old Italian bread, cut into 1-inch cubes (about 4 cups)
¼ cup red wine vinegar
2 tablespoons extra-virgin olive oil
½ teaspoon salt
½ teaspoon freshly ground black pepper
3 cups chopped cooked chicken breast
2½ cups chopped tomato
1¾ cups English cucumber slices (about ¼ inch thick)
1 cup chopped yellow bell pepper
½ cup vertically sliced red onion
¼ cup chopped fresh basil
Additional freshly ground black pepper (optional)

1. Preheat oven to 350°.
2. Place bread cubes in a single layer on a jelly-roll pan. Bake at 350° for 7 minutes or until toasted.
3. While bread toasts, combine vinegar and next 3 ingredients (through black pepper) in a large bowl, stirring with a whisk. Add bread cubes, chicken, and next 5 ingredients (through basil), tossing to coat. Sprinkle with additional black pepper, if desired. Serve immediately. **YIELD: 6 SERVINGS (SERVING SIZE: 2 CUPS).**

PER SERVING: Calories 237; Fat 8g (sat 1.6g, mono 4.6g, poly 1.3g); Protein 24.9g; Carb 15.5g; Fiber 2.5g; Chol 60mg; Iron 1.7mg; Sodium 369mg; Calc 41mg

ROASTED CHICKEN, ARUGULA, AND BEET SALAD WITH RASPBERRY-WALNUT VINAIGRETTE

PointsPlus value per serving: 9

HANDS-ON TIME: 12 min. ▪ **TOTAL TIME:** 12 min.

This salad is a wonderful blend of fall flavors and also offers a burst of color from the beets and oranges.

2 large navel oranges
½ cup low-fat raspberry walnut salad dressing
6 cups loosely packed arugula
1 (11.5-ounce) package refrigerated precooked beets, drained and cut into wedges
2 cups shredded skinless, boneless rotisserie chicken breast
1 ounce shaved fresh Parmesan cheese (about ¼ cup)
¼ cup coarsely chopped walnuts, toasted

1. Grate ½ teaspoon rind from 1 orange. Peel and section oranges over a bowl; squeeze membranes to extract juice. Set sections aside; reserve ¼ cup juice. Discard membranes. Combine juice, ½ teaspoon rind, and dressing in small bowl, stirring with a whisk.
2. Combine orange sections and arugula in a medium bowl; add ¼ cup dressing mixture, tossing to coat. Combine beets and ¼ cup dressing mixture in a medium bowl, tossing gently to coat. Combine chicken and ¼ cup dressing mixture in a small bowl, tossing to coat. Divide arugula mixture among 4 plates; top with chicken mixture, beet mixture, cheese, and nuts. **YIELD: 4 SERVINGS (SERVING SIZE: ABOUT 1½ CUPS ARUGULA MIXTURE, ½ CUP CHICKEN MIXTURE, ABOUT ⅓ CUP BEET MIXTURE, 1 TABLESPOON CHEESE, AND 1 TABLESPOON NUTS).**

PER SERVING: Calories 357; Fat 16.6g (sat 4g, mono 5.9g, poly 5.6g); Protein 30.2g; Carb 23.3g; Fiber 3.9g; Chol 72mg; Iron 1.6mg; Sodium 661mg; Calc 255mg

ARUGULA

Leafy arugula is actually an herb with a peppery bite. It's most often served raw and used as a salad green or sandwich topper. Because of its assertive flavor, arugula is often mixed with milder greens like romaine and spinach. It is packed full of vitamins A, C, and K and is a good source of iron, potassium, folate, and calcium.

GREEK CHICKEN SALAD

PointsPlus value per serving: 5

HANDS-ON TIME: 9 min. ■ **TOTAL TIME:** 9 min.

Both kalamata olives and feta cheese contribute a good bit of sodium to a traditional Greek salad, but the salt-free vinaigrette in this recipe keeps total sodium within a healthy range.

¼ cup red wine vinegar
1 tablespoon olive oil
2 teaspoons chopped fresh oregano
¼ teaspoon freshly ground black pepper
2 cups shredded skinless, boneless rotisserie chicken breast
2 cups grape tomatoes, halved
1 cup vertically sliced red onion
¼ cup chopped pitted kalamata olives (about 10)
1 English cucumber, halved lengthwise and thinly sliced (1 cup)
5 cups chopped romaine lettuce
3 ounces crumbled feta cheese (about ¾ cup)

1. Combine first 4 ingredients in a large bowl, stirring with a whisk. Add chicken and next 4 ingredients (through cucumber); toss well.
2. Divide lettuce among 5 bowls; top with chicken mixture, and sprinkle with cheese. **YIELD: 5 SERVINGS (SERVING SIZE: 1 CUP LETTUCE, ABOUT 1⅓ CUPS CHICKEN SALAD, AND ABOUT 2 TABLESPOONS CHEESE).**

PER SERVING: Calories 215; Fat 10.5g (sat 3.2g, mono 5.1g, poly 1.2g); Protein 22.7g; Carb 8.7g; Fiber 3g; Chol 60mg; Iron 1.8mg; Sodium 532mg; Calc 95mg

MOROCCAN CHICKEN ON GREENS

PointsPlus value per serving: 7

HANDS-ON TIME: 15 min. ■ **TOTAL TIME:** 15 min.

For added crunch, add 1 tablespoon almonds for an additional *PointsPlus* value per serving of 1.

2 navel oranges, divided
2 tablespoons white wine vinegar
2 tablespoons olive oil
½ teaspoon Moroccan seasoning
¼ teaspoon salt
8 cups chopped romaine lettuce
2 cups shredded skinless, boneless rotisserie chicken breast
⅓ cup whole pitted dates, chopped
1 (8.8-ounce) package cooked beets, coarsely diced

1. Grate rind and squeeze juice from 1 orange to measure ½ teaspoon rind and ¼ cup juice. Combine orange rind, orange juice, vinegar, and next 3 ingredients (through salt) in a small bowl, stirring with a whisk.
2. Peel 1 orange, and cut crosswise into thin slices. Divide lettuce among 4 bowls. Arrange chicken, orange slices, dates, and beets over romaine. Drizzle with vinaigrette. **YIELD: 4 SERVINGS (SERVING SIZE: 2 CUPS LETTUCE, ½ CUP CHICKEN, ¼ OF ORANGE SLICES, 4 TEASPOONS DATES, ABOUT 2 OUNCES BEETS, AND 2 TABLESPOONS VINAIGRETTE).**

PER SERVING: Calories 283; Fat 9.7g (sat 1.7g, mono 5.8g, poly 1.5g); Protein 24.7g; Carb 25.9g; Fiber 5g; Chol 60mg; Iron 2.4mg; Sodium 463mg; Calc 75mg

OLIVE VARIETIES

Olives may be one of the most versatile foods. Used as an appetizer, a topping, ground or chopped into a spread, tossed into pilafs and salads, added to savory sauces, pressed into oil, or served straight-up with a drink, the uses for olives are endless in the culinary realm.

These days there are also many types of olives to choose from, so it can be helpful to know the key differences between varieties. Green olives are typically unripe while dark purple olives are ripe, but there are some varieties that are green when ripe. Both colors of olives are cured or pickled once harvested. Three of the most common types are kalamata, manzanilla, and niçoise. Tastes vary based on the type of olive and the curing solution.

- **Kalamata olives** are large, deep purple or black olives that are almond-shaped. They have a rich, salty flavor and are associated with Greek cuisines.
- **Manzanilla olives** are large green olives often stuffed with pimientos and cured in a brine solution.
- **Niçoise olives** are small black olives often with cured herbs.

Olives are considered a fat in one's diet, but they are composed primarily of heart-healthy monounsaturated fats and contain the fat-soluble vitamin E. The only downside to olives is that they can be high in sodium since they are cured in brine or salt solutions. The good news, though, is that a little olive in a salad or sauce goes a long way in flavor, so sodium and fat content is not typically an issue.

LAYERED COBB SALAD

PointsPlus value per serving: 6 *(pictured on page 6)*

HANDS-ON TIME: 12 min. ▪ **TOTAL TIME:** 12 min.

If you'd prefer to make individual salads, just layer the ingredients in each of 8 bowls.

8 cups chopped romaine lettuce (2 romaine hearts)
3½ cups chopped cooked chicken breast
2 cups chopped tomato
1 peeled avocado, diced
2 hard-cooked large eggs, sliced
4 center-cut bacon slices, cooked and crumbled
½ cup refrigerated light blue cheese dressing
¼ cup nonfat buttermilk

1. Place lettuce in bottom of a 6-quart glass serving bowl. Layer chicken, tomato, avocado, egg, and bacon over lettuce. Combine dressing and buttermilk, stirring until blended. Serve dressing with salad. YIELD: 8 SERVINGS (SERVING SIZE: ABOUT 2 CUPS SALAD AND 1½ TABLESPOONS DRESSING).

PER SERVING: Calories 230; Fat 12.4g (sat 3.2g, mono 5.3g, poly 2.7g); Protein 24.2g; Carb 5.8g; Fiber 2.7g; Chol 107mg; Iron 1.5mg; Sodium 223mg; Calc 38mg

PERFECT HARD-COOKED EGGS

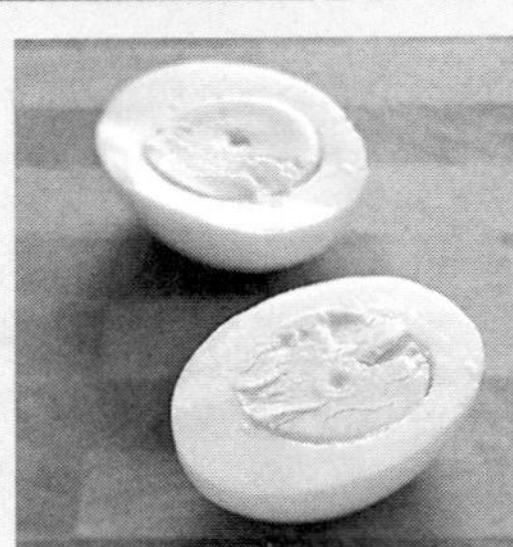

Tired of greenish-gray yolks or rubbery egg whites? Here's a no-fail method for cooking the perfect hard-cooked eggs.

1. Place eggs in a saucepan and cover with 1 to 2 inches of cold water. Place the pan over high heat.
2. When water has reached a full boil, remove the pan from heat, and place a lid on the pan. Let eggs stand covered in pan for 10 minutes.
3. If you need to use your eggs immediately, remove from pan, cool, and peel under cold running water. If eggs are for use later, remove them from pan, and place them in a bowl of ice water until cool.

WASABI

Often referred to as Japanese horseradish, wasabi is a root commonly used in Asian cooking to add intense hotness. It is a common ingredient and condiment for sushi but can also be used to add a touch of heat to sauces, marinades, salads, and noodle dishes. The wasabi root is sliced and finely grated, and then it can be used fresh, dried, or as a paste in recipes. Dried wasabi is most common in markets and can be found in the ethnic produce or spice section. It can be added directly to dressings or sauces, or it can be reconstituted with water to make a paste.

ASIAN CHICKEN SALAD WITH SWEET AND SPICY WASABI DRESSING

PointsPlus value per serving: 8

HANDS-ON TIME: 10 min. ▪ **TOTAL TIME:** 10 min.

Wasabi powder adds flavor as well as heat to the dressing. Cut back on the amount, if you like, to cool this dish down.

2 tablespoons rice vinegar
2 tablespoons maple syrup
2 tablespoons olive oil
¾ teaspoon wasabi powder (dried Japanese horseradish)
¼ teaspoon salt
⅛ teaspoon freshly ground black pepper
1 (11.4-ounce) package Asian supreme salad mix
2 cups shredded cooked chicken breast
1 (8¼-ounce) can mandarin oranges in light syrup, drained
1 diagonally cut green onion

1. Combine first 6 ingredients in a large bowl, stirring well with a whisk.
2. Add salad mix including cranberries to vinegar mixture, reserving wonton strips for topping and sesame-orange dressing for another use. Add chicken and oranges; toss gently to coat. Top with green onion and reserved wonton strips. YIELD: 4 SERVINGS (SERVING SIZE: ABOUT 1½ CUPS SALAD, ¼ OF GREEN ONION, AND 3 WONTON STRIPS).

PER SERVING: Calories 316; Fat 14g (sat 3.6g, mono 5.9g, poly 1.6g); Protein 25.3g; Carb 23.5g; Fiber 2.5g; Chol 67mg; Iron 1.5mg; Sodium 279mg; Calc 100mg

CHICKEN AND PEAR SALAD

PointsPlus value per serving: 7

HANDS-ON TIME: 11 min. ■ **TOTAL TIME:** 11 min.

If you're especially conscious of your sodium intake, just omit the salt in this dressing, and the sodium will drop to about 120 milligrams per serving.

- **2 tablespoons 100% cranberry juice**
- **2 tablespoons olive oil**
- **1 tablespoon honey**
- **1 teaspoon Dijon mustard**
- **¼ teaspoon freshly ground black pepper**
- **¼ teaspoon salt**
- **8 cups mixed salad greens**
- **2 cups shredded cooked chicken breast**
- **1 medium Bartlett pear, thinly sliced**
- **¼ cup chopped walnuts, toasted**

1. Combine first 6 ingredients in a large bowl. Add salad greens, chicken, and pear. Toss to coat. Divide salad among 4 bowls. Sprinkle with walnuts. **YIELD: 4 SERVINGS (SERVING SIZE: ABOUT 2 CUPS SALAD AND 1 TABLESPOON WALNUTS).**

PER SERVING: Calories 290; Fat 14g (sat 2.1g, mono 6.4g, poly 4.7g); Protein 24.4g; Carb 18.2g; Fiber 4.7g; Chol 60mg; Iron 2mg; Sodium 270mg; Calc 25mg

SELECTING PEARS

Whether eaten alone or added to a salad, pears have a delicious, subtle sweetness when ripe. However, they don't fully ripen until they're picked. If your pears need some additional ripening time, allow the unripe fruit to sit at room temperature. If you're in a hurry, you can speed up the ripening process by placing unripe pears in a paper bag with a ripe banana or apple. As fruits ripen, they give off ethylene gas, which speeds the ripening process of fruits that are nearby.

The best way to determine when a pear is ripe is to check the neck of the pear (the area right around the stem). It should be firm, but should give when pressed with your finger. If it's still hard, allow to ripen for a few more days. Once ripe, pears should either be eaten or placed in the refrigerator.

CHOPPED BUFFALO CHICKEN SALAD

PointsPlus value per serving: 5

HANDS-ON TIME: 8 min. ■ **TOTAL TIME:** 8 min.

A healthy take on a pub-favorite—buffalo chicken—this salad can be made and served in just a few minutes when you use leftover chicken breast or rotisserie chicken breast.

- **6 cups chopped romaine lettuce**
- **1⅓ cups grape tomatoes, halved**
- **1¼ cups shredded carrot**
- **1 cup chopped celery**
- **2 cups chopped cooked chicken breast**
- **¼ cup bottled buffalo sauce**
- **½ cup light ranch dressing**

1. Combine first 4 ingredients in a large bowl. Divide among 5 plates.
2. Combine chicken and buffalo sauce, tossing to coat. Top salads with chicken mixture; drizzle with dressing. **YIELD: 5 SERVINGS (SERVING SIZE: 2 CUPS SALAD MIXTURE AND ABOUT 1½ TABLESPOONS DRESSING).**

PER SERVING: Calories 196; Fat 7.8g (sat 1.1g, mono 2.3g, poly 3.4g); Protein 19.3g; Carb 11.5g; Fiber 3.4g; Chol 54mg; Iron 1.3mg; Sodium 724mg; Calc 64mg

TURKEY WALDORF SALAD

PointsPlus value per serving: 5

HANDS-ON TIME: 10 min. ■ **TOTAL TIME:** 10 min.

Serve this salad over a bed of spinach or mixed greens. Chicken can be substituted for turkey.

¼ cup plain fat-free yogurt
1 tablespoon fresh lemon juice
2 teaspoons chopped fresh chives
¼ teaspoon salt
¼ teaspoon freshly ground black pepper
2 cups shredded skinless, boneless rotisserie turkey or chicken breast
1 cup chopped Granny Smith apple
1 cup seedless red grapes, halved
¼ cup chopped walnuts, toasted
¼ cup chopped celery

1. Combine first 5 ingredients in a large bowl, stirring with a whisk. Add turkey and remaining ingredients, tossing gently to coat. Cover and chill until ready to serve. **YIELD: 4 SERVINGS (SERVING SIZE: ABOUT 1 CUP).**

PER SERVING: Calories 216; Fat 7.4g (sat 1.2g, mono 1.5g, poly 4g); Protein 24g; Carb 13.8g; Fiber 1.7g; Chol 60mg; Iron 1.1mg; Sodium 424mg; Calc 55mg

CHIVES

Chives are a perennial favorite that adds a hint of onion flavor to dishes. Store them in a produce bag in the vegetable bin in your refrigerator for up to a week. When cooking, toss them in at the end as heat destroys their flavor.

ORANGE–WILD RICE SALAD WITH SMOKED TURKEY

PointsPlus value per serving: 5

HANDS-ON TIME: 14 min. ■ **TOTAL TIME:** 1 hr. 14 min.

The myriad of textures and sweet and tangy flavors make this salad a standout. It's perfect for a potluck or a brown bag lunch.

6 cups water
1 cup uncooked wild rice
1 cup orange sections (about 4 oranges)
½ cup diced celery
⅓ cup dried sweet cherries or sweetened dried cranberries
½ pound smoked turkey breast, diced
¼ cup thawed orange juice concentrate, undiluted
2 tablespoons fresh lemon juice
2 tablespoons water
1 tablespoon Dijon mustard
1½ teaspoons olive oil
½ teaspoon salt
¼ teaspoon freshly ground black pepper

1. Bring water to a boil in a medium saucepan; stir in rice. Partially cover, reduce heat, and simmer 1 hour or until tender. Drain; cool. Combine rice, oranges, celery, cherries, and turkey in a bowl.
2. Combine orange juice concentrate and remaining ingredients; stir well with a whisk. Pour over rice mixture; toss well. Cover and chill. **YIELD: 7 SERVINGS (SERVING SIZE: 1 CUP).**

PER SERVING: Calories 192; Fat 3.3g (sat 0.8g, mono 1.6g, poly 0.8g); Protein 11.9g; Carb 30.4g; Fiber 2.9g; Chol 18mg; Iron 1.6mg; Sodium 465mg; Calc 29mg

sandwiches

Pulled Chicken Ciabatta Sandwiches, *page 112*

PIMIENTO CHEESE GRILLED CHEESE

PointsPlus value per serving: 6 *(pictured on page 8)*

HANDS-ON TIME: 13 min. ■ **TOTAL TIME:** 13 min.

This pimiento cheese can also be served on crackers as a snack. Make sure to grate the cheese yourself to ensure better melting and spreading consistency.

- **3 ounces reduced-fat sharp cheddar cheese, shredded (about ¾ cup)**
- **2 ounces reduced-fat sharp white cheddar cheese, shredded (about ½ cup)**
- **3 tablespoons fat-free mayonnaise**
- **2 tablespoons chopped green onions**
- **2 tablespoons diced pimiento, drained**
- **¼ teaspoon freshly ground black pepper**
- **2 center-cut bacon slices, cooked and crumbled**
- **8 (0.5-ounce) slices very thin white bread**
- **Cooking spray**

1. Combine first 7 ingredients in a medium bowl. Spread cheese mixture evenly over 4 bread slices. Top with remaining 4 bread slices. Coat both sides of sandwiches with cooking spray.

2. Heat a large skillet over medium heat. Add sandwiches to pan; cook 1 to 2 minutes on each side or until lightly browned and cheese melts. **YIELD: 4 SERVINGS (SERVING SIZE: 1 SANDWICH).**

PER SERVING: Calories 202; Fat 9.9g (sat 4.7g, mono 2.7g, poly 1.3g); Protein 12.8g; Carb 18.1g; Fiber 0.7g; Chol 28mg; Iron 1.1mg; Sodium 575mg; Calc 432mg

SAUTÉED VEGETABLE PITAS

PointsPlus value per serving: 6 *(pictured on page 130)*

HANDS-ON TIME: 15 min. ■ **TOTAL TIME:** 15 min.

Look for prepared hummus in the deli section of your local grocery store. Change up the recipe by trying different flavors.

- **1 teaspoon olive oil**
- **1 cup sliced red bell pepper**
- **1 cup sliced red onion**
- **1 zucchini, halved lengthwise and sliced (about 1 cup)**
- **1 yellow squash, halved lengthwise and sliced (about 1 cup)**
- **¼ teaspoon salt**
- **¼ teaspoon freshly ground black pepper**
- **½ cup hummus**
- **2 (6-inch) whole-wheat pitas, cut in half**
- **3 ounces crumbled feta cheese (about ¾ cup)**
- **1 cup fresh baby spinach**

1. Heat a large skillet over medium-high heat. Add oil to pan; swirl to coat. Add bell pepper and next 3 ingredients (through yellow squash), and sauté 8 minutes or until tender. Remove from heat, and stir in salt and pepper.

2. Spread 2 tablespoons hummus in each pita half. Fill each pita half with about ½ cup vegetable mixture, 3 tablespoons feta cheese, and ¼ cup spinach. **YIELD: 4 SERVINGS (SERVING SIZE: 1 STUFFED PITA HALF).**

PER SERVING: Calories 237; Fat 9.6g (sat 2.8g, mono 3.1g, poly 1.8g); Protein 10g; Carb 31.3g; Fiber 6g; Chol 16mg; Iron 2.4mg; Sodium 709mg; Calc 90mg

TOMATO-PROVOLONE SANDWICHES WITH PESTO MAYO

PointsPlus value per serving: 9

HANDS-ON TIME: 7 min. ■ **TOTAL TIME:** 7 min.

Mayonnaise and pesto form the savory dressing for fresh tomatoes, arugula, and cheese.

- **3 tablespoons organic canola mayonnaise**
- **5 teaspoons refrigerated pesto**
- **8 (1½-ounce) slices sourdough bread**
- **4 (½-ounce) slices provolone cheese**
- **1 cup arugula leaves**
- **8 (¼-inch-thick) tomato slices**
- **¼ teaspoon freshly ground black pepper**
- **⅛ teaspoon salt**

1. Preheat broiler.

2. Combine mayonnaise and pesto in a small bowl, stirring well.

3. Arrange bread in a single layer on a baking sheet. Broil bread 2 minutes or until toasted. Turn bread over; place 1 cheese slice on each of 4 bread slices. Broil 1 minute or until cheese is bubbly. Spread about 2 teaspoons pesto mixture over each cheese-topped bread slice. Arrange ¼ cup arugula and 2 tomato slices over pesto mixture; sprinkle tomato slices evenly with pepper and salt. Spread about 1½ teaspoons remaining pesto mixture evenly over one side of each remaining bread slice; place 1 slice, pesto side down, on top of each sandwich. **YIELD: 4 SERVINGS (SERVING SIZE: 1 SANDWICH)**

PER SERVING: Calories 329; Fat 16.7g (sat 3.4g, mono 5.8g, poly 6.3g); Protein 11g; Carb 35.7g; Fiber 2.9g; Chol 15mg; Iron 3.3mg; Sodium 630mg; Calc 194mg

ROASTED BELL PEPPERS

Broiling transforms crisp, plump bell peppers into smoky-sweet versions of themselves with a velvety texture. Use them on sandwiches and pizzas, or stir them into hummus for a flavorful dip. All bell peppers—green, yellow, orange, and red—can be broiled. Cutting the peppers in half before broiling them simplifies the process. Plus, lining the baking sheet with foil makes cleanup a snap.

EGGPLANT AND GOAT CHEESE SANDWICHES

PointsPlus value per serving: 11

HANDS-ON TIME: 22 min. ■ **TOTAL TIME:** 37 min.

Transform Sandwich Night with this hearty veggie-laden stacker. You can peel the eggplant, but the sandwiches are prettier with the deep-purple skin intact.

8 (½-inch-thick) slices eggplant
2 teaspoons olive oil, divided
1 large red bell pepper
4 (1-ounce) slices ciabatta bread
2 tablespoons refrigerated pesto
1 cup baby arugula
⅛ teaspoon freshly ground black pepper
2 ounces soft goat cheese (about ¼ cup)

1. Preheat broiler.

2. Arrange eggplant slices in a single layer on a foil-lined baking sheet. Brush both sides of eggplant with 1 teaspoon oil. Cut bell pepper in half lengthwise; discard seeds and membrane. Arrange bell pepper halves, skin sides up, on baking sheet with eggplant; flatten with hand. Broil 4 minutes; turn eggplant over (do not turn bell pepper over). Broil an additional 4 minutes; remove eggplant from pan. Broil bell pepper an additional 7 minutes or until blackened. Place bell pepper in a zip-top plastic bag; seal. Let stand 15 minutes; peel and discard skin.

3. Broil bread slices 2 minutes or until lightly browned, turning once. Spread 1 tablespoon pesto on each of 2 bread slices. Layer each bread slice, pesto side up, with 2 eggplant slices, 1 bell pepper half, and 2 eggplant slices. Toss arugula with 1 teaspoon oil and black pepper; divide arugula mixture evenly between sandwiches. Spread 2 tablespoons goat cheese over each of 2 remaining bread slices; place, cheese side down, on sandwiches. **YIELD: 2 SERVINGS (SERVING SIZE: 1 SANDWICH)**

PER SERVING: Calories 395; Fat 20.4g (sat 6.4g, mono 11.6g, poly 1.4g); Protein 14g; Carb 43.1g; Fiber 6.7g; Chol 18mg; Iron 3.5mg; Sodium 635mg; Calc 108mg

HAM AND SWISS EGG SANDWICHES

PointsPlus value per serving: 9

HANDS-ON TIME: 12 min. ■ **TOTAL TIME:** 12 min.

Cooking spray
4 ounces thinly sliced lower-sodium deli ham
4 large eggs
4 English muffins, split and toasted
4 (1-ounce) slices Emmentaler or Swiss cheese

1. Preheat broiler.

2. Heat a nonstick skillet over medium-high heat. Coat pan with cooking spray. Add ham to pan; sauté 2 minutes or until lightly browned. Remove from pan. Recoat pan with cooking spray. Crack eggs into pan. Cover and cook 4 minutes or until desired degree of doneness. Remove from heat.

3. Place 4 muffin halves, cut sides up, on a baking sheet. Top each half with 1 cheese slice. Broil for 2 minutes or until cheese is melted. Divide ham among cheese-topped muffin halves; top each with 1 egg and 1 muffin half. **YIELD: 4 SERVINGS (SERVING SIZE: 1 SANDWICH)**

PER SERVING: Calories 344; Fat 14.7g (sat 6.7g, mono 4.1g, poly 1.5g); Protein 23.5g; Carb 29.1g; Fiber 0g; Chol 250mg; Iron 2mg; Sodium 553mg; Calc 351mg

HOW TO CHOP FENNEL

Fennel is an aromatic vegetable with a slight licorice flavor whose taste mellows when cooked. The bulb, leaves, and seeds can all be used in different ways to season foods. In Tuscan Tuna Sandwiches, the bulb is used to add crunch and a kick of flavor to the tuna salad. Look for small, heavy white bulbs that are firm and free of cracks, browning, and moist areas. The stalks should be crisp, with feathery, bright-green fronds. Wrapped in plastic, fennel keeps for just a few days in the refrigerator; the flavor fades as it dries out.

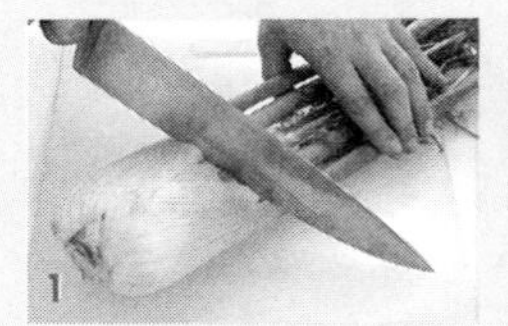

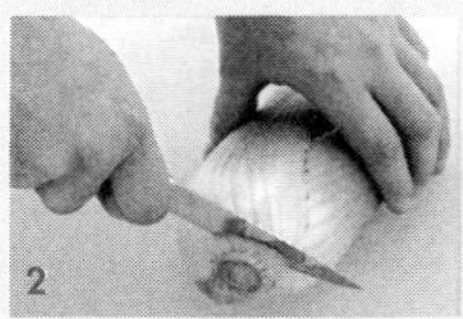

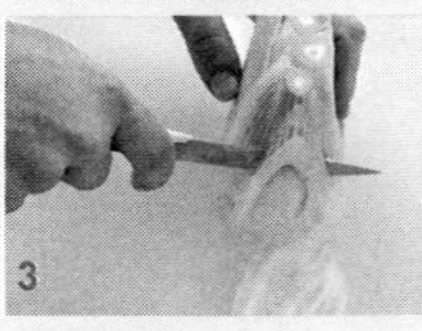

1. Trim the stalks about an inch above the bulb.
2. If you want the pieces to stay together for grilling, keep the root end intact. Otherwise, trim about ½ inch off the root end.
3. To chop the fennel bulb, stand it on the root end, and cut vertically. Chop the slices.
4. You can use the stalks in place of celery in soups. The fronds can be used as a garnish, or chop them and use as you would other herbs like dill or parsley.

TUSCAN TUNA SANDWICHES

PointsPlus value per serving: 7

HANDS-ON TIME: 6 min. ▪ **TOTAL TIME:** 6 min.

Chopped fennel bulb, fresh basil, and capers lend this speedy, no-cook supper vibrant Italian flair. Toasted bread adds a nice texture, but it's an optional step. Serve the sandwich with baked potato chips.

¼ cup finely chopped fennel bulb
¼ cup prechopped red onion
¼ cup chopped fresh basil
2 tablespoons drained capers
2 tablespoons fresh lemon juice
2 tablespoons extra-virgin olive oil
¼ teaspoon freshly ground black pepper
2 (6-ounce) cans solid white tuna in water, drained
1 (4-ounce) jar chopped roasted red bell peppers, drained
8 (1-ounce) slices sourdough bread, toasted

1. Combine first 9 ingredients in a large bowl, stirring well. Spoon ½ cup tuna mixture on each of 4 bread slices. Top each serving with 1 bread slice. Cut each sandwich in half. **YIELD: 4 SERVINGS (SERVING SIZE: 1 SANDWICH)**

PER SERVING: Calories 292; Fat 10g (sat 1.6g, mono 5.6g, poly 1.7g); Protein 25.2g; Carb 24.3g; Fiber 3.3g; Chol 36mg; Iron 2.4mg; Sodium 878mg; Calc 85mg

SALMON SALAD SANDWICHES

PointsPlus value per serving: 7 *(pictured on page 134)*

HANDS-ON TIME: 6 min. ▪ **TOTAL TIME:** 6 min.

Canned salmon is the star in this take on tuna salad. Salmon is a good source of heart-healthy omega-3s.

¼ cup light mayonnaise
2 tablespoons chopped celery
1 tablespoon finely chopped red onion
2 teaspoons chopped fresh dill
2 teaspoons fresh lemon juice
¼ teaspoon freshly ground black pepper
2 (5-ounce) cans skinless, boneless pink salmon in water, drained
1 hard-cooked large egg, chopped
8 (1.1-ounce) slices dark pumpernickel bread
4 green leaf lettuce leaves

1. Combine first 8 ingredients in a medium bowl; spread about ⅓ cup over each of 4 bread slices. Top with 1 lettuce leaf and 1 bread slice. **YIELD: 4 SERVINGS (SERVING SIZE: 1 SANDWICH).**

PER SERVING: Calories 281; Fat 9.6g (sat 1.7g, mono 2.5g, poly 4.2g); Protein 16.7g; Carb 31.7g; Fiber 4.4g; Chol 69mg; Iron 2.5mg; Sodium 596mg; Calc 57mg

ASIAN CATFISH WRAPS

PointsPlus value per serving: 9

HANDS-ON TIME: 14 min. ■ **TOTAL TIME:** 14 min.

Catfish nuggets are fresh catfish pieces that are less expensive than fillets. If they're not available, buy fillets, and cut them into bite-sized pieces.

1 teaspoon dark sesame oil, divided
1 pound catfish nuggets
3 cups thinly sliced napa (Chinese) cabbage
1 cup thinly sliced shiitake mushroom caps
¾ cup preshredded carrot
½ cup sliced green onions
1 tablespoon bottled minced fresh ginger
1 tablespoon bottled minced garlic
¼ cup hoisin sauce
1 teaspoon chili garlic sauce
4 (8-inch) fat-free flour tortillas

1. Heat a large nonstick skillet over medium-high heat. Add ½ teaspoon dark sesame oil to pan; swirl to coat. Add catfish nuggets; cook 3 minutes or until done, stirring frequently. Remove from pan.
2. Add ½ teaspoon dark sesame oil to pan; swirl to coat. Add cabbage, sliced mushroom caps, carrot, green onions, ginger, and garlic to pan; sauté 2 minutes or until carrot is crisp-tender. Stir in catfish nuggets, hoisin, and chili garlic sauce, and cook 1 minute or until thoroughly heated. Remove from heat.
3. Warm tortillas according to package directions. Divide catfish mixture evenly among tortillas; roll up. **YIELD: 4 SERVINGS (SERVING SIZE: 1 WRAP)**

PER SERVING: Calories 344; Fat 10.4g (sat 2.3g, mono 4.7g, poly 2.6g); Protein 22.8g; Carb 37.8g; Fiber 3.7g; Chol 54mg; Iron 0.9mg; Sodium 650mg; Calc 58mg

ROAST BEEF AND CARAMELIZED ONION SANDWICHES

PointsPlus value per serving: 6 *(pictured on page 132)*

HANDS-ON TIME: 13 min. ■ **TOTAL TIME:** 15 min.

Using water to cook the onions helps speed up the process of caramelizing them and keeps them from burning.

4 (1.5-ounce) frozen artisan French rolls
1¼ cups vertically sliced onion
Cooking spray
¼ teaspoon salt
¼ teaspoon freshly ground black pepper
6 tablespoons water
¼ cup light mayonnaise
2 teaspoons prepared horseradish
1 cup trimmed watercress
8 ounces thinly sliced lower-sodium roast beef

1. Heat rolls according to package directions. Cut rolls in half.
2. While rolls cook, heat a medium nonstick skillet over medium-high heat. Add onion to pan. Coat onion with cooking spray; stir in salt and pepper. Sauté 8 minutes or until onion is tender and golden brown.
3. While onion cooks, add 2 tablespoons water; cook until liquid evaporates, scraping pan to loosen browned bits. Repeat procedure twice with remaining water.
4. Combine mayonnaise and horseradish in a small bowl. Spread mayonnaise mixture evenly on cut sides of rolls. Layer ¼ cup watercress, 2 ounces roast beef, and ¼ of onion on bottom half of each roll. Cover each with top half of roll. **YIELD: 4 SERVINGS (SERVING SIZE: 1 SANDWICH).**

PER SERVING: Calories 248; Fat 7.6g (sat 2g, mono 2.1g, poly 2.8g); Protein 19.8g; Carb 25.8g; Fiber 1.8g; Chol 35mg; Iron 1.9mg; Sodium 594mg; Calc 20mg

GRILLED BEEF AND PEPPER SANDWICHES

PointsPlus value per serving: 11

HANDS-ON TIME: 33 min. ▪ **TOTAL TIME:** 1 hr. 3 min.

If you need to shave time off this recipe, it's better to omit the resting time beforehand and let the steak rest 10 minutes after it's grilled, which allows the juices to redistribute throughout the steak.

2 teaspoons grated fresh lemon rind
1 teaspoon dried rosemary
1 teaspoon olive oil
1 teaspoon Dijon mustard
½ teaspoon freshly ground black pepper
¼ teaspoon salt
2 garlic cloves, minced
1 (1-pound) flank steak, trimmed
Cooking spray
2 red bell peppers
⅓ cup reduced-fat mayonnaise
3 tablespoons finely grated Parmesan cheese
1 tablespoon fresh lemon juice
1 garlic clove, minced
1 (10-ounce) round focaccia bread, cut in half horizontally

1. Prepare grill.
2. Combine first 7 ingredients in a small bowl. Rub spice mixture over one side of steak, and let stand 10 minutes.
3. Place steak on grill rack coated with cooking spray; grill 8 minutes on each side or until desired degree of doneness. Let steak stand 10 minutes. Cut steak diagonally across grain into thin slices.
4. Cut bell peppers in half lengthwise; discard seeds and membranes. Flatten peppers with hand. Place peppers, skin sides down, on grill rack; grill 12 minutes or until blackened. Place peppers in a zip-top plastic bag; seal. Let stand 10 minutes. Peel and cut each half into quarters.
5. Combine mayonnaise, cheese, juice, and 1 garlic clove in a small bowl, stirring well. Spread about ¼ cup mayonnaise mixture onto cut side of each bread half. Arrange beef evenly over bottom half; top with peppers. Cover with top bread half, pressing gently. Cut sandwich into 4 wedges. YIELD: 4 SERVINGS (SERVING SIZE: 1 WEDGE)

PER SERVING: Calories 427; Fat 13.9g (sat 4.6g, mono 5.9g, poly 2.4g); Protein 31g; Carb 45.3g; Fiber 2.8g; Chol 48mg; Iron 4.2mg; Sodium 719mg; Calc 69mg

TACO BURGERS

PointsPlus value per serving: 6

HANDS-ON TIME: 15 min. ▪ **TOTAL TIME:** 15 min.

Pureed pumpkin helps keep extra lean ground beef moist without adding any extra fat.

1 pound ground sirloin
½ cup canned pumpkin
2 teaspoons 25%-less-sodium taco seasoning
½ teaspoon freshly ground black pepper
1 tablespoon olive oil, divided
6 (1.8-ounce) white-wheat hamburger buns
¾ cup refrigerated fresh salsa
1½ cups shredded iceberg lettuce

1. Combine first 4 ingredients in a large bowl. Divide sirloin mixture into 6 equal portions, shaping each into a ¾-inch-thick patty.
2. Heat a large nonstick skillet over medium-high heat. Add 1½ teaspoons oil to pan; swirl to coat. Add 3 patties to pan; cover and cook 3 minutes on each side or until done. Remove patties from pan, and keep warm. Repeat procedure with 1½ teaspoons oil and remaining patties.
3. Place 1 patty on bottom half of each bun. Top each patty with 2 tablespoons salsa, ¼ cup lettuce, and top half of bun. YIELD: 6 SERVINGS (SERVING SIZE: 1 BURGER).

PER SERVING: Calories 249; Fat 8.7g (sat 2.3g, mono 3.6g, poly 1.1g); Protein 18.9g; Carb 25.7g; Fiber 5.1g; Chol 37mg; Iron 3.8mg; Sodium 383mg; Calc 257mg

GROUND BEEF

Purchasing ground beef can be confusing depending on the terminology used on the packaging. Typically, a ratio such as 90/10, 85/15, or 80/20 is used to express amount of lean meat and fat in the beef. This first number tells you the percentage that is lean meat; the second number tells you the percentage that is fat. Packages may also use different terms to describe where the cut came from (see chart below). Beef with a higher percentage of fat is usually less expensive, and if you're browning the meat, most of the extra fat can be drained off. Remember though that because the meat had a higher starting percentage of fat, there will be slightly less cooked meat.

Ground beef type	Fat percentage
Ground sirloin	7 to 10% fat
Ground round	10 to 15% fat
Ground chuck	15 to 20% fat

GARLICKY SPINACH AND FETA BURGERS

PointsPlus value per serving: 9 *(pictured on page 133)*

HANDS-ON TIME: 14 min. ■ **TOTAL TIME:** 14 min.

Feta cheese, spinach, and garlic give plain ground sirloin a Mediterranean twist. Add 1 teaspoon fresh lemon juice to the yogurt-garlic sauce for a burst of bright flavor.

1 pound ground sirloin
4 ounces crumbled feta cheese (about 1 cup)
1 cup chopped fresh baby spinach
2 teaspoons minced fresh garlic, divided
¾ teaspoon freshly ground black pepper, divided
Cooking spray
½ cup plain fat-free Greek yogurt
⅛ teaspoon salt
4 (1.8-ounce) white-wheat hamburger buns
4 green leaf lettuce leaves

1. Combine beef, feta cheese, spinach, 1 teaspoon garlic, and ½ teaspoon black pepper in a large bowl. Divide beef mixture into 4 equal portions, shaping each into a ½-inch-thick patty.
2. Heat a grill pan over medium heat. Coat pan with cooking spray. Add patties to pan; cook 5 minutes on each side or until done.
3. While patties cook, combine yogurt, salt, 1 teaspoon garlic, and ¼ teaspoon pepper in a small bowl, stirring until smooth.
4. Place 1 burger on bottom half of each bun. Top each with 2 tablespoons yogurt mixture and a lettuce leaf, if desired. Cover each with top half of bun. **YIELD: 4 SERVINGS (SERVING SIZE: 1 BURGER).**

PER SERVING: Calories 359; Fat 14.9g (sat 6.5g, mono 4.5g, poly 1.2g); Protein 34g; Carb 26.2g; Fiber 5.1g; Chol 76mg; Iron 5.4mg; Sodium 702mg; Calc 380mg

GARLIC-ROSEMARY LAMB PITAS

PointsPlus value per serving: 10

HANDS-ON TIME: 9 min. ■ **TOTAL TIME:** 9 min.

Stuff whole-wheat pitas with savory cubes of lamb and a cool cucumber and yogurt tzatziki sauce for a fresh and flavorful meal from the Mediterranean. Make extra tzatziki sauce to use as a dip for whole-wheat pita wedges for a healthy snack. One-fourth cup of tzatziki sauce has a ***PointsPlus*** value per serving of just 1.

2 teaspoons olive oil
1 tablespoon chopped fresh rosemary
1 teaspoon bottled minced garlic
½ teaspoon salt, divided
⅜ teaspoon black pepper, divided
1 pound boneless leg of lamb, cut into (¾-inch) cubes
1½ cups finely chopped seeded cucumber
1 tablespoon fresh lemon juice
1 (6-ounce) container plain low-fat yogurt
4 (6-inch) whole-wheat pitas

1. Heat a large nonstick skillet over medium-high heat. Add oil to pan; swirl to coat. Combine rosemary, garlic, ¼ teaspoon salt, ¼ teaspoon pepper, and lamb, tossing to coat. Add lamb mixture to pan; sauté 4 minutes or until done.
2. While lamb cooks, combine ¼ teaspoon salt, ⅛ teaspoon pepper, cucumber, lemon juice, and yogurt. Divide lamb mixture evenly among each of 4 pitas, and drizzle with sauce. **YIELD: 4 SERVINGS (SERVING SIZE: ABOUT 3 OUNCES LAMB, 1 PITA, AND ⅔ CUP SAUCE)**

PER SERVING: Calories 391; Fat 11.5g (sat 3.5g, mono 4.8g, poly 1.5g); Protein 32.7g; Carb 40.8g; Fiber 5.3g; Chol 77mg; Iron 4.4mg; Sodium 742mg; Calc 117mg

ROSEMARY

Rosemary is one of the most aromatic and pungent of all herbs. Its needlelike leaves have a pronounced lemon-pine flavor. Use a light hand because its strong flavor can overpower a dish.

CHICKEN BLTS

PointsPlus value per serving: 9

HANDS-ON TIME: 14 min. ■ **TOTAL TIME:** 14 min.

Although peak-season tomatoes are unrivaled in flavor, you don't have to wait for tomato season to enjoy this BLT. Use commercial tomato bruschetta topping instead of sliced fresh tomatoes for a great off-season substitute.

½ cup tomato bruschetta topping
¼ cup light mayonnaise
8 (0.9-ounce) slices whole-wheat bread, toasted
4 green leaf lettuce leaves
6 center-cut bacon slices, cooked
2 cups shredded cooked chicken breast

1. Combine bruschetta topping and mayonnaise in a small bowl. Spread mixture over bread slices. Top each of 4 bread slices with 1 lettuce leaf, 1½ bacon slices, and ½ cup chicken. Cover with remaining bread slices. **YIELD: 4 SERVINGS (SERVING SIZE: 1 SANDWICH).**

PER SERVING: Calories 328; Fat 14.5g (sat 3.2g, mono 4.4g, poly 4.5g); Protein 32.8g; Carb 22g; Fiber 4.6g; Chol 76mg; Iron 2.3mg; Sodium 801mg; Calc 114mg

BACON

Most would agree that bacon makes most anything better. It's delicious as a simple breakfast protein; seasoning for cooking vegetables; crumbled as a topping on potatoes, soups, dips, and even cupcakes—there are myriad culinary uses for bacon and its smoky, salty flavor. Thankfully, a little bacon goes a long way flavor-wise since this cured meat is high in both fat and sodium. One slice of regular cooked bacon has about 40 calories, 3 grams of fat, and a ***PointsPlus*** value per serving of 1; or you can have 2 slices for a ***PointsPlus*** value of 3. To save calories and still get real bacon flavor, try center-cut bacon. It's bacon that's cut closer to the bone so it's lower in fat. Two slices has a ***PointsPlus*** value per serving of 1.

HUMMUS AND CHICKEN SALAD PITAS

PointsPlus value per serving: 7

HANDS-ON TIME: 11 min. ■ **TOTAL TIME:** 11 min.

We used roasted red bell pepper hummus, but spicy three-pepper hummus would be a good choice, too.

2 cups sliced romaine lettuce
1 cup chopped skinless, boneless rotisserie chicken breast
⅔ cup diced seeded cucumber
¼ cup thinly sliced red onion
1 ounce crumbled feta cheese (about ¼ cup)
2 tablespoons fresh lemon juice
2 tablespoons olive oil
¼ teaspoon salt
¼ teaspoon freshly ground black pepper
6 tablespoons roasted red bell pepper hummus
2 (6-inch) whole-wheat pitas, cut in half

1. Combine first 5 ingredients in a large bowl. Add lemon juice, olive oil, salt, and pepper; toss gently.
2. Spread 1½ tablespoons hummus inside each pita half; spoon salad mixture into pita halves. Serve immediately. **YIELD: 4 SERVINGS (SERVING SIZE: 1 PITA HALF).**

PER SERVING: Calories 278; Fat 13.5g (sat 2.9g, mono 7.3g, poly 1.8g); Protein 16.7g; Carb 24.6g; Fiber 4.1g; Chol 38mg; Iron 2mg; Sodium 669mg; Calc 71mg

PESTO CHICKEN CLUBS

PointsPlus value per serving: 10 *(pictured on page 129)*

HANDS-ON TIME: 10 min. ■ **TOTAL TIME:** 10 min.

2 cups shredded cooked chicken breast
6 tablespoons refrigerated reduced-fat pesto
4 green leaf lettuce leaves
8 (1.8-ounce) slices white-wheat bread, toasted
4 (¼-inch-thick) slices tomato
8 center-cut bacon slices, cooked

1. Combine chicken and pesto in medium bowl. Place 1 lettuce leaf on each of 4 bread slices; top each with ½ cup chicken mixture, 1 tomato slice, 2 bacon slices, and 1 bread slice. **YIELD: 4 SERVINGS (SERVING SIZE: 1 SANDWICH).**

PER SERVING: Calories 382; Fat 15.2g (sat 4.2g, mono 7.1g, poly 2g); Protein 33.8g; Carb 27.8g; Fiber 4.2g; Chol 80mg; Iron 3.8mg; Sodium 746mg; Calc 394mg

CHICKEN MUFFULETTAS

PointPlus value serving: 8

HANDS-ON TIME: 32 min. ▪ **TOTAL TIME:** 42 min.

This make-ahead sandwich is a lighter take on an old New Orleans favorite, and this recipe can easily be cut in half if you want fewer servings. Use a fork to scrape the bread and hollow the loaves.

3 cups chopped seeded tomato (about 2 medium)
Cooking spray
8 cups diced peeled eggplant (about 1 pound)
1½ cups chopped onion
2 teaspoons chopped fresh thyme
¼ teaspoon freshly ground black pepper
¾ cup chopped pimiento-stuffed olives (about 4 ounces)
3 tablespoons chopped pepperoncini (about 3 medium)
4 ounces sharp provolone cheese, finely diced (about 1 cup)
⅔ cup chopped reduced-fat hard salami (about 2 ounces)
1 tablespoon olive oil
1 tablespoon balsamic vinegar
4 (8-ounce) loaves French bread
1 pound skinless, boneless rotisserie chicken breast, thinly sliced

1. Spread tomato evenly onto several layers of heavy-duty paper towels. Cover with additional paper towels; let stand 10 minutes.
2. Heat a large skillet over medium-high heat. Coat pan with cooking spray. Add eggplant and onion; sauté 10 minutes or until eggplant is tender and beginning to brown. Stir in thyme and pepper; cook 1 minute, stirring occasionally. Spoon eggplant mixture into a large bowl.
3. Coat pan with cooking spray. Add tomato, and cook 2 minutes, stirring frequently. Stir tomato into eggplant mixture. Cool to room temperature.
4. Stir olives and next 5 ingredients (through vinegar) into eggplant mixture.
5. Cut French bread loaves in half horizontally. Hollow out top and bottom halves of bread, leaving a ½-inch-thick shell; reserve torn bread for another use. Spread about 2 tablespoons eggplant mixture over bottom half of each loaf. Arrange chicken evenly on bottom halves. Top chicken evenly with 2 tablespoons eggplant mixture; cover with top halves of loaves. Wrap loaves with plastic wrap; refrigerate up to 24 hours. Cut each loaf into 3 pieces just before serving. YIELD: 12 SERVINGS (SERVING SIZE: 1 PIECE)

PER SERVING: Calories 318; Fat 7.2g (sat 2.8g, mono 2.0g, poly 0.4g); Protein 21.7g; Carb 44g; Fiber 3.1g; Chol 45mg; Iron 3.1mg; Sodium 799mg; Calc 96mg

CHICKEN CREMINI SANDWICHES

PointsPlus value per serving: 9

HANDS-ON TIME: 17 min. ▪ **TOTAL TIME:** 17 min.

Since mascarpone is a full-fat cheese, use it sparingly to add richness and flavor to this upscale sandwich.

Cooking spray
1 pound cremini mushrooms, sliced
¼ teaspoon freshly ground black pepper
¼ teaspoon salt
2 tablespoons mascarpone cheese
8 (1.2-ounce) slices ciabatta bread
1⅓ cups thinly sliced deli chicken breast
2 cups packed arugula

1. Preheat panini grill.
2. Heat a medium nonstick skillet over medium-high heat. Coat pan with cooking spray. Add mushrooms and pepper to pan, and cook 6 minutes or until mushrooms are lightly browned and tender; drain and return to pan. Stir in salt.
3. Spread ½ tablespoon mascarpone cheese on each of 4 bread slices; top with chicken, mushrooms, arugula, and another bread slice.
4. Coat both sides of sandwiches with cooking spray. Place sandwiches on panini grill. Grill 3 minutes or until golden brown. Serve immediately. YIELD: 4 SERVINGS (SERVING SIZE: 1 SANDWICH).

PER SERVING: Calories 331; Fat 11g (sat 4.3g, mono 3.5g, poly 1g); Protein 23.4g; Carb 36g; Fiber 1.9g; Chol 57mg; Iron 2.9mg; Sodium 587mg; Calc 64mg

PULLED CHICKEN CIABATTA SANDWICHES

PointsPlus value per serving: 9 *(pictured on page 103)*

HANDS-ON TIME: 8 min. ▪ **TOTAL TIME:** 12 min.

Frozen herbed ciabatta rolls make this speedy sandwich taste like a gourmet sandwich. Keep the leftover rolls in the freezer for later use.

4 (1½-ounce) frozen ciabatta sandwich rolls with rosemary and olive oil
2 cups shredded cooked chicken breast
1 ounce crumbled feta cheese with basil and sun-dried tomatoes (about ¼ cup)
1 tablespoon chopped fresh parsley
7 pitted kalamata olives, finely chopped
2 tablespoons balsamic vinegar
5 teaspoons extra-virgin olive oil
½ teaspoon freshly ground black pepper
1 garlic clove, minced
4 thin tomato slices

1. Heat rolls according to package directions.
2. While rolls cook, combine chicken, cheese, parsley, and olives in a bowl. Combine vinegar and next 3 ingredients (through garlic clove) in a small bowl, stirring with a whisk. Pour vinaigrette over chicken mixture; toss well.
3. Cut rolls in half horizontally; arrange tomato slices on bottom halves of rolls. Spoon chicken salad onto tomato slices. Cover with roll tops. **YIELD: 4 SERVINGS (SERVING SIZE: 1 SANDWICH).**

PER SERVING: Calories 339; Fat 13.1g (sat 2.5g, mono 8g, poly 1.8g); Protein 27.6g; Carb 26g; Fiber 1.7g; Chol 65mg; Iron 1.3mg; Sodium 482mg; Calc 43mg

BALSAMIC ONION CHICKEN SANDWICHES

PointsPlus value per serving: 9

HANDS-ON TIME: 15 min. ▪ **TOTAL TIME:** 15 min.

A small amount of strong blue cheese combined with caramelized onion goes a long way to boost the flavor in these pita sandwiches.

1 teaspoon olive oil
1 cup sliced red onion
1 tablespoon balsamic vinegar
½ cup light mayonnaise
1 ounce crumbled Gorgonzola cheese (about ¼ cup)
2 (6-inch) whole-wheat pitas, cut in half
4 Bibb lettuce leaves
2 cups shredded cooked chicken

1. Heat a large nonstick skillet over medium-high heat. Add oil to pan; swirl to coat. Add onion to pan; sauté 5 minutes or until tender. Add vinegar; cook 1 minute or until liquid almost evaporates, stirring constantly.
2. Combine mayonnaise and cheese in a small bowl. Spread cheese mixture inside each pita half. Line each pita half with 1 lettuce leaf. Fill each pita half with about 2 tablespoons onion mixture and ½ cup chicken. **YIELD: 4 SERVINGS (SERVING SIZE: 1 PITA HALF).**

PER SERVING: Calories 353; Fat 16.5g (sat 4.3g, mono 4.8g, poly 6.5g); Protein 26.9g; Carb 23.6g; Fiber 3g; Chol 76mg; Iron 2mg; Sodium 561mg; Calc 66mg

SPINACH-ARTICHOKE CHICKEN SANDWICHES

PointsPlus value per serving: 9

HANDS-ON TIME: 15 min. ▪ **TOTAL TIME:** 15 min.

Spinach, artichokes, and two kinds of cheese create a flavorful spread for these chicken and vegetable–filled sandwiches.

1 cup chopped fresh spinach
½ cup drained canned chopped artichoke hearts
4 ounces ⅓-less-fat cream cheese (about ½ cup), softened
¼ teaspoon grated fresh lemon rind
1 teaspoon fresh lemon juice
⅛ teaspoon freshly ground black pepper
8 (½-inch-thick) slices Chicago-style Italian bread (about 6 ounces)
2 cups chopped cooked chicken breast
1 ounce grated Asiago cheese (about ¼ cup)
Olive oil–flavored cooking spray

1. Preheat panini grill.
2. Combine first 6 ingredients in a medium bowl; spread onto 4 slices of bread. Top with chicken, Asiago cheese, and remaining bread slices.
3. Coat outsides of sandwiches with cooking spray. Place sandwiches on panini grill; cook 3 minutes or until golden brown and cheese melts. YIELD: 4 SERVINGS (SERVING SIZE: 1 SANDWICH).

PER SERVING: Calories 343; Fat 12.7g (sat 6g, mono 3.5g, poly 1.5g); Protein 30.4g; Carb 24.9g; Fiber 1.6g; Chol 87mg; Iron 2.6mg; Sodium 535mg; Calc 132mg

CHICKEN AND SUN-DRIED TOMATO SANDWICHES

PointsPlus value per serving: 9

HANDS-ON TIME: 13 min. ■ **TOTAL TIME:** 13 min.

You can swap out the peppery arugula for baby spinach, if desired.

4 sun-dried tomato and basil light mozzarella spreadable cheese wedges
8 (1.3-ounce) slices sourdough bread (½ inch thick)
1 cup arugula
8 (¼-inch-thick) slices tomato
2 cups shredded skinless, boneless rotisserie chicken breast
½ cup (¼-inch-thick) vertically sliced red onion
Cooking spray

1. Preheat panini grill.
2. Spread ½ cheese wedge on each of 8 bread slices. Top 4 slices evenly with arugula, tomato slices, chicken, and onion. Cover with remaining bread slices.
3. Coat sandwiches with cooking spray. Place sandwiches on panini grill. Grill 2 to 3 minutes or until golden brown. Serve immediately. YIELD: 4 SERVINGS (SERVING SIZE: 1 SANDWICH).

PER SERVING: Calories 378; Fat 6g (sat 2.1g, mono 1.7g, poly 1.3g); Protein 33g; Carb 46.7g; Fiber 2.6g; Chol 65mg; Iron 3.6mg; Sodium 861mg; Calc 118mg

CHIMICHURRI CHICKEN WRAPS

PointsPlus value per serving: 8

HANDS-ON TIME: 12 min. ■ **TOTAL TIME:** 12 min.

Loaded with fresh parsley and garlic, chimichurri sauce is the traditional accompaniment to steak in Argentina. Try this recipe, and you'll see how tasty chimichurri-dressed chicken can be.

Cooking spray
1 cup vertically sliced red onion
4 garlic cloves, peeled
2 cups fresh parsley leaves
2 tablespoons olive oil
2 tablespoons red wine vinegar
1 tablespoon fresh lemon juice
¼ teaspoon salt
¼ teaspoon freshly ground black pepper
⅛ teaspoon crushed red pepper
4 (8-inch) whole-wheat tortillas
2 cups shredded cooked chicken breast

1. Heat a medium skillet over medium-high heat. Coat pan with cooking spray. Add onion to pan; cook 5 minutes or until tender.
2. Drop garlic through food chute with processor on; process until minced. Add parsley and next 6 ingredients (through crushed red pepper); process 1 minute or until finely minced, scraping sides once.
3. Spread 2 tablespoons parsley mixture on each tortilla. Divide onion and chicken among tortillas; roll up. YIELD: 4 SERVINGS (SERVING SIZE: 1 WRAP).

PER SERVING: Calories 334; Fat 11.6g (sat 1.7g, mono 6.8g, poly 1.8g); Protein 27.2g; Carb 31g; Fiber 4.6g; Chol 60mg; Iron 4.2mg; Sodium 558mg; Calc 215mg

CHICKEN BURGERS WITH FIG RELISH

PointsPlus value per serving: 7

HANDS-ON TIME: 15 min. ■ **TOTAL TIME:** 15 min.

Be sure to purchase ground chicken that is made of both light and dark meat and not just ground chicken breast. The additional fat in the dark meat will ensure the burgers stay juicy and moist during cooking.

1 pound ground chicken
1 tablespoon olive oil
¼ teaspoon salt
¼ teaspoon freshly ground black pepper
Cooking spray
2 tablespoons finely chopped shallot (1 large)
½ cup chopped dried figs (about 10)
2 tablespoons fig preserves
2 tablespoons water
1 tablespoon balsamic vinegar
½ teaspoon chopped fresh rosemary
6 (1.3-ounce) wheat slider buns
¾ cup arugula

1. Combine first 4 ingredients in a medium bowl. Divide chicken mixture into 6 equal portions. With moist hands, shape each into a ½-inch-thick patty.
2. Heat a large skillet over medium-high heat. Coat pan with cooking spray. Add patties; cook 5 to 6 minutes on each side or until a thermometer registers 165°.
3. While burgers cook, heat a small saucepan over medium-high heat. Coat pan with cooking spray. Add shallot to pan; cook 2 minutes. Add figs and next 3 ingredients (through balsamic vinegar). Cook 2 minutes or until liquid almost evaporates. Remove from heat. Stir in rosemary.
4. Place 1 burger on bottom half of each bun. Top with fig mixture, arugula, and bun tops. **YIELD: 6 SERVINGS (SERVING SIZE: 1 BURGER).**

PER SERVING: Calories 273; Fat 9.4g (sat 2g, mono 4.6g, poly 1.9g); Protein 19.6g; Carb 31.4g; Fiber 6.4g; Chol 50mg; Iron 0.4mg; Sodium 305mg; Calc 27mg

CHICKEN, APPLE, AND CHEDDAR WAFFLE SANDWICHES

PointsPlus value per serving: 9

HANDS-ON TIME: 6 min. ■ **TOTAL TIME:** 6 min.

To keep the sodium in check, be sure to check the nutrition label on the waffles; aim for under 120 milligrams of sodium per waffle.

8 (1.12-ounce) frozen multigrain waffles
3 tablespoons canola mayonnaise
2 teaspoons spicy brown mustard
1 teaspoon honey
8 ounces thinly sliced lower-sodium deli chicken
4 (0.7-ounce) slices reduced-fat sharp cheddar cheese
1 cup thinly sliced Granny Smith apple

1. Heat waffles according to package directions.
2. Combine mayonnaise, mustard, and honey in a small bowl. Spread 1 tablespoon mayonnaise mixture on each of 4 waffles. Top each with 2 ounces chicken, 1 cheese slice, ¼ cup apple slices, and 1 waffle. **YIELD: 4 SERVINGS (SERVING SIZE: 1 SANDWICH).**

PER SERVING; Calories 336; Fat 14.4g (sat 2.8g, mono 6.7g, poly 3.1g); Protein 21.4g; Carb 34.6g; Fiber 6.8g; Chol 48mg; Iron 1.5mg; Sodium 860mg; Calc 151mg

REDUCED-FAT CHEESES

Shredded, grated, melted, or crumbled, cheese is something that makes almost any dish better. Though it's a good source of protein and calcium, cheese is also high in fat. Thankfully, there are lots of reduced-fat cheeses available, so a little sprinkle or crumble adds richness to your favorite dishes without adding as many calories. Plus, the quality has improved greatly over the past few years, and often they melt and taste like full-fat versions. Most reduced-fat cheeses are made with reduced-fat or 2% milks, which cuts about 25% of the fat. In 1 ounce of cheese, there is a substantial difference between full-fat cheese with 7 to 10 grams of fat and a ***PointsPlus*** value per serving of 3 and reduced-fat cheese with 4 to 8 grams of fat and a ***PointsPlus*** value per serving of 2. To get the most impact from the cheese, opt for sharp and extra-sharp varieties that offer more flavor than milder varieties.

SPICY CHICKEN SANDWICHES

PointsPlus value per serving: 8

HANDS-ON TIME: 13 min. ▪ **TOTAL TIME:** 13 min.

Satisfy your spicy cravings with this chipotle-laced sandwich. To turn down the heat, use only 1 teaspoon of the chiles.

2 teaspoons canola oil
4 (4-ounce) chicken cutlets
¼ teaspoon ground red pepper
4 (0.67-ounce) slices reduced-fat Monterey Jack cheese with jalapeño peppers
⅓ cup fat-free mayonnaise
1 tablespoon chopped fresh cilantro
2 teaspoons chopped chipotle chiles, canned in adobo sauce
4 (1.8-ounce) white-wheat hamburger buns
4 romaine lettuce leaves

1. Heat a large nonstick skillet over medium-high heat. Add oil to pan; swirl to coat. Sprinkle chicken with ground red pepper. Add chicken to pan. Cook 3 minutes on each side or until done. Top each cutlet with 1 cheese slice. Cover and cook 1 minute or until cheese melts.
2. While chicken cooks, combine mayonnaise, cilantro, and chipotle chiles in a small bowl. Spread about ½ tablespoon mayonnaise mixture on cut sides of each bun half. Top bottom halves with 1 lettuce leaf and 1 chicken cutlet. Cover with bun tops. **YIELD: 4 SERVINGS (SERVING SIZE: 1 SANDWICH).**

PER SERVING: Calories 332; Fat 11g (sat 3.4g, mono 3.8g, poly 1.8g); Protein 34.3g; Carb 26.2g; Fiber 5.3g; Chol 85mg; Iron 2.5mg; Sodium 731mg; Calc 414mg

CHICKEN REUBENS

PointsPlus value per serving: 9

HANDS-ON TIME: 17 min. ▪ **TOTAL TIME:** 17 min.

We used chicken instead of corned beef to create this lightened version of the classic Reuben sandwich.

4 (4-ounce) chicken cutlets
¼ teaspoon freshly ground black pepper
Cooking spray
¼ cup light Thousand Island dressing
8 (1-ounce) slices rye bread
½ cup drained refrigerated sauerkraut
4 (0.75-ounce) slices reduced-fat Swiss cheese

1. Sprinkle chicken with pepper. Heat a large nonstick skillet over medium-high heat. Coat pan with cooking spray. Add chicken to pan; cook 3 minutes on each side or until done. Remove chicken from pan, and keep warm. Wipe pan with a paper towel.
2. Spread 1 tablespoon dressing on 1 side of each of 4 bread slices. Top each with 2 tablespoons sauerkraut, 1 chicken cutlet, 1 cheese slice, and 1 bread slice.
3. Heat a large skillet over medium heat. Coat both sides of sandwiches with cooking spray. Add sandwiches to pan; cook 2 minutes on each side or until bread is browned and cheese melts. Remove sandwiches from pan, and cut in half. Serve immediately. **YIELD: 4 SERVINGS (SERVING SIZE: 1 SANDWICH).**

PER SERVING: Calories 369; Fat 8.5g (sat 2.8g, mono 2.1g, poly 1.1g); Protein 38.1g; Carb 34g; Fiber 3.9g; Chol 81mg; Iron 2.4mg; Sodium 823mg; Calc 257mg

PEAR-CHICKEN MONTE CRISTO SANDWICHES

PointsPlus value per serving: 8 *(pictured on page 131)*

HANDS-ON TIME: 14 min. ■ **TOTAL TIME:** 14 min.

A Monte Cristo is a classic ham and cheese sandwich in which the bread is dipped in an egg mixture, cooked, and then often dusted with powdered sugar. This chicken variation includes thinly sliced fresh pear for a touch of sweetness. Serve the sandwich immediately, while the crust is still warm and crisp.

3 tablespoons honey mustard
8 (¾-ounce) slices low-calorie white bread
4 (0.7-ounce) thin slices reduced-fat Swiss cheese
4 ounces shaved deli maple-glazed roasted chicken breast
1 cup thin peeled pear slices (1 medium)
⅓ cup fat-free milk
2 large egg whites
1 teaspoon canola oil
2 teaspoons powdered sugar
8 teaspoons pear preserves

1. Spread about 1 teaspoon mustard over each bread slice. Place 1 cheese slice on each of 4 bread slices. Arrange chicken and pear slices over cheese. Cover with remaining bread slices, mustard sides down.
2. Combine milk and egg whites in a shallow dish, stirring with a whisk. Heat a large nonstick skillet over medium heat. Add oil to pan; swirl to coat.
3. Dip both sides of 2 sandwiches into milk mixture; place in pan. Cook sandwiches 1 to 2 minutes on each side or until lightly browned. Repeat procedure with remaining 2 sandwiches and egg mixture.
4. Sift ½ teaspoon sugar over each sandwich; top each with 2 teaspoons preserves. Serve immediately. **YIELD: 4 SERVINGS (SERVING SIZE: 1 SANDWICH).**

PER SERVING: Calories 279; Fat 7.4g (sat 2.1g, mono 1.8g, poly 1.1g); Protein 21.3g; Carb 37.9g; Fiber 5.4g; Chol 28mg; Iron 1.9mg; Sodium 557mg; Calc 284mg

TURKEY-AVOCADO MELTS

PointsPlus value per serving: 9

HANDS-ON TIME: 9 min. ■ **TOTAL TIME:** 9 min.

1 ripe peeled avocado, coarsely mashed
1 tablespoon canola mayonnaise
1 teaspoon chopped chipotle chiles, canned in adobo sauce
8 (1-ounce) slices Italian bread
8 ounces thinly sliced no-salt-added deli turkey breast
4 (0.67-ounce) slices reduced-fat Monterey Jack cheese with jalapeño peppers
Cooking spray

1. Preheat panini grill. Combine first 3 ingredients in a small bowl. Spread about 2 tablespoons avocado mixture on each of 4 bread slices. Top each with 2 ounces turkey, 1 cheese slice, and 1 bread slice.
2. Coat both sides of sandwiches with cooking spray. Place sandwiches on panini grill; grill 3 to 4 minutes or until bread is lightly browned and cheese melts. **YIELD: 4 SERVINGS (SERVING SIZE: 1 SANDWICH).**

PER SERVING: Calories 353; Fat 13.3g (sat 3.9g, mono 5.7g, poly 2.2g); Protein 25.8g; Carb 31.7g; Fiber 4.2g; Chol 51mg; Iron 2.3mg; Sodium 610mg; Calc 199mg

TURKEY-CRANBERRY MELTS

PointsPlus value per serving: 8

HANDS-ON TIME: 10 min. ■ **TOTAL TIME:** 10 min.

¼ cup tub light cream cheese with garden vegetables
1 tablespoon Dijon mustard
8 (0.9-ounce) slices 100% whole-wheat bread
4 (0.63-ounce) slices Swiss cheese
8 ounces thinly sliced lower-sodium deli turkey breast
¼ cup whole-berry cranberry sauce
Cooking spray

1. Combine cream cheese and mustard in a small bowl. Spread cream cheese mixture evenly over each of 4 bread slices. Top each with 1 Swiss cheese slice and 2 ounces turkey. Spread cranberry sauce evenly over remaining bread slices; place on top of sandwiches.
2. Coat both sides of sandwiches with cooking spray. Heat a large nonstick skillet over medium heat. Add sandwiches to pan. Cook 3 to 4 minutes on each side or until bread is browned and cheese melts. **YIELD: 4 SERVINGS (SERVING SIZE: 1 SANDWICH).**

PER SERVING: Calories 321; Fat 8.8g (sat 4.3g, mono 1.8g, poly 0.9g); Protein 25g; Carb 34.8g; Fiber 4.3g; Chol 43mg; Iron 1.9mg; Sodium 710mg; Calc 239mg

soups & stews

Pumpkin-Chicken Chili, *page 128*

CREAMY CHILLED CUCUMBER SOUP

PointsPlus value per serving: 3

HANDS-ON TIME: 14 min. ■ **TOTAL TIME:** 14 min.

Pureed avocado and Greek yogurt help to make this vegetable soup extra creamy. If you have time, chill this soup for 2 hours or until cold. It's delicious cold or at room temperature.

2½ tablespoons extra-virgin olive oil, divided
½ cup chopped Vidalia or other sweet onion
3 garlic cloves, chopped
4 English cucumbers, peeled and coarsely chopped (about 6¾ cups)
1 peeled avocado, halved
1½ cups fat-free, lower-sodium chicken broth
3 tablespoons fresh lemon juice
¼ teaspoon freshly ground black pepper
⅛ teaspoon salt
⅛ teaspoon ground red pepper
¾ cup cilantro leaves, divided
½ cup plain fat-free Greek yogurt

1. Heat a medium skillet over medium-high heat. Add 1 tablespoon oil to pan; swirl to coat. Add onion and garlic to pan; sauté 3 minutes or until tender. Remove from heat; cool 5 minutes.
2. While onion mixture cools, combine cucumber and next 6 ingredients (through ground red pepper). Place half of cucumber mixture in a blender; process until smooth. Pour pureed mixture into a large bowl. Place remaining cucumber mixture in blender; process until smooth. Add onion mixture, ½ cup cilantro, and yogurt. Process until smooth; add to cucumber mixture in bowl, stirring well. Ladle soup into bowls; top evenly with remaining cilantro, and drizzle with remaining olive oil. YIELD: 8 SERVINGS (SERVING SIZE: ABOUT ¾ CUP SOUP, 1½ TEASPOONS CILANTRO, AND ABOUT ½ TEASPOON OLIVE OIL).

PER SERVING: Calories 100; Fat 7g (sat 1g, mono 5g, poly 0.7g); Protein 3.9g; Carb 6.6g; Fiber 2.7g; Chol 0mg; Iron 0.2mg; Sodium 153mg; Calc 27mg

BUTTERNUT SQUASH AND APPLE SOUP

PointsPlus value per serving: 3

HANDS-ON TIME: 15 min. ■ **TOTAL:** 15 min.

Packages of frozen butternut squash are a huge time-saver when making this seasonal soup.

2 teaspoons olive oil
1¼ cups chopped peeled apple (1 medium)
1 cup chopped Vidalia or other sweet onion
3 garlic cloves, chopped
1 cup fat-free, lower-sodium chicken broth
1 cup water
¾ teaspoon dried rubbed sage
¼ teaspoon freshly ground black pepper
2 (12-ounce) packages frozen butternut squash, thawed
⅓ cup reduced-fat sour cream
3 tablespoons chopped fresh chives

1. Heat a large Dutch oven over medium-high heat. Add oil to pan; swirl to coat. Add apple, onion, and garlic to pan; sauté 5 minutes or until tender. Stir in broth and next 4 ingredients (through butternut squash); cook 2 minutes or until thoroughly heated.
2. Place half of soup mixture in a blender. Remove center piece of blender lid (to allow steam to escape); secure blender lid on blender. Place a clean towel over opening in blender lid (to avoid splatters). Blend until smooth. Pour into a large bowl. Repeat procedure with remaining soup mixture. Ladle soup into individual bowls; top with sour cream and chives. YIELD: 6 SERVINGS (SERVING SIZE: ABOUT ¾ CUP SOUP, ABOUT 1 TABLESPOON SOUR CREAM, AND 1½ TEASPOONS CHIVES).

PER SERVING: Calories 124; Fat 3.2g (sat 1.3g, mono 1.6g, poly 0.3g); Protein 3g; Carb 21.1g; Fiber 2.5g; Chol 7mg; Iron 0.6mg; Sodium 107mg; Calc 61mg

CREAMY TOMATO-BALSAMIC SOUP

PointsPlus value per serving: 3

HANDS-ON TIME: 10 min. ▪ **TOTAL TIME:** 1 hr.

Cooking the vegetables at the high temperature of 500° caramelizes their natural sugars and deepens their flavor; the liquid poured over them ensures they won't burn. Prepare the soup up to two days ahead; reheat over medium heat before serving.

1 cup fat-free lower-sodium beef broth, divided
1 tablespoon brown sugar
3 tablespoons balsamic vinegar
1 tablespoon lower-sodium soy sauce
1 cup coarsely chopped onion
5 garlic cloves
2 (28-ounce) cans whole tomatoes, drained
Cooking spray
¾ cup half-and-half
Cracked black pepper (optional)

1. Preheat oven to 500°.
2. Combine ½ cup broth, sugar, vinegar, and soy sauce in a small bowl. Place onion, garlic, and tomatoes in a 13 x 9–inch baking pan coated with cooking spray. Pour broth mixture over tomato mixture. Bake at 500° for 50 minutes or until vegetables are lightly browned.
3. Place tomato mixture in a blender. Add remaining ½ cup broth and half-and-half, and process until smooth. Strain mixture through a sieve into a bowl; discard solids. Garnish with cracked black pepper, if desired. **YIELD: 4 SERVINGS (SERVING SIZE: ABOUT ½ CUP).**

PER SERVING: Calories 120; Fat 4.7g (sat 3g, mono 1.5g, poly 0.1g); Protein 3.8g; Carb 14.9g; Fiber 1.7g; Chol 23mg; Iron 1.7mg; Sodium 452mg; Calc 120mg

POTATO-KALE SOUP

PointsPlus value per serving: 6

HANDS-ON TIME: 15 min. ▪ **TOTAL TIME:** 15 min.

Already diced potatoes with garlic cut down on prep time and increase the flavor of this speedy soup.

1 (22-ounce) package frozen red potato wedges with olive oil, Parmesan, and roasted garlic
Olive oil–flavored cooking spray
3 cups packed prechopped kale
1 cup chopped onion
3 cups fat-free, lower-sodium chicken broth
1 cup water
½ teaspoon freshly ground black pepper
2 (15.5-ounce) cans cannellini beans, rinsed and drained
2 ounces shredded fresh Parmesan cheese (about ½ cup)
Crushed red pepper (optional)

1. Place potatoes in a large glass bowl. Microwave at MEDIUM (50% power) 2 minutes or until thawed.
2. Heat a large Dutch oven over medium-high heat. Coat pan with cooking spray. Add kale and onion to pan; sauté 4 minutes. Add potatoes, broth, and next 3 ingredients (through beans) to pan. Increase heat to high; cover and cook 8 minutes or until potatoes are tender, stirring occasionally. Ladle soup into bowls; sprinkle with cheese and red pepper, if desired. **YIELD: 8 SERVINGS (SERVING SIZE: 1 CUP SOUP AND 1 TABLESPOON CHEESE).**

PER SERVING: Calories 228; Fat 5.6g (sat 1.5g, mono 2.9g, poly 0.5g); Protein 12.6g; Carb 32.9g; Fiber 6g; Chol 5mg; Iron 1.7mg; Sodium 710mg; Calc 177mg

LEGUMES

Looking for foods to keep you full and your energy high? Legumes are a great choice. Legumes include lentils, black-eyed peas, and lots of varieties of beans including black beans, pinto beans, cannellini beans, chickpeas, and lima beans. Legumes are a unique food because they are good sources of both complex carbohydrates and lean protein. In fact, they are one of the healthiest and least expensive protein foods available. This protein combined with legumes' high fiber content slows digestion to help keep you full longer while their complex carbs provide a source of sustained energy. Legumes are also rich in iron, magnesium, and folate.

HOW TO PREPARE AVOCADOS

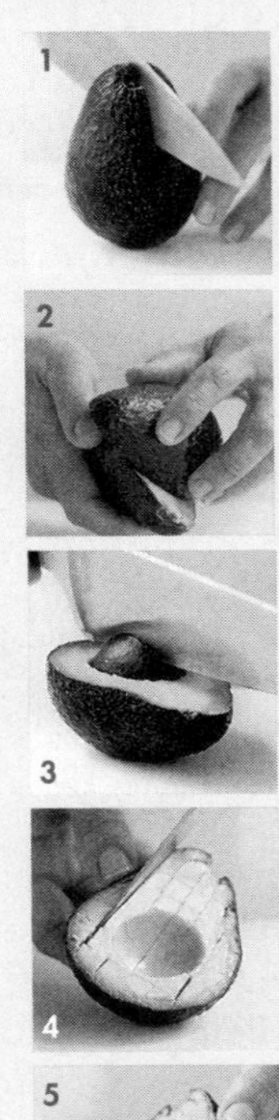

Add the buttery texture and mild, nutty flavor of avocados to sandwiches, salads, and soups. To easily dice, start with an 8- to 10-inch chef's knife. Insert it into the top where the stem was (it will be a darker area), and gently press down until you reach the pit. Then follow these steps.

1. Holding the knife steady, rotate the fruit so the knife moves around the pit, cutting the entire avocado.
2. Remove the knife, then slowly and gently twist the two sides away from each other to separate.
3. Strike the pit, and pierce it with the blade. Then twist and remove the knife; the pit will come with it.
4. Use the knife's tip to cut the flesh in horizontal and vertical rows. Be careful not to cut through the skin.
5. Remove the flesh gently with a spoon. To prevent browning, squeeze lemon or lime juice on the flesh.

LOCRO

PointsPlus value per serving: 5

HANDS-ON TIME: 14 min. ■ **TOTAL TIME:** 14 min.

Locro **is a traditional Ecuadorian potato and cheese soup that is simmered slowly and topped with cheese and diced avocado.**

Cooking spray
½ cup chopped onion
3 garlic cloves, crushed
¾ teaspoon ground cumin
4 cups 1% low-fat milk
1¼ cups instant potato flakes
1 cup water
½ teaspoon salt
½ teaspoon freshly ground black pepper
4 ounces preshredded reduced-fat 4-cheese Mexican-blend cheese (about 1 cup)
⅓ cup diced peeled avocado
1 ounce queso fresco, crumbled (about ¼ cup)

1. Heat a large Dutch oven over medium-high heat. Coat pan with cooking spray. Add onion, garlic, and cumin to pan; sauté 3 minutes. Stir in milk and next 4 ingredients (through black pepper). Bring to a simmer; cook 3 minutes, stirring frequently. Remove from heat; add Mexican-blend cheese, stirring until cheese melts.
2. Ladle soup into individual bowls; top with avocado and queso fresco. **YIELD: 6 SERVINGS (SERVING SIZE: 1 CUP SOUP, ABOUT 1 TABLESPOON AVOCADO, AND ABOUT 2 TEASPOONS QUESO FRESCO).**

PER SERVING: Calories 195; Fat 7.8g (sat 3.5g, mono 2.8g, poly 0.5g); Protein 12.8g; Carb 20.3g; Fiber 2g; Chol 23mg; Iron 0.6mg; Sodium 424mg; Calc 395mg

CABBAGE AND CHICKPEA MINESTRONE

PointsPlus value per serving: 5

HANDS-ON TIME: 4 min. ■ **TOTAL TIME:** 15 min.

Prepare this hearty soup on cold evenings when you want something satisfying and filling—and fast.

Cooking spray
⅓ cup chopped carrot
1 (8-ounce) package refrigerated prechopped celery, onion, and bell pepper mix
2 cups packaged angel hair coleslaw
2 cups fat-free, lower-sodium chicken broth
½ cup hot water
⅓ cup uncooked orzo (rice-shaped pasta)
½ teaspoon freshly ground black pepper
2 (14.5-ounce) cans unsalted diced tomatoes with basil, garlic, and oregano, undrained
1 (16-ounce) can chickpeas (garbanzo beans), rinsed and drained
1½ ounces grated fresh Parmesan cheese (about 6 tablespoons)

1. Heat a large Dutch oven over medium-high heat. Coat pan with cooking spray. Add carrot and celery mix; sauté 3 minutes or until tender. Stir in coleslaw and next 6 ingredients (through chickpeas). Cover and cook 11 minutes. Ladle soup into individual bowls; sprinkle with cheese. **YIELD: 6 SERVINGS (SERVING SIZE: 1⅓ CUPS SOUP AND 1 TABLESPOON CHEESE).**

PER SERVING: Calories 194; Fat 3.2g (sat 1.2g, mono 0.8g, poly 0.5g); Protein 10.9g; Carb 30.9g; Fiber 5.1g; Chol 5mg; Iron 1.2mg; Sodium 471mg; Calc 143mg

EASY BLACK BEAN SOUP

PointsPlus value per serving: 4

HANDS-ON TIME: 15 min. ■ **TOTAL TIME:** 15 min.

Queso fresco is a mild, white cheese commonly used in Mexican dishes.

- 1 tablespoon olive oil
- 1 small onion, chopped
- 3 garlic cloves, chopped
- ¼ teaspoon crushed red pepper
- 1 cup water
- 1½ teaspoons ground cumin
- ½ teaspoon salt
- ¼ teaspoon freshly ground black pepper
- 2 (15-ounce) cans unsalted black beans, rinsed and drained
- 1 (14.5-ounce) can fat-free, lower-sodium chicken broth
- ¼ cup chopped fresh cilantro
- 2 tablespoons fresh lime juice
- ¼ cup sliced green onions
- 1 ounce queso fresco (about ¼ cup)

1. Heat a large saucepan over medium-high heat. Add oil to pan; swirl to coat. Add onion, garlic, and red pepper to pan; cook 3 minutes or until tender, stirring occasionally. Add 1 cup water and next 5 ingredients (through broth). Bring to a boil. Reduce heat, and simmer 5 minutes.
2. Mash soup with a potato masher until slightly thick. Stir in cilantro and lime juice. Ladle soup into individual bowls; top with green onions and queso fresco. **YIELD: 4 SERVINGS (SERVING SIZE: 1¼ CUPS SOUP, 1 TABLESPOON GREEN ONIONS, AND 1 TABLESPOON QUESO FRESCO).**

PER SERVING: Calories 181; Fat 4.2g (sat 0.8g, mono 2.6g, poly 0.4g); Protein 11g; Carb 25.5g; Fiber 7.8g; Chol 2mg; Iron 2.5mg; Sodium 623mg; Calc 110mg

SALMON CORN CHOWDER

PointsPlus value per serving: 6 *(pictured on page 9)*

HANDS-ON TIME: 15 min. ■ **TOTAL TIME:** 15 min.

Cream-style corn and potatoes provide the perfect base for this creamy salmon soup topped with savory bacon crumbles and cheese.

- 4 cups diced red potato (about 4 medium)
- 2 tablespoons water
- 4 center-cut bacon slices
- 1 (1-pound) skinless salmon fillet, cut into 1-inch pieces
- 2 cups 1% low-fat milk
- ¾ teaspoon salt
- ½ teaspoon freshly ground black pepper
- 2 (14¾-ounce) cans unsalted cream-style corn
- ⅓ cup shredded reduced-fat cheddar cheese
- Chopped green onions (optional)

1. Place potato and 2 tablespoons water in a large microwave-safe bowl. Cover with plastic wrap. Microwave at HIGH 8 minutes or until tender.
2. While potato cooks, cook bacon in a large Dutch oven over medium-high heat until crisp. Remove bacon from pan, reserving 2 teaspoons drippings in pan. Crumble bacon, and set aside.
3. Add fish to Dutch oven; cook 3 minutes or until browned, stirring occasionally. Stir in potato, milk, and next 3 ingredients (through corn); cover and bring to a simmer. Ladle soup into bowls; sprinkle with bacon, cheese, and green onions, if desired. **YIELD: 8 SERVINGS (SERVING SIZE: ABOUT 1¼ CUPS SOUP, ABOUT 1 TABLESPOON BACON, AND ABOUT 2 TEASPOONS CHEESE).**

PER SERVING: Calories 242; Fat 7.5g (sat 2.3g, mono 2.9g, poly 1.6g); Protein 18.1g; Carb 27.3g; Fiber 3g; Chol 38mg; Iron 1.1mg; Sodium 386mg; Calc 129mg

HERBED FISH AND RED POTATO CHOWDER

PointsPlus value per serving: 8

HANDS-ON TIME: 18 min. ■ **TOTAL TIME:** 24 min.

Any flaky white fish can be used in place of the halibut. Serve with a mixed green salad topped with balsamic vinaigrette.

2 bacon slices
3 cups diced red potato (about 1 pound)
1 cup chopped onion
3 tablespoons all-purpose flour
2 (8-ounce) bottles clam juice
2 cups 2% reduced-fat milk
1 tablespoon chopped fresh thyme
¼ teaspoon salt
¼ teaspoon black pepper
12 ounces skinless halibut fillets, cut into 1-inch pieces
2 tablespoons chopped fresh flat-leaf parsley

1. Cook bacon in a large Dutch oven over medium-high heat until crisp. Remove bacon from pan, reserving 1 tablespoon drippings in pan. Crumble bacon; set aside.
2. Add potato and onion to drippings in pan; sauté 3 minutes or until onion is tender. Add flour to pan; cook 1 minute, stirring constantly. Stir in clam juice; bring to a boil. Cover, reduce heat, and simmer 6 minutes or until potato is tender. Stir in milk; bring to a simmer over medium-high heat, stirring constantly (do not boil). Stir in thyme, salt, pepper, and fish; cook 3 minutes or until fish flakes easily when tested with a fork. Stir in parsley. Sprinkle with bacon. **YIELD: 4 SERVINGS (SERVING SIZE: 2 CUPS SOUP AND 1½ TEASPOONS CRUMBLED BACON).**

PER SERVING: Calories 307; Fat 8.1g (sat 3.5g, mono 3g, poly 0.9g); Protein 24.4g; Carb 33.9g; Fiber 2.5g; Chol 57mg; Iron 2.2mg; Sodium 611mg; Calc 198mg

SHRIMP AND OKRA GUMBO

PointsPlus value per serving: 7

HANDS-ON TIME: 24 min. ■ **TOTAL TIME:** 38 min.

Thanks to savory spices and a quick-cooking roux, this gumbo cuts back on time (and calories!) while keeping the rich flavor.

2 tablespoons canola oil, divided
3 tablespoons all-purpose flour
10 tablespoons fat-free, lower-sodium chicken broth
1 cup chopped onion
4 ounces smoked ham, chopped
1 cup chopped green bell pepper
⅔ cup diced celery
½ teaspoon dried thyme
3 garlic cloves, minced
½ pound fresh okra pods, sliced
¼ cup water
½ teaspoon ground red pepper
½ teaspoon paprika
½ teaspoon freshly ground black pepper
¼ teaspoon salt
¼ teaspoon ground allspice
1 (28-ounce) can diced tomatoes, drained
12 ounces peeled and deveined large shrimp
2 tablespoons chopped fresh flat-leaf parsley

1. Heat a large saucepan over medium-high heat. Add 1 tablespoon oil to pan; swirl to coat. Add flour; cook 1 minute or until lightly browned, stirring constantly with a whisk. Add broth; stir with a whisk until thick. Pour into a bowl; set aside. Wipe pan clean with paper towels.
2. Heat pan over medium heat. Add 1 tablespoon oil to pan; swirl to coat. Add onion and ham; cook 10 minutes, stirring occasionally. Add bell pepper and next 4 ingredients (through okra); cook 5 minutes or until vegetables are almost tender, stirring occasionally. Add broth mixture, ¼ cup water, and next 6 ingredients (through tomatoes). Bring to a boil; reduce heat, and simmer 10 minutes or until vegetables are tender. Stir in shrimp; cook 4 minutes or until shrimp are done. Sprinkle with parsley. **YIELD: 4 SERVINGS (SERVING SIZE: 1½ CUPS GUMBO AND 1½ TEASPOONS PARSLEY).**

PER SERVING: Calories 300; Fat 10.5g (sat 1.4g, mono 4.4g, poly 2.9g); Protein 26.6g; Carb 26.5g; Fiber 7.3g; Chol 143mg; Iron 4mg; Sodium 918mg; Calc 162mg

BACON, HAM, AND LENTIL SOUP

PointsPlus value per serving: 8

HANDS-ON TIME: 22 min. ▪ **TOTAL TIME:** 52 min.

With a little bacon and some leftover ham, that bag of lentils in your pantry turns into a hearty, satisfying soup. Leftovers are great, as most legume soups benefit from being made a day ahead so their flavors meld. Substitute green split peas for the lentils, if you prefer; they take less time to cook, so monitor the soup accordingly.

5 slices thick-sliced bacon, cut crosswise into ½-inch strips
1½ cups (½-inch) cubed ham (about 8 ounces)
1 cup chopped onion
1 cup chopped fennel bulb
1 cup chopped celery
½ cup chopped leek
½ cup chopped carrot
3 (14-ounce) cans fat-free, lower-sodium chicken broth
2 cups water
1 teaspoon chopped fresh or ¼ teaspoon dried thyme
½ teaspoon freshly ground black pepper
1 cup canned diced tomatoes with basil, garlic, and oregano
1 pound dried lentils
2 bay leaves
¼ cup chopped fresh chives

1. Cook bacon in a Dutch oven over medium heat until crisp. Remove from pan, reserving 2 tablespoons drippings in pan. Crumble bacon, and set aside.
2. Add ham to drippings in pan; cook 2 minutes, stirring frequently. Add onion and next 4 ingredients (through carrot); cover and cook 10 minutes, stirring occasionally. Add broth and next 6 ingredients (through bay leaves). Bring to a boil; cover, reduce heat, and simmer 30 minutes or until lentils are tender. Discard bay leaves; sprinkle with bacon and chives just before serving. **YIELD: 8 SERVINGS (SERVING SIZE: 1¾ CUPS, ABOUT 2 TEASPOONS BACON, AND ½ TABLESPOON CHIVES).**

PER SERVING: Calories 359; Fat 11g (sat 4g, mono 4.8g, poly 1.4g); Protein 25.2g; Carb 40.6g; Fiber 18.9g; Chol 21mg; Iron 6.1mg; Sodium 956mg; Calc 72mg

MUSHROOM, BARLEY, AND BEEF SOUP

PointsPlus value per serving: 8

HANDS-ON TIME: 24 min. ▪ **TOTAL TIME:** 2 hr. 39 min.

½ cup dried porcini mushrooms (about ¼ ounce)
1 cup boiling water
Cooking spray
3½ cups sliced cremini mushrooms (about 8 ounces)
1½ cups chopped onion (about 1 medium)
½ cup finely chopped carrot (about 1 medium)
½ cup finely chopped celery
½ cup finely chopped parsnip (about 1 small)
2 garlic cloves, minced
1 tablespoon olive oil
12 ounces lean beef stew meat, cut into bite-sized pieces
6 cups lower-sodium beef broth, divided
2 cups water
½ teaspoon salt
¼ teaspoon freshly ground black pepper
2 thyme sprigs
1 cup uncooked barley
2 tablespoons chopped fresh parsley

1. Place porcini mushrooms in a medium bowl; cover with boiling water. Cover and let stand 30 minutes or until tender. Drain mushrooms in a colander over a bowl, reserving liquid. Chop mushrooms; set aside.
2. Heat a Dutch oven over medium-high heat. Coat pan with cooking spray. Add cremini mushrooms and onion; sauté 10 minutes or until lightly browned. Spoon onion mixture into a medium bowl. Recoat pan with cooking spray. Add carrot, celery, parsnip, and garlic; sauté 4 minutes or until lightly browned. Add carrot mixture to onion mixture in bowl.
3. Heat pan over medium-high heat. Add oil to pan; swirl to coat. Add beef to pan; cook 3 minutes, browning on all sides. Add 1 cup broth to pan, scraping pan to loosen browned bits. Add 5 cups broth, chopped porcini mushrooms, porcini liquid, onion mixture, 2 cups water, salt, pepper, and thyme. Bring to a boil; cover, reduce heat to medium-low, and simmer 1 hour or until beef is just tender.
4. Discard thyme sprigs. Stir in barley; cover and cook 30 minutes or until barley is al dente. Uncover and cook 15 minutes. Remove from heat; sprinkle with parsley. **YIELD: 6 SERVINGS (SERVING SIZE: ABOUT 1½ CUPS SOUP AND 1 TEASPOON PARSLEY).**

PER SERVING: Calories 318; Fat 9.6g (sat 2.9g, mono 4.6g, poly 0.9g); Protein 25.7g; Carb 32.5g; Fiber 7.4g; Chol 58mg; Iron 3.8mg; Sodium 700mg; Calc 47mg

PORK AND WILD RICE SOUP

PointsPlus value per serving: 7

HANDS-ON TIME: 11 min. ▪ **TOTAL TIME:** 26 min.

1 tablespoon extra-virgin olive oil, divided
1 (1 pound) pork tenderloin, trimmed and cut into ½-inch pieces
⅓ cup brown and wild rice blend
¼ cup finely chopped onion
3 garlic cloves, minced
2 serrano chiles, seeded and minced
1 cup water
1 teaspoon chopped fresh oregano
1 (32-ounce) carton fat-free, lower-sodium chicken broth
1 (15-ounce) can black beans, rinsed and drained
¼ cup chopped fresh cilantro
2½ tablespoons fresh lime juice
¼ teaspoon kosher salt
¼ teaspoon freshly ground black pepper
3 tablespoons crumbled queso fresco
1 sliced peeled avocado
24 baked tortilla chips

1. Heat a Dutch oven over medium-high heat. Add 1½ teaspoons oil to pan; swirl to coat. Add pork to pan, and cook 5 minutes, browning on all sides. Remove from pan.
2. Add 1½ teaspoons oil to pan, scraping pan to loosen browned bits. Add rice, onion, garlic, and chiles; sauté 3 minutes or until onion is tender. Add pork, 1 cup water, oregano, broth, and beans; bring to a boil. Cover, reduce heat, and simmer 15 minutes or until rice is tender. Stir in cilantro, juice, salt, and black pepper; simmer 2 minutes. Top each serving evenly with cheese, avocado, and chips. YIELD: 6 SERVINGS (SERVING SIZE: 1⅓ CUPS SOUP, ABOUT 2 AVOCADO SLICES, 1½ TEASPOONS CHEESE, AND 4 CHIPS).

PER SERVING: Calories 282; Fat 12.1g (sat 2.7g, mono 6.7g, poly 1.7g); Protein 21.6g; Carb 24.6g; Fiber 5.1g; Chol 52mg;Iron 2.3mg; Sodium 638mg; Calc 61mg

CURRIED CHICKEN NOODLE SOUP

PointsPlus value per serving: 5

HANDS-ON TIME: 8 min. ▪ **TOTAL TIME:** 13 min.

Try this Thai-inspired take on a traditional favorite. The addition of edamame gives this soup a protein bonus.

6 ounces dried wide rice noodles
3 cups fat-free, lower-sodium chicken broth
2 cups chopped cooked chicken breast
1 tablespoon red curry paste
2 teaspoons fish sauce
1 (13.5-ounce) can light coconut milk
3 cups baby spinach leaves
½ cup frozen shelled edamame, thawed

1. Prepare noodles according to package directions, omitting salt and fat.
2. While noodles cook, bring broth and next 4 ingredients (through coconut milk) to a boil in a large saucepan; cook 5 minutes. Stir in noodles, spinach, and edamame. Cook 2 minutes or until thoroughly heated.
YIELD: 8 SERVINGS (SERVING SIZE: 1 CUP).

PER SERVING: Calories 182; Fat 4.3g (sat 2.7g, mono 0.6g, poly 0.5g); Protein 14.7g; Carb 20.4g; Fiber 0.8g; Chol 30mg; Iron 0.9mg; Sodium 438mg; Calc 17mg

COCONUT MILK

Thick, fragrant, and creamy, coconut milk is the liquid that comes from the fruit of the coconut when it's grated and mixed with a little water. Coconut milk is a common ingredient in curries, sauces, and soups. Because coconuts are naturally high in fat, coconut milk is also high in fat. There are "lite" or lower-fat coconut milks available. These lighter versions have been thinned with some water, but still add rich flavor to dishes. Do not use coconut water or cream of coconut in place of coconut milk. Coconut water is a mixture of the thin liquid inside unripe coconuts and water, and it doesn't offer the thick consistency, flavor, or richness that the milk does, while cream of coconut is a thickened mixture of coconut milk and sugar that is more suited for desserts and tropical drinks.

COLOMBIAN CHICKEN SOUP

PointsPlus value per serving: 8

HANDS-ON TIME: 13 min. ▪ **TOTAL TIME:** 13 min.

This soup, traditionally known as *ajiaco*, is a specialty around the mountainous region of Bogotá, Colombia. If you don't have a pouch of microwaveable brown rice, you can cook ⅔ cup brown rice to get the 2 cups cooked rice needed.

3 cups fat-free, lower-sodium chicken broth
1 (8.8-ounce) pouch microwaveable precooked whole-grain brown rice
½ teaspoon ground cumin
¼ teaspoon crushed red pepper
¼ teaspoon freshly ground black pepper
2 garlic cloves, minced
1 cup cubed peeled baking potato
½ cup water
2 ears shucked corn, each cut crosswise into 4 pieces
2 cups shredded cooked chicken breast
¼ cup chopped fresh cilantro
2 tablespoons fresh lime juice
¼ cup diced peeled avocado
Cilantro leaves (optional)

1. Place first 6 ingredients in a large Dutch oven; bring to a boil.
2. While broth mixture comes to a boil, place potato cubes, ½ cup water, and corn in a microwave-safe bowl. Cover with heavy-duty plastic wrap; vent. Microwave at HIGH 7 minutes or until potato and corn are tender.
3. Add vegetables and cooking liquid to broth mixture. Stir in chicken, cilantro, and lime juice. Cook 3 minutes or until thoroughly heated. Ladle soup into bowls; top with avocado and cilantro leaves, if desired. **YIELD: 4 SERVINGS (SERVING SIZE: 1 CUP SOUP, 2 PIECES OF CORN, AND 1 TABLESPOON AVOCADO).**

PER SERVING: Calories 339; Fat 6.2g (sat 1.3g, mono 2.5g, poly 1.5g); Protein 29.6g; Carb 39.5g; Fiber 4g; Chol 60mg; Iron 2mg; Sodium 500mg; Calc 24mg

CHICKEN POT PIE SOUP

PointsPlus value per serving: 5

HANDS-ON TIME: 15 min. ▪ **TOTAL TIME:** 15 min.

Using canned creamed soups helps keep the preparation time down for this favorite comfort food dish. Serve with seedless grapes or other fresh fruit.

1 teaspoon canola oil
1 teaspoon minced fresh garlic
¾ teaspoon dried thyme, divided
½ teaspoon freshly ground black pepper
1 (16-ounce) package frozen mixed vegetables, thawed
2 cups chopped skinless, boneless rotisserie chicken
1 (10¾-ounce) can condensed reduced-fat, reduced-sodium cream of celery soup, undiluted
1 (10¾-ounce) can condensed reduced-fat, reduced-sodium cream of mushroom soup, undiluted
1 (14.5-ounce) can fat-free, lower-sodium chicken broth
7 reduced-fat round buttery crackers
Cooking spray

1. Preheat broiler.
2. Heat a large deep skillet over medium-high heat. Add oil to pan; swirl to coat. Add garlic, ½ teaspoon thyme, pepper, and vegetables to pan; sauté 3 minutes. Add chicken, soups, and broth. Bring to a boil; reduce heat, and simmer, uncovered, 8 to 10 minutes, stirring occasionally.
3. While soup cooks, coat crackers with cooking spray; place on a baking sheet. Sprinkle crackers with ¼ teaspoon thyme. Broil 1 minute. Remove from oven. Ladle soup into bowls, and top with crackers. **YIELD: 7 SERVINGS (SERVING SIZE: 1 CUP SOUP AND 1 CRACKER).**

PER SERVING: Calories 194; Fat 5.5g (sat 1.2g, mono 1.9g, poly 1.8g); Protein 14.7g; Carb 19.5g; Fiber 2.3g; Chol 39mg; Iron 1.1mg; Sodium 639mg; Calc 100mg

ESCAROLE

Escarole is a light-colored, leafy green with a slightly bitter taste. Part of the endive family, its leaves are usually broad and curly and are a common addition to mixed salad greens. It is also good sautéed or cooked similar to collard greens. Escarole is a great source of vitamins A and K, as well as fiber. If you can't find it, substitute kale, collard greens, or spinach.

CHICKEN-ESCAROLE SOUP

PointsPlus value per serving: 6

HANDS-ON TIME: 10 min. ■ **TOTAL TIME:** 15 min.

1 (14½-ounce) can Italian-style stewed tomatoes, undrained and chopped
1 (14.5-ounce) can fat-free, lower-sodium chicken broth
2 cups coarsely chopped escarole (about 1 small head)
1 cup chopped cooked chicken breast
2 teaspoons extra-virgin olive oil

1. Combine tomatoes and broth in a large saucepan. Cover and bring to a boil over high heat. Reduce heat to low; simmer 5 minutes. Add escarole, chicken, and oil; cook 5 minutes or until heated. YIELD: 4 SERVINGS (SERVING SIZE: 1 CUP).

PER SERVING: Calories 118; Fat 4g (sat 0.7g, mono 2.1g, poly 0.6g); Protein 13.5g; Carb 7.9g; Fiber 1.5g; Chol 30mg; Iron 1.1mg; Sodium 535mg; Calc 49mg

CHICKEN TORTILLA SOUP

PointsPlus value per serving: 7

HANDS-ON TIME: 15 min. ■ **TOTAL TIME:** 15 min.

Simple to prepare but big on flavor, this classic Mexican soup is even better when served for leftovers. If you have extra time, coat the tortilla strips with cooking spray, and toast until golden and crispy.

1½ cups frozen whole-kernel corn
1 cup water
1 (14.5-ounce) can fat-free, lower-sodium chicken broth
1 (10-ounce) can diced tomatoes with green chiles, undrained
2 cups shredded cooked chicken breast
½ cup diced peeled avocado
40 mini corn tortilla strips (about 2½ ounces)
Freshly ground black pepper (optional)
Lime wedges (optional)

1. Combine first 4 ingredients in a medium saucepan; bring to a boil. Stir in chicken; reduce heat, and simmer 2 minutes or until thoroughly heated. Ladle soup into bowls, and top with avocado and tortilla strips. Sprinkle with pepper, and serve with lime wedges, if desired. YIELD: 4 SERVINGS (SERVING SIZE: 1½ CUPS, 2 TABLESPOONS AVOCADO, AND 10 TORTILLA STRIPS).

PER SERVING: Calories 299; Fat 9.2g (sat 1.7g, mono 5.5g, poly 1.2g); Protein 26.5g; Carb 27g; Fiber 3.5g; Chol 60mg; Iron 1.2mg; Sodium 678mg; Calc 47mg

COCONUT CORN CHOWDER WITH CHICKEN

PointsPlus value per serving: 8

HANDS-ON TIME: 10 min. ■ **TOTAL TIME:** 10 min.

Cooking the potatoes in the microwave is the perfect way to jump-start this creamy creation. The other big time-saver is to purchase a rotisserie chicken. If you use a combination of white and dark meat instead of all chicken breast, the ***PointsPlus*** value will increase to 9.

3½ cups (½-inch) cubed medium-sized red potatoes (6 potatoes)
3 cups pulled skinless, boneless rotisserie chicken breast
2 (14¾-ounce) cans no-salt-added cream-style corn
1 (13.5-ounce) can light coconut milk
¼ teaspoon salt
¼ teaspoon freshly ground black pepper
Chopped green onions (optional)
Chopped fresh cilantro (optional)

1. Place potato in a large microwave-safe bowl. Cover with plastic wrap; vent. Microwave at HIGH 3 minutes or until tender.
2. While potato cooks, combine chicken and next 4 ingredients (through black pepper) in a medium saucepan. Cook over medium heat 3 minutes or just until bubbly, stirring occasionally.
3. Stir potato into chicken mixture. Bring to a boil; reduce heat, and simmer 2 minutes. Ladle soup into 6 bowls; sprinkle evenly with green onions and cilantro, if desired. YIELD: 6 SERVINGS (SERVING SIZE: 1⅓ CUPS).

PER SERVING: Calories 323; Fat 7.3g (sat 3.9g, mono 1.4g, poly 1.1g); Protein 26.5g; Carb 39.2g; Fiber 4.2g; Chol 60mg; Iron 2.1mg; Sodium 386mg; Calc 21mg

SPICY CHICKEN AND OKRA GUMBO

PointsPlus value per serving: 6

HANDS-ON TIME: 15 min. ■ **TOTAL TIME:** 15 min.

1 tablespoon olive oil
1 (16-ounce) package frozen sliced okra, thawed
1 (8-ounce) container refrigerated prechopped celery, onion, and bell pepper mix
1 tablespoon salt-free Cajun seasoning
3 cups fat-free, lower-sodium chicken broth
2 cups chopped skinless, boneless rotisserie chicken breast
1 teaspoon smoked paprika
1 (10-ounce) can diced tomatoes with green chiles, undrained
3 cups hot cooked rice

1. Heat a large Dutch oven over medium-high heat. Add oil to pan; swirl to coat. Add okra, bell pepper mix, and Cajun seasoning to pan, and sauté 4 minutes or until okra is tender.
2. Add chicken broth and next 3 ingredients (through diced tomatoes). Bring to a boil; reduce heat to medium, and cook 8 to 10 minutes or until thoroughly heated, stirring occasionally.
3. Ladle soup into bowls over rice. YIELD: 6 SERVINGS (SERVING SIZE: 1⅓ CUPS SOUP AND ½ CUP RICE).

PER SERVING: Calories 254; Fat 4.2g (sat 0.9g, mono 2.3g, poly 0.7g); Protein 19.4g; Carb 32.4g; Fiber 3.2g; Chol 40mg; Iron 1.7mg; Sodium 631mg; Calc 86mg

CHICKEN AND CHICKPEA STEW

PointsPlus value per serving: 4

HANDS-ON TIME: 14 min. ■ **TOTAL TIME:** 14 min.

1 tablespoon olive oil
1 (8-ounce) container refrigerated prechopped celery, onion, and bell pepper mix
2 tablespoons chopped golden raisins
1 tablespoon biryani curry paste
1 teaspoon smoked paprika
½ teaspoon salt
1 cup drained canned no-salt-added tomatoes
1 cup water
1 (16-ounce) can lower-sodium chickpeas (garbanzo beans), rinsed and drained
1 (12-ounce) jar roasted red bell peppers, drained and chopped
2 cups chopped skinless, boneless rotisserie chicken breast

1. Heat a large nonstick skillet over medium-high heat. Add oil to pan; swirl to coat. Add bell pepper mix and next 4 ingredients (through salt) to pan. Reduce heat to medium, and cook 5 minutes, stirring twice.
2. Add tomatoes and next 3 ingredients (through roasted bell peppers); cook 4 minutes, stirring once. Add chicken; cook 4 minutes, stirring once. YIELD: 6 SERVINGS (SERVING SIZE: 1 CUP).

PER SERVING: Calories 189; Fat 5.7g (sat 1g, mono 2.8g, poly 1.3g); Protein 18.3g; Carb 15.4g; Fiber 4.5g; Chol 40mg; Iron 1.6mg; Sodium 631mg; Calc 40mg

BBQ CHICKEN AND VEGETABLE STEW

PointsPlus value per serving: 5

HANDS-ON TIME: 9 min. ■ **TOTAL TIME:** 14 min.

Bake a batch of cornbread muffins for this homey stew. A typical muffin weighing about 2 ounces has a *PointsPlus* value of 5.

Cooking spray
2 (8-ounce) containers refrigerated prechopped celery, onion, and bell pepper mix
1½ cups frozen mixed vegetables
1¼ cups fat-free, lower-sodium chicken broth
½ cup frozen baby lima beans
½ cup water
½ cup barbecue sauce
2 tablespoons unsalted tomato paste
2 teaspoons Worcestershire sauce
½ teaspoon freshly ground black pepper
2⅔ cups pulled smoked rotisserie chicken

1. Heat a large Dutch oven over medium-high heat. Coat pan with cooking spray. Add bell pepper mix; sauté 5 minutes or until tender. Stir in mixed vegetables and next 7 ingredients (through black pepper). Bring to a boil; stir in chicken. Cover, reduce heat, and simmer 5 minutes. YIELD: 6 SERVINGS (SERVING SIZE: 1 CUP).

PER SERVING: Calories 218; Fat 4.8g (sat 1.3g, mono 1.7g, poly 1.1g); Protein 21.3g; Carb 21g; Fiber 3.2g; Chol 55mg; Iron 1.5mg; Sodium 655mg; Calc 47mg

BUFFALO CHICKEN CHILI

PointsPlus value per serving: 5

HANDS-ON TIME: 13 min. ■ **TOTAL TIME:** 13 min.

Cooking spray
1½ cups sliced celery
2⅓ cups chopped cooked chicken breast
½ cup fat-free, lower-sodium chicken broth
3 tablespoons hot pepper sauce
1 (15-ounce) can reduced-sodium black beans, rinsed and drained
1 (14.5-ounce) can diced tomatoes with green pepper, celery, and onion
1 (8-ounce) can unsalted tomato sauce
1½ ounces crumbled blue cheese (about 6 tablespoons)

1. Heat a large saucepan over medium heat. Coat pan with cooking spray. Add celery; sauté 6 minutes or until crisp-tender. Stir in chicken and next 5 ingredients (through tomato sauce). Bring to a boil; boil 2 minutes, stirring occasionally.
2. Ladle chili into bowls; sprinkle with cheese. YIELD: 6 SERVINGS (SERVING SIZE: 1 CUP CHILI AND 1 TABLESPOON CHEESE).

PER SERVING: Calories 197; Fat 4.2g (sat 1.8g, mono 1.3g, poly 0.4g); Protein 22g; Carb 17.8g; Fiber 4g; Chol 53mg; Iron 2.3mg; Sodium 589mg; Calc 101mg

PUMPKIN-CHICKEN CHILI

PointsPlus value per serving: 4 *(pictured on page 136)*

HANDS-ON TIME: 8 min. ■ **TOTAL TIME:** 13 min.

Canned pumpkin is the surprise ingredient in this hearty fall chili, adding unique taste and texture.

Cooking spray
1 cup prechopped onion
2 teaspoons chili powder
1 teaspoon ground cumin
2 cups shredded cooked chicken breast
½ cup water
½ teaspoon salt
1 (16-ounce) can reduced-sodium pinto beans, rinsed and drained
1 (15-ounce) can pumpkin
1 (14.5-ounce) can fat-free, lower-sodium chicken broth
1 (14.5-ounce) can fire-roasted diced tomatoes with garlic, drained
¼ cup chopped fresh cilantro

1. Heat a large Dutch oven over medium-high heat. Coat pan with cooking spray. Add onion, chili powder, and cumin to pan; sauté 4 minutes or until onion is tender.
2. Add chicken and next 6 ingredients (through diced tomatoes). Cover, reduce heat, and simmer 5 minutes or until thoroughly heated. Ladle soup into individual bowls; sprinkle with cilantro. YIELD: 6 SERVINGS (SERVING SIZE: 1¼ CUPS CHILI AND 2 TEASPOONS CILANTRO).

PER SERVING: Calories 161; Fat 2.2g (sat 0.5g, mono 0.6g, poly 0.4g); Protein 19.7g; Carb 17.6g; Fiber 7.1g; Chol 40mg; Iron 2.2mg; Sodium 599mg; Calc 62mg

CHICKEN ORZO SOUP

PointsPlus value per serving: 5

HANDS-ON TIME: 26 min. ■ **TOTAL TIME:** 26 min.

The addition of the optional fresh basil and lemon brightens the flavor of this comforting soup.

1 teaspoon olive oil
8 ounces skinless, boneless chicken breast, chopped
1 cup matchstick-cut carrots
1 (8-ounce) container refrigerated prechopped onion
5 cups fat-free, lower-sodium chicken broth
1½ cups water
½ teaspoon freshly ground black pepper
¼ teaspoon salt
1 cup uncooked orzo (rice-shaped pasta)
Thinly sliced basil leaves (optional)
Lemon wedges (optional)

1. Heat a large nonstick saucepan over medium-high heat. Add oil to pan; swirl to coat. Add chicken to pan, and sauté 5 minutes or until browned. Add carrots and onion; sauté 5 minutes or until vegetables are tender.
2. Add broth and next 3 ingredients (through salt). Cover and bring to a boil. Stir in pasta. Reduce heat to medium; cook 13 minutes or until pasta is done, stirring occasionally.
3. Ladle soup into bowls. Garnish with basil, and serve with lemon wedges, if desired. YIELD: 6 SERVINGS (SERVING SIZE: ABOUT 1 CUP).

PER SERVING: Calories 203; Fat 2.3g (sat 0.5g, mono 0.9g, poly 0.5g); Protein 15.5g; Carb 30.3g; Fiber 2.3g; Chol 24mg; Iron 1.3mg; Sodium 635mg; Calc 24mg

Pesto Chicken Clubs,
page 110

Sautéed Vegetable Pitas,
page 104

Pear-Chicken Monte Cristo Sandwiches, *page 116*

Roast Beef and Caramelized Onion Sandwiches, *page 107*

Garlicky Spinach and Feta Burgers,
page 109

Salmon Salad Sandwiches, *page 106*

Green Soup, *page 146*

Sautéed Squash and Peppers with Tarragon, *page 153*

Pumpkin-Chicken Chili,
page 128

Bacon-Walnut Brussels Sprouts,
page 150

Blue Cheese Asparagus,
page 148

Cilantro Corn,
page 151

Pomegranate Sorbet,
page 167

Dark Chocolate–Blueberry Bark, *page 174*

Broiled Citrus with Crystallized Ginger, *page 160*

Broiled Grapefruit with Vanilla Bean Cream, *page 160*

Mixed Berry Pavlova Parfaits, *page 162*

Chocolate Chip Cake Cookies, *page 172*

CHICKEN SAUSAGE TORTELLINI SOUP

PointsPlus value per serving: 4

HANDS-ON TIME: 15 min. ▪ **TOTAL TIME:** 15 min.

Cooking spray
1 cup chopped onion
6 ounces spinach and feta chicken sausage, sliced
3 garlic cloves, chopped
3 cups fat-free, lower-sodium chicken broth
1½ cups fresh three-cheese tortellini
1 cup water
1 cup chopped carrot
½ teaspoon freshly ground black pepper
½ teaspoon dried basil
1 cup chopped fresh baby spinach
Basil leaves (optional)

1. Heat a large saucepan over medium-high heat. Coat pan with cooking spray. Add onion and sausage to pan; cook 3 minutes, stirring occasionally. Add garlic; cook 1 minute or until sausage is browned, stirring constantly.
2. Stir in broth and next 5 ingredients (through basil). Bring to a boil; reduce heat, and simmer 3 to 4 minutes or until carrot and tortellini are tender. Stir in spinach just before serving. Sprinkle with basil, if desired. YIELD: 6 SERVINGS (SERVING SIZE: 1 CUP).

PER SERVING: Calories 162; Fat 5.2g (sat 1.7g, mono 1.9g, poly 0.7g); Protein 10.6g; Carb 19.3g; Fiber 2.4g; Chol 42mg; Iron 0.8mg; Sodium 641mg; Calc 58mg

CHICKEN GNOCCHI SOUP

PointsPlus value per serving: 6

HANDS-ON TIME: 15 min. ▪ **TOTAL TIME:** 15 min.

6 ounces ground chicken
2 cups water
¼ teaspoon freshly ground black pepper
1 (14.5-ounce) can fat-free, lower-sodium chicken broth
1 (14.5-ounce) can unsalted diced tomatoes with basil, garlic, and oregano, undrained
1 (16-ounce) package vacuum-packed gnocchi
1 cup packed baby spinach leaves
¼ cup commercial basil pesto, divided
3 tablespoons preshredded fresh Parmesan cheese

1. Heat a large saucepan over medium-high heat. Add chicken to pan; cook 4 minutes or until browned, stirring to crumble.
2. Add 2 cups water and next 3 ingredients (through diced tomatoes). Cover and bring to a boil. Stir in gnocchi; return to a boil. Uncover and boil 2 to 3 minutes or until gnocchi float to top of mixture. Stir in spinach and 2 tablespoons pesto.
3. Ladle soup into bowls; sprinkle with cheese. Dollop remaining pesto on top of soup. YIELD: 6 SERVINGS (SERVING SIZE: ABOUT 1½ CUPS SOUP, 1½ TEASPOONS CHEESE, AND 1 TEASPOON PESTO).

PER SERVING: Calories 241; Fat 7.1g (sat 1.7g, mono 3.7g, poly 0.7g); Protein 10.2g; Carb 33.6g; Fiber 2.8g; Chol 22mg; Iron 0.5mg; Sodium 648mg; Calc 76mg

SAUSAGE AND SPINACH SOUP

PointsPlus value per serving: 6

HANDS-ON TIME: 14 min. ▪ **TOTAL TIME:** 14 min.

Fresh herbs are added after the soup cooks so they'll retain their bright color and flavor. You can substitute 1 teaspoon dried herbs for each tablespoon fresh, but add them with the tomatoes.

Cooking spray
10 ounces sweet turkey Italian sausage
1 cup prechopped onion
2 teaspoons bottled minced garlic
½ cup water
1 (15-ounce) can cannellini beans, rinsed and drained
1 (14.5-ounce) can organic stewed tomatoes, undrained
1 (14-ounce) can fat-free, lower-sodium chicken broth
2 cups baby spinach
1 tablespoon chopped fresh basil
2 teaspoons chopped fresh oregano
2 tablespoons grated fresh Romano cheese

1. Heat a large saucepan over high heat. Coat pan with cooking spray. Remove casings from sausage. Add sausage to pan, and cook 4 minutes or until browned, stirring to crumble. Add onion and garlic to pan; cook 2 minutes. Stir in ½ cup water, beans, tomatoes, and broth. Cover and bring to a boil. Uncover and cook 3 minutes or until slightly thick. Remove from heat, and stir in spinach, basil, and oregano. Ladle soup into bowls, and sprinkle with cheese. YIELD: 4 SERVINGS (SERVING SIZE: 1½ CUPS SOUP AND 1½ TEASPOONS CHEESE).

PER SERVING: Calories 261; Fat 8.6g (sat 2.8g, mono 2.7g, poly 2.5g); Protein 20.9g; Carb 23.1g; Fiber 5.4g; Chol 62mg; Iron 3.4mg; Sodium 842mg; Calc 105mg

GREEN SOUP

PointsPlus value per serving: 3 *(pictured on page 135)*

HANDS-ON TIME: 15 min. ▪ **TOTAL TIME:** 15 min.

Turkey kielbasa imparts a hearty flavor to this soup, which is chock full of vegetables. Andouille or hot Italian sausage would also work well.

1 tablespoon olive oil
8 ounces turkey kielbasa, halved lengthwise and cut into ½-inch-thick slices
1 (8-ounce) package refrigerated prechopped celery, onion, and bell pepper mix
3 garlic cloves, chopped
2 cups chopped broccoli florets
1 pound asparagus, cut into 1-inch pieces
3 cups fat-free, lower-sodium chicken broth
3 cups water
1 (6-ounce) package fresh baby spinach
½ teaspoon freshly ground black pepper
2 ounces grated fresh Parmesan cheese (about ½ cup)

1. Heat a Dutch oven over medium-high heat. Add oil to pan; swirl to coat. Add kielbasa to pan, and sauté 1 to 2 minutes or until lightly browned. Add bell pepper mix and garlic, and sauté 3 minutes or until vegetables are tender. Add broccoli and asparagus, and sauté 2 minutes. Stir in broth and 3 cups water. Bring to a boil; reduce heat, and simmer 2 minutes. Add spinach and black pepper to pan, stirring until spinach wilts. Ladle soup into individual bowls; sprinkle with cheese. **YIELD: 8 SERVINGS (SERVING SIZE: 1¼ CUPS SOUP AND ABOUT 1 TABLESPOON CHEESE).**

PER SERVING: Calories 132; Fat 6.4g (sat 2g, mono o 2.7g, poly 0.9g); Protein 11.3g; Carb 9.6g; Fiber 3.3g; Chol 23mg; Iron 1.5mg; Sodium 635mg; Calc 157mg

PRECHOPPED VEGETABLES

Most grocery stores now offer an assortment of pre-prepped produce. Although they may cost a little more, washed and chopped vegetables can be a huge timesaver. The most widely available are prechopped onions and bell peppers—key starting ingredients in many recipes. If you're watching your pocketbook, purchase prechopped ingredients only on days when you're really in a time crunch. Also, make sure to inspect the package to ensure the vegetables look fresh and haven't been sitting in the case for several days. Vegetables lose a small amount of nutrients once chopped and the flesh is exposed to air.

TURKEY CHILI

PointsPlus value per serving: 5

HANDS-ON TIME: 5 min. ▪ **TOTAL TIME:** 1 hr. 20 min.

If you add the optional toppings, each serving of this hearty chili will have a *PointsPlus* value of 6.

Cooking spray
1 pound ground turkey
2 (15-ounce) cans unsalted pinto beans, rinsed, drained, and divided
1 (8-ounce) container refrigerated prechopped celery, onion, and bell pepper mix
1½ tablespoons chili powder
1 cup water
¼ teaspoon salt
2 (10-ounce) cans diced tomatoes with green chiles, undrained
6 tablespoons reduced-fat shredded cheddar cheese (optional)
6 tablespoons reduced-fat sour cream (optional)
6 tablespoons sliced green onions (optional)

1. Heat a large Dutch oven over medium-high heat. Coat pan with cooking spray. Add turkey to pan; cook 7 minutes or until turkey is done, stirring frequently. Remove turkey from pan. Set aside.
2. While turkey cooks, place 1 can of pinto beans in a food processor; process 2 minutes or until beans are smooth.
3. Add bell pepper mix to pan, and cook 3 minutes or until vegetables are crisp-tender, stirring frequently. Stir in turkey, bean puree, remaining can of beans, chili powder, and next 3 ingredients (through diced tomatoes). Bring to a boil; cover, reduce heat, and simmer 1 hour. Ladle chili into bowls. Top each serving with 1 tablespoon each cheese, sour cream, and green onions, if desired. **YIELD: 6 SERVINGS (SERVING SIZE: 1 CUP).**

PER SERVING: Calories 215; Fat 6.1g (sat 1.6g, mono 2.1g, poly 1.8g); Protein 19.8g; Carb 19.4g; Fiber 6.4g; Chol 52mg; Iron 2.8mg; Sodium 581mg; Calc 85mg

sides

Sautéed Squash and Peppers with Tarragon, *page 153*

BLUE CHEESE ASPARAGUS

PointsPlus value per serving: 2 *(pictured on page 138)*

HANDS-ON TIME: 12 min. ■ **TOTAL TIME:** 12 min.

With tangy balsamic vinegar and blue cheese, this will become your go-to asparagus recipe.

1 pound asparagus spears
1 tablespoon chopped fresh parsley
1 tablespoon olive oil
1 tablespoon balsamic vinegar
¼ teaspoon freshly ground black pepper
2 tablespoons crumbled blue cheese

1. Snap off tough ends of asparagus. Add water to a large skillet to a depth of 1 inch; bring to a boil. Add asparagus in a single layer; cook 3 minutes or until crisp-tender. Drain asparagus; arrange on a serving platter.
2. Combine parsley and next 3 ingredients (through black pepper) in a small bowl, stirring with a whisk. Spoon parsley mixture over asparagus. Sprinkle with cheese. **YIELD: 4 SERVINGS (SERVING SIZE: ¼ OF ASPARAGUS).**

PER SERVING: Calories 69; Fat 4.5g (sat 1.1g, mono 2.8g, poly 0.4g); Protein 3.3g; Carb 5.4g; Fiber 2.4g; Chol 3mg; Iron 2.5mg; Sodium 51mg; Calc 49mg

ASPARAGUS

Asparagus is at its peak from April through late June. Look for stalks with smooth skin and uniform color. All asparagus should have a dry, compact tip. Fibrous stems and shriveled stalks are signs of age. To prepare the asparagus, trim the fibrous ends from all the spears. Just hold the spear and bend—it'll break at the right spot.

GREEN BEANS WITH PANCETTA

PointsPlus value per serving: 2 *(pictured on page 10)*

HANDS-ON TIME: 9 min. ■ **TOTAL TIME:** 9 min.

These salty sautéed green beans are the perfect accompaniment to a grilled chicken breast or steak.

1 (12-ounce) bag trimmed fresh green beans
4 thin slices pancetta (1 ounce)
¼ teaspoon freshly ground black pepper
⅛ teaspoon salt
2 tablespoons chopped walnuts, toasted

1. Microwave green beans according to package directions. Let stand 1 minute.
2. Heat a large nonstick skillet over medium-high heat. Add pancetta to pan; cook 2 minutes or until crisp. Remove pancetta from pan; drain on paper towels. Crumble pancetta. Add green beans, pepper, and salt to drippings in pan. Cook 2 minutes or until thoroughly heated. Sprinkle with pancetta and walnuts. **YIELD: 4 SERVINGS (SERVING SIZE: ABOUT ⅔ CUP).**

PER SERVING: Calories 76; Fat 4.6g (sat 1g, mono 1.1g, poly 2g); Protein 3.7g; Carb 6.5g; Fiber 2.6g; Chol 5mg; Iron 1.2mg; Sodium 218mg; Calc 36mg

SESAME BROCCOLI

PointsPlus value per serving: 2

HANDS-ON TIME: 11 min. ■ **TOTAL TIME:** 11 min.

Toasted sesame seeds are often available in the spice section of most groceries.

2 teaspoons dark sesame oil
1 teaspoon minced peeled fresh ginger
¼ teaspoon salt
2 garlic cloves, chopped
2 (12-ounce) packages broccoli florets
2 teaspoons honey
2 teaspoons toasted sesame seeds

1. Heat a large nonstick skillet over medium heat. Add oil to pan; swirl to coat. Add ginger, salt, and garlic; sauté 2 minutes. Add broccoli; sauté 5 minutes or until crisp-tender. Add honey; cook 2 minutes, stirring constantly. Sprinkle with sesame seeds. **YIELD: 6 SERVINGS (SERVING SIZE: ABOUT 1 CUP).**

PER SERVING: Calories 61; Fat 2.5g (sat 0.4g, mono 0.9g, poly 1.1g); Protein 3.7g; Carb 8.3g; Fiber 3.5g; Chol 0mg; Iron 1.1mg; Sodium 131mg; Calc 59mg

LEMON-SCENTED BROCCOLINI

PointsPlus value per serving: 1

HANDS-ON TIME: 10 min. ■ **TOTAL TIME:** 10 min.

Be careful not to overcook Broccolini—its flavor and texture are best when it's served crisp-tender.

2 bunches Broccolini (about 14 ounces)
1 tablespoon olive oil
2 garlic cloves, chopped
1 tablespoon grated fresh lemon rind
½ teaspoon freshly ground black pepper
¼ teaspoon salt

1. Cook Broccolini in boiling water to cover in a large saucepan 3 minutes or until crisp-tender. Drain and plunge Broccolini into ice water. Drain and pat dry with paper towels.
2. Heat a large skillet over medium-high heat. Add oil to pan; swirl to coat. Add garlic; sauté 30 seconds or until garlic begins into brown. Add Broccolini, and cook 2 minutes or until thoroughly heated, stirring constantly. Stir in lemon rind, pepper, and salt. **YIELD: 6 SERVINGS (SERVING SIZE: ⅙ OF BROCCOLINI).**

PER SERVING: Calories 45; Fat 2.5g (sat 0.3g, mono 1.6g, poly 0.3g); Protein 2g; Carb 5g; Fiber 1.9g; Chol 0mg; Iron 0.5mg; Sodium 121mg; Calc 35mg

BROCCOLINI

Although common perception is that Broccolini is the younger, less mature broccoli plants and stems, it's actually a hybrid vegetable that was made by crossing broccoli with Chinese cabbage. The end result is a plant similar in shape to broccoli but with thinner, longer stems and heads. Most any recipe or cooking method for broccoli, such as steaming, sautéing, or stir-frying, is also suitable for Broccolini although you may need to cut down on the cooking time slightly.

REMOVING BEET STAINS

Their vibrant red-purple hue is what beets are best known for, and they can add a wonderful pop of color to the dinner table. However, beets' rich color can also stain your hands during the preparation process. Washing with soap will get some of the color off, but here are some additional tips to help avoid staining.

- Consider using disposable plastic gloves when handling.
- If stains get on hands, try scrubbing hands with a coarse salt under warm water—just be careful of any cuts or open wounds.
- If stains are on clothes, rinse immediately, and treat with stain remover.

ORANGE-SCENTED BEETS

PointsPlus value per serving: 2

HANDS-ON TIME: 5 min. ■ **TOTAL TIME:** 5 min.

Precooked beets can be found in the produce section of your local grocery store. Serve this side at room temperature, or cover and chill until you're ready to serve.

1 teaspoon grated fresh orange rind
2 tablespoons fresh orange juice
1 tablespoon olive oil
1 tablespoon white wine vinegar
1 teaspoon chopped fresh rosemary
¼ teaspoon freshly ground black pepper
⅛ teaspoon salt
2 (8.8-ounce) packages refrigerated precooked beets, drained and cut into wedges
2 tablespoons crumbled feta cheese

1. Combine first 7 ingredients in a medium bowl, stirring with a whisk. Add beets; toss to coat. Sprinkle with cheese before serving. **YIELD: 6 SERVINGS (SERVING SIZE: 1 CUP BEETS AND 1 TEASPOON CHEESE).**

PER SERVING: Calories 74; Fat 3g (sat 0.7g, mono 1.8g, poly 0.3g); Protein 2.3g; Carb 10.8g; Fiber 2.1g; Chol 2mg; Iron 0.9mg; Sodium 207mg; Calc 26mg

MAPLE-ORANGE BRUSSELS SPROUTS

PointsPlus value per serving: 4

HANDS-ON TIME: 16 min. ■ **TOTAL TIME:** 16 min.

Remove the skillet from the heat before adding the syrup mixture; otherwise, the syrup may burn.

1 navel orange
2 tablespoons maple syrup
¼ teaspoon salt
¼ teaspoon freshly ground black pepper
2 teaspoons olive oil
4½ cups trimmed Brussels sprouts, halved
¼ cup coarsely chopped pecans

1. Grate rind and squeeze juice from orange to measure ½ teaspoon rind and 2 tablespoons juice. Combine rind, juice, syrup, salt, and pepper in a small bowl.
2. Heat a large nonstick skillet over medium-high heat. Add oil to pan; swirl to coat. Add Brussels sprouts to pan; sauté 6 minutes or until tender. Add pecans; sauté 1 minute or until pecans are toasted. Remove pan from heat; stir in syrup mixture. **YIELD: 4 SERVINGS (SERVING SIZE: ABOUT ¾ CUP).**

PER SERVING: Calories 146; Fat 7.5g (sat 0.8g, mono 4.5g, poly 1.9g); Protein 4.5g; Carb 18.8g; Fiber 5g; Chol 0mg; Iron 1.8mg; Sodium 177mg; Calc 64mg

BACON-WALNUT BRUSSELS SPROUTS

PointsPlus value per serving: 3 *(pictured on page 137)*

HANDS-ON TIME: 15 min. ■ **TOTAL TIME:** 15 min.

2 center-cut bacon slices
4½ cups thinly sliced Brussels sprouts (about 1 pound)
¼ cup sliced shallots (about 2)
¼ teaspoon freshly ground black pepper
2 tablespoons chopped walnuts, toasted
2 tablespoons grated fresh Parmesan cheese

1. Cook bacon in a large nonstick skillet over medium heat until crisp. Remove bacon from pan; crumble.
2. Add Brussels sprouts and shallots to drippings in pan; sauté 5 minutes or until tender. Stir in pepper. Sprinkle with walnuts, cheese, and reserved bacon. **YIELD: 4 SERVINGS (SERVING SIZE: ¾ CUP).**

PER SERVING: Calories 111; Fat 4.7g (sat 1.3g, mono 1.1g, poly 2g); Protein 7.4g; Carb 13.2g; Fiber 4.6g; Chol 6mg; Iron 1.9mg; Sodium 158mg; Calc 102mg

SPICY ROASTED CAULIFLOWER

PointsPlus value per serving: 1

HANDS-ON TIME: 9 min. ■ **TOTAL TIME:** 15 min.

A head of cauliflower can be used in place of the two (10-ounce) bags.

2 (10-ounce) bags fresh cauliflower florets
1 tablespoon olive oil
½ teaspoon crushed red pepper
¼ teaspoon salt
1 ounce grated fresh Parmesan cheese (about ¼ cup)

1. Preheat oven to 500°.
2. Place cauliflower on a rimmed baking sheet; drizzle with olive oil. Sprinkle with red pepper and salt; toss gently. Bake at 500° for 12 minutes or until lightly browned, stirring after 6 minutes. Sprinkle with cheese. **YIELD: 8 SERVINGS (SERVING SIZE: ¾ CUP).**

PER SERVING: Calories 48; Fat 2.9g (sat 0.8g, mono 1.5g, poly 0.2g); Protein 2.9g; Carb 3.6g; Fiber 1.4g; Chol 3mg; Iron 0.3mg; Sodium 158mg; Calc 66mg

LEMON-DILL CARROT AND PARSNIP HASH

PointsPlus value per serving: 2

HANDS-ON TIME: 12 min. ■ **TOTAL TIME:** 12 min.

Try this hash in place of the standard potato dish that you usually serve with fish or chicken.

2 teaspoons olive oil
½ pound carrot, grated (about 1½ cups)
½ pound parsnip, grated (about 1½ cups)
1 tablespoon chopped fresh dill
1 teaspoon grated fresh lemon rind
1 tablespoon fresh lemon juice
¼ teaspoon salt
¼ teaspoon freshly ground black pepper

1. Heat a large nonstick skillet over medium-high heat. Add oil to pan; swirl to coat. Add carrot and parsnip to pan; sauté 5 minutes or until tender. Remove from heat; stir in dill and remaining ingredients. **YIELD: 4 SERVINGS (SERVING SIZE: ½ CUP).**

PER SERVING: Calories 87; Fat 2.6g (sat 0.4g, mono 1.7g, poly 0.3g); Protein 1.3g; Carb 16.1g; Fiber 4.5g; Chol 0mg; Iron 0.5mg; Sodium 193mg; Calc 41mg

CILANTRO CORN

PointsPlus value per serving: 3 *(pictured on page 139)*

HANDS-ON TIME: 12 min. ■ **TOTAL TIME:** 12 min.

Cilantro and red bell pepper dress up plain corn, and a sprinkle of lime juice at the end makes it an ideal side to pair with cheesy Mexican dishes.

1 tablespoon butter
3 cups frozen whole-kernel corn, thawed
⅓ cup chopped red bell pepper
¼ teaspoon salt
1 jalapeño pepper, seeded and minced
3 tablespoons chopped fresh cilantro
1 tablespoon fresh lime juice

1. Melt butter in a 12-inch cast-iron skillet over medium-high heat. Add corn, bell pepper, salt, and jalapeño pepper. Cook 8 minutes or until corn is lightly browned, stirring frequently. Remove from heat; stir in cilantro and lime juice. **YIELD: 5 SERVINGS (SERVING SIZE: ½ CUP).**

PER SERVING: Calories 97; Fat 3g (sat 1.6g, mono 0.8g, poly 0.4g); Protein 2.6g; Carb 18g; Fiber 2g; Chol 6mg; Iron 0.4mg; Sodium 142mg; Calc 6mg

HERBED WILD MUSHROOMS

PointsPlus value per serving: 2

HANDS-ON TIME: 15 min. ■ **TOTAL TIME:** 15 min.

The earthy flavors of the mushroom blend are accentuated by thyme and soy sauce. Serve as a topping for grilled steak.

1 tablespoon olive oil
2 garlic cloves, minced
4 (4-ounce) packages presliced exotic mushroom blend (such as shiitake, cremini, and oyster)
1 teaspoon chopped fresh thyme
4 teaspoons lower-sodium soy sauce
½ teaspoon freshly ground black pepper

1. Heat a large nonstick skillet over medium-high heat. Add oil to pan; swirl to coat. Add garlic to pan, and cook 30 seconds, stirring constantly. Add mushrooms; cook 9 minutes or until mushrooms are tender and lightly browned, stirring frequently. Stir in thyme and remaining ingredients; cook 2 minutes or until thoroughly heated. **YIELD: 4 SERVINGS (SERVING SIZE: ABOUT ½ CUP).**

PER SERVING: Calories 62; Fat 3.5g (sat 0.5g, mono 2.5g, poly 0.4g); Protein 3.3g; Carb 6g; Fiber 0.8g; Chol 0mg; Iron 0.6mg; Sodium 199mg; Calc 25mg

MUSHROOM, CORN, AND LEEK SAUTÉ

PointsPlus value per serving: 2

HANDS-ON TIME: 12 min. ■ **TOTAL TIME:** 12 min.

Wash the leek slices by placing them in a bowl of water and swirling them around vigorously.

Cooking spray
1 (8-ounce) package presliced button mushrooms
1 cup frozen whole-kernel corn, thawed and drained
1 cup sliced leek
1 teaspoon thyme leaves
¼ teaspoon freshly ground black pepper
⅛ teaspoon salt
2 tablespoons water
1 teaspoon light stick butter

1. Heat a large skillet over medium-high heat. Coat pan with cooking spray. Add mushrooms; coat mushrooms with cooking spray. Cook 5 minutes or until lightly browned, stirring occasionally.
2. Add corn and next 4 ingredients (through salt); coat lightly with cooking spray. Sauté 4 minutes or until vegetables are lightly browned. Stir in 2 tablespoons water, scraping pan to loosen browned bits. Add butter; stir until butter melts. **YIELD: 4 SERVINGS (SERVING SIZE: ½ CUP).**

PER SERVING: Calories 61; Fat 0.9g (sat 0.3g, mono 0.3g, poly 0.2g); Protein 2.4g; Carb 12.3g; Fiber 1.2g; Chol 1mg; Iron 0.8mg; Sodium 91mg; Calc 19mg

LEMONY KALE

PointsPlus value per serving: 2

HANDS-ON TIME: 11 min. ■ **TOTAL TIME:** 11 min.

Eliminate the need to trim and chop fresh kale by using packages of prechopped kale. They can be found near the bagged lettuce in the grocery store.

10 cups chopped kale (about 1 pound)
1 tablespoon olive oil
¼ teaspoon crushed red pepper
¼ cup apple juice
2 teaspoons grated fresh lemon rind
3 tablespoons fresh lemon juice
¼ teaspoon salt

1. Cook kale, covered, in boiling water 3 minutes. Drain well; place kale in a large bowl.
2. Heat a small skillet over medium-high heat. Add oil to pan; swirl to coat. Add red pepper; sauté 1 minute. Remove from heat; stir in apple juice and remaining ingredients. Return to medium-high heat; cook 1 minute, stirring constantly with a whisk. Pour apple juice mixture over kale; toss well to coat. YIELD: 6 SERVINGS (SERVING SIZE: 1 CUP).

PER SERVING: Calories 81; Fat 3.3g (sat 0.4g, mono 1.7g, poly 0.6g); Protein 4.8g; Carb 11.7g; Fiber 2.3g; Chol 0mg; Iron 1.7mg; Sodium 141mg; Calc 169mg

CREAMED SPINACH

PointsPlus value per serving: 3

HANDS-ON TIME: 11 min. ■ **TOTAL TIME:** 11 min.

Prewashed baby spinach cuts down on preparation time. Pair this creamy side dish with grilled chicken or pork chops.

2½ teaspoons canola oil, divided
2 (6-ounce) packages fresh baby spinach
¼ cup finely chopped shallots (about 2)
2 teaspoons minced fresh garlic
⅓ cup fat-free milk
1 tablespoon all-purpose flour
¼ teaspoon freshly ground black pepper
⅛ teaspoon salt
2 ounces tub-style light cream cheese (about ¼ cup)
3 tablespoons grated fresh Parmesan cheese

1. Heat a large skillet over medium-high heat. Add 1½ teaspoons oil to pan; swirl to coat. Add spinach; sauté 2 to 3 minutes or until spinach wilts. Remove from heat; keep warm.
2. Heat a small saucepan over medium heat. Add 1 teaspoon oil to pan; swirl to coat. Add shallots and garlic; cook 1 minute, stirring constantly. Combine milk and flour in a small bowl; stir with a whisk. Gradually add milk mixture to pan, stirring with a whisk until blended. Stir in pepper and salt; cook 1 minute or until thick, stirring constantly. Remove from heat; add cheeses, stirring until smooth. Add milk mixture to spinach, stirring until smooth. YIELD: 4 SERVINGS (SERVING SIZE: ½ CUP).

PER SERVING: Calories 117; Fat 6.2g (sat 2.2g, mono 2.8g, poly 1g); Protein 5.9g; Carb 8.8g; Fiber 2.4g; Chol 10mg; Iron 3mg; Sodium 279mg; Calc 181mg

WARM FINGERLING POTATOES WITH FETA

PointsPlus value per serving: 4

HANDS-ON TIME: 3 min. ■ **TOTAL TIME:** 10 min.

Add visual interest to your plate by using colored fingerling potatoes, including red, purple, gold, and the more traditional white.

1 pound fingerling potatoes, cut into wedges
1 tablespoon water
1 tablespoon chopped fresh parsley
1 tablespoon balsamic vinegar
1 tablespoon olive oil
½ teaspoon Dijon mustard
¼ teaspoon freshly ground black pepper
⅛ teaspoon salt
2 ounces crumbled feta cheese (about ½ cup)

1. Place potato wedges and 1 tablespoon water in a large microwave-safe bowl. Cover with plastic wrap; vent (do not allow plastic wrap to touch food). Microwave at HIGH 7 minutes or until tender; drain.
2. Combine parsley and next 5 ingredients (through salt) in a small bowl; pour over potatoes, tossing gently to coat. Sprinkle with cheese. YIELD: 4 SERVINGS (SERVING SIZE: ABOUT ⅔ CUP POTATOES AND 2 TABLESPOONS CHEESE).

PER SERVING: Calories 160; Fat 6.4g (sat 2.2g, mono 3.1g, poly 0.5g); Protein 5.3g; Carb 21.6g; Fiber 2.9g; Chol 10mg; Iron 1.3mg; Sodium 260mg; Calc 58mg

WHITE CHEDDAR MASHED POTATOES

PointsPlus value per serving: 4

HANDS-ON TIME: 15 min. ■ **TOTAL TIME:** 15 min.

No one can resist cheesy mashed potatoes. Choose a sharp white cheddar for extra flavor.

4 cups cubed peeled baking potato (about 2 pounds)
3 ounces shredded white cheddar cheese (about ¾ cup)
⅓ cup 2% reduced-fat milk
¼ cup reduced-fat sour cream
¼ teaspoon salt
¼ teaspoon freshly ground black pepper

1. Cook potato in boiling water 10 minutes or until tender; drain. Return potato to pan. Add cheese and remaining ingredients; mash with a potato masher to desired consistency. **YIELD: 6 SERVINGS (SERVING SIZE: ½ CUP).**

PER SERVING: Calories 155; Fat 6.2g (sat 4g, mono 1.8g, poly 0.2g); Protein 6.5g; Carb 19.4g; Fiber 2.2g; Chol 21mg; Iron 0.8mg; Sodium 208mg; Calc 146mg

MAPLE-BACON SWEET POTATOES

PointsPlus value per serving: 4

HANDS-ON TIME: 10 min. ■ **TOTAL TIME:** 10 min.

Garnish these maple-glazed potatoes with thin slices of scallion for the perfect balance of sweet and savory.

2 (9-ounce) individually wrapped microwaveable sweet potatoes
2 tablespoons chopped cooked bacon
2 tablespoons maple syrup
4 teaspoons light butter, softened
¼ teaspoon freshly ground black pepper

1. Cook potatoes according to package directions. Cut potatoes in half horizontally. Combine bacon and remaining ingredients in a small bowl. Top each potato half with bacon mixture. Serve immediately. **YIELD: 4 SERVINGS (SERVING SIZE: ½ POTATO AND ABOUT 4 TEASPOONS BACON MIXTURE).**

PER SERVING: Calories 157; Fat 3.3g (sat 1.9g, mono 1.1g, poly 0.2g); Protein 2.8g; Carb 29.4g; Fiber 4g; Chol 7mg; Iron 0.8mg; Sodium 131mg; Calc 33mg

SAUTÉED SQUASH AND PEPPERS WITH TARRAGON

PointsPlus value per serving: 2 *(pictured on page 135)*

HANDS-ON TIME: 16 min. ■ **TOTAL TIME:** 16 min.

This tasty side is ideal in summer when summer squash are plentiful. Just about any herb will work here: Try basil, thyme, or oregano for variety.

Cooking spray
2 teaspoons olive oil
4 cups sliced zucchini (about 1 pound)
4 cups sliced yellow squash (about 1 pound)
1 cup chopped red bell pepper
¼ teaspoon salt
⅛ teaspoon freshly ground black pepper
2 tablespoons chopped fresh tarragon
2 ounces shaved fresh Parmesan cheese (about ½ cup)

1. Heat a large nonstick skillet over medium-high heat. Coat pan with cooking spray. Add oil to pan. Add zucchini and next 4 ingredients (through black pepper); sauté 8 minutes or until crisp-tender. Stir in tarragon. Sprinkle with cheese just before serving. **YIELD: 6 SERVINGS (SERVING SIZE: 1 CUP AND ABOUT 4 TEASPOONS CHEESE).**

PER SERVING: Calories 84; Fat 4.2g (sat 1.6g, mono 1.8g, poly 0.3g); Protein 5g; Carb 7.4g; Fiber 2.7g; Chol 7mg; Iron 0.7mg; Sodium 236mg; Calc 133mg

SWEET POTATOES

What's not to love about sweet potatoes? They're inexpensive, naturally sweet, and full of vitamins and minerals. In fact, they are considered nutritionally superior to regular potatoes thanks to their high levels of beta-carotene, vitamin C, and iron. In addition, sweet potatoes have a lower glycemic index compared to white potatoes. This is a measure of how your blood sugar and insulin levels respond after eating a food. The lower the gylcemic index number, the more stable your overall blood sugar remains so you don't have sugar highs or lows. In addition to the health perks, sweet potatoes offer a ton of versatility when cooking. They're tasty when simply baked, but they're also great when roasted, mashed, grilled, and incorporated into casseroles, soups, and stews. To bake, scrub sweet potatoes clean, and place in the oven at 450° for 30 to 45 minutes. Season with salt and pepper or Greek yogurt and cinnamon-sugar.

MOROCCAN COUSCOUS

PointsPlus value per serving: 4

HANDS-ON TIME: 6 min. ■ **TOTAL TIME:** 11 min.

Raisins may be substituted for currants, if desired.

- **¾ cup fat-free, lower-sodium chicken broth**
- **½ teaspoon ground turmeric**
- **½ teaspoon ground cumin**
- **¾ cup uncooked couscous**
- **1½ tablespoons chopped dried apricots**
- **1 tablespoon dried currants**
- **1 teaspoon toasted pine nuts**
- **Chopped fresh mint (optional)**

1. Bring first 3 ingredients to a boil in a small saucepan; gradually stir in couscous. Remove from heat; cover and let stand 5 minutes. Add apricots, currants, and pine nuts; fluff with fork. Garish with mint, if desired. **YIELD: 4 SERVINGS (SERVING SIZE: ABOUT ½ CUP).**

PER SERVING: Calories 141; Fat 0.9g (sat 0.1g, mono 0.1g, poly 0.4g); Protein 5.4g; Carb 29.9g; Fiber 1.3g; Chol 0mg; Iron 1mg; Sodium 108mg; Calc 7mg

ISRAELI COUSCOUS WITH BUTTERNUT SQUASH

PointsPlus value per serving: 3

HANDS-ON TIME: 8 min. ■ **TOTAL TIME:** 8 min.

Israeli couscous granules are twice as big as regular couscous and have a slightly nuttier flavor.

- **1 cup uncooked whole-wheat Israeli couscous**
- **¼ teaspoon salt, divided**
- **1½ cups diced peeled butternut squash**
- **½ cup chopped red onion**
- **1 garlic clove, thinly sliced**
- **Olive oil–flavored cooking spray**
- **½ cup organic vegetable broth**
- **1 teaspoon chopped fresh sage**
- **½ teaspoon freshly ground black pepper**
- **2 tablespoons grated fresh Parmesan cheese**
- **Sage leaves (optional)**

1. Cook couscous according to package directions, omitting fat and using ⅛ teaspoon salt.

2. While couscous cooks, heat a large nonstick skillet over medium-high heat. Add squash, onion, and garlic to pan. Coat vegetables with cooking spray; cook 5 minutes, stirring frequently. Add broth; cover and cook 3 minutes or until squash is tender. Stir in cooked couscous, ⅛ teaspoon salt, chopped sage, and pepper; sprinkle with cheese, and garnish with sage leaves, if desired. Serve warm. **YIELD: 6 SERVINGS (SERVING SIZE: ABOUT ½ CUP COUSCOUS AND 1 TEASPOON CHEESE).**

PER SERVING: Calories 128; Fat 1.1g (sat 0.3g, mono 0.1g, poly 0.2g); Protein 4.7g; Carb 25.2g; Fiber 3.5g; Chol 1mg; Iron 0.3mg; Sodium 175mg; Calc 43mg

PEELING & CUTTING BUTTERNUT SQUASH

The bright orange flesh of butternut squash has a slightly sweet nuttiness that's similar to a sweet potato and a texture that's even silkier. But to reach the flesh, you must first remove the squash's thick, shiny skin.

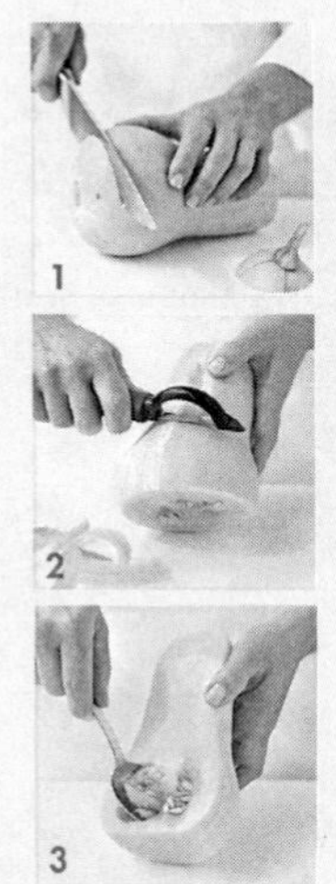

1. For stability, use a sharp kitchen knife to cut 1 inch from the top and bottom of the squash, and discard.
2. Using a vegetable peeler, peel away the thick skin until you reach the deeper orange flesh of the squash.
3. Cut squash in half vertically. With a spoon, scoop away the seeds and membranes; discard. Then cut the flesh according to your recipe directions.

PINE NUT COUSCOUS

PointsPlus value per serving: 6

HANDS-ON TIME: 5 min. ■ **TOTAL TIME:** 10 min.

Toasted pine nuts transform plain couscous to a flavorful Middle Eastern–inspired side dish. Have a smaller ⅓-cup serving for a *PointsPlus* value of 3 if you desire.

- **2 teaspoons olive oil**
- **¾ cup whole-wheat couscous**
- **1 cup water**
- **2 tablespoons golden raisins**
- **¼ teaspoon salt**
- **¼ cup pine nuts, toasted**
- **2 tablespoons chopped fresh parsley**
- **½ teaspoon grated fresh lemon rind**

1. Heat a medium saucepan over medium heat. Add oil to pan; swirl to coat. Add couscous to pan; sauté 1 minute. Stir in 1 cup water, raisins, and salt. Bring to a boil; remove from heat. Cover and let stand 5 minutes or until liquid is absorbed.
2. Add pine nuts, parsley, and lemon rind; fluff with a fork. **YIELD: 4 SERVINGS (SERVING SIZE: ABOUT ⅔ CUP).**

PER SERVING: Calories 214; Fat 7.2g (sat 1.3g, mono 3g, poly 2.6g); Protein 6.6g; Carb 32.8g; Fiber 5.4g; Chol 0mg; Iron 1.8mg; Sodium 153mg; Calc 22mg

SOUTHWESTERN COUSCOUS

PointsPlus value per serving: 3

HANDS-ON TIME: 10 min. ■ **TOTAL TIME:** 10 min.

To quickly thaw frozen corn, place in a colander, and run warm water over it until thawed, being sure to remove any excess water.

- **1 cup water**
- **½ teaspoon salt**
- **¾ cup uncooked couscous**
- **2½ tablespoons fresh lime juice**
- **1½ tablespoons olive oil**
- **½ teaspoon ground cumin**
- **½ cup rinsed and drained canned black beans**
- **½ cup frozen corn kernels, thawed**
- **½ cup chopped tomato**
- **⅓ cup chopped fresh cilantro**

1. Bring 1 cup water and salt to a boil in a medium saucepan; gradually stir in couscous. Remove from heat; cover and let stand 5 minutes. Fluff with a fork.
2. While couscous stands, combine lime juice, olive oil, and cumin in a large bowl, stirring with a whisk. Stir in beans and remaining ingredients. Add couscous; toss gently with a fork. **YIELD: 8 SERVINGS (SERVING SIZE: ½ CUP).**

PER SERVING: Calories 102; Fat 2.9g (sat 0.4g, mono 1.9g, poly 0.3g); Protein 3.5g; Carb 17.5g; Fiber 1.6g; Chol 0mg; Iron 0.6mg; Sodium 207mg; Calc 8mg

WHITE CHEDDAR CHEESE GRITS

PointsPlus value per serving: 5

HANDS-ON TIME: 7 min. ■ **TOTAL TIME:** 12 min.

Reduced-fat sharp cheddar cheese can be substituted for the white cheddar cheese, or use a combination of both.

- **1½ cups fat-free milk**
- **¾ cup water**
- **¼ teaspoon salt**
- **¼ teaspoon freshly ground black pepper**
- **¾ cup uncooked quick-cooking grits**
- **3 ounces reduced-fat sharp white cheddar cheese (about ¾ cup), shredded**

1. Combine first 4 ingredients in a large saucepan. Bring to a boil over medium heat. Gradually stir in grits. Cover, reduce heat, and simmer 5 minutes or until thick, stirring occasionally. Remove from heat; add cheese, stirring until cheese melts. Serve immediately. **YIELD: 4 SERVINGS (SERVING SIZE: ABOUT ⅔ CUP).**

PER SERVING: Calories 193; Fat 4g (sat 2.4g, mono 1.1g, poly 0.4g); Protein 11.4g; Carb 27.8g; Fiber 1.4g; Chol 13mg; Iron 0.9mg; Sodium 316mg; Calc 266mg

PARMESAN POLENTA WITH GARLIC

PointsPlus value per serving: 4

HANDS-ON TIME: 11 min. ▪ **TOTAL TIME:** 11 min.

This creamy Parmesan- and garlic-spiked polenta makes a hearty, flavor-packed side dish for beef, lamb, or pork.

1 teaspoon olive oil
2 garlic cloves, minced
1¼ cups fat-free milk
1 cup water
⅛ teaspoon salt
½ cup quick-cooking polenta
2 ounces grated fresh Parmesan cheese (about ½ cup)
¼ teaspoon freshly ground black pepper

1. Heat a medium saucepan over medium heat. Add oil to pan; swirl to coat. Add garlic; sauté 1 minute or until golden.
2. Add milk, 1 cup water, and salt to pan; bring to a boil. Add polenta, stirring with a whisk. Cook 2 minutes or until thick, stirring frequently with a whisk.
3. Remove from heat; add cheese and pepper, stirring until cheese melts. Serve immediately. **YIELD: 4 SERVINGS (SERVING SIZE: ½ CUP).**

PER SERVING: Calories 173; Fat 5.2g (sat 2.2g, mono 2g, poly 0.3g); Protein 10.1g; Carb 20.4g; Fiber 0.6g; Chol 12mg; Iron 0.5mg; Sodium 359mg; Calc 299mg

GRITS VERSUS POLENTA

Grits and polenta are both made of the same thing—dried, ground corn—and they are both cooked in liquid like broth or water until they're thick and creamy. But, they differ in where they originated from and the type of corn used. Grits are made from dried white corn that's ground into fine granules. Grits are thought to have originated from Native Americans and are popular still today in the Southern states as a breakfast dish. Polenta originated in Italian cuisine and is made from dried yellow corn that is ground into slightly coarser granules. Polenta is often cooked thicker than grits so that it can be cooled and cut into shapes. Both grits and polenta have become popular side dishes for seafood, meat, and poultry. Since the main difference is color and the size of the granules, grits and polenta can be substituted when in a pinch. Just be aware that the smaller the granules, the less cooking time will be required.

GOAT CHEESE AND SPINACH POLENTA

PointsPlus value per serving: 2

HANDS-ON TIME: 11 min. ▪ **TOTAL TIME:** 11 min.

1 cup fat-free, lower-sodium chicken broth
⅔ cup water
⅓ cup quick-cooking polenta
2 tablespoons grated fresh Parmesan cheese
1 ounce crumbled goat cheese (about ¼ cup)
¼ teaspoon freshly ground black pepper
2 cups fresh baby spinach

1. Bring broth and ⅔ cup water to a boil in a medium saucepan; gradually add polenta, stirring constantly with a whisk. Reduce heat, and simmer, uncovered, 3 minutes or until thick, stirring constantly. Remove from heat.
2. Add cheeses and pepper, stirring until cheeses melt. Stir in spinach. Serve immediately. **YIELD: 4 SERVINGS (SERVING SIZE: ½ CUP).**

PER SERVING: Calories 96; Fat 2.5g (sat 1.5g, mono 0.3g, poly 0g); Protein 5.2g; Carb 13.6g; Fiber 1.9g; Chol 6mg; Iron 0.8mg; Sodium 250mg; Calc 69mg

CILANTRO RICE

PointsPlus value per serving: 2

HANDS-ON TIME: 3 min. ▪ **TOTAL TIME:** 13 min.

Refrigerated ginger is available in 4-ounce tubes in the produce section of the grocery store. Fresh gingerroot that has been peeled and chopped can also be used.

1 (3½-ounce) bag boil-in-bag rice
½ cup chopped fresh cilantro
1 teaspoon grated fresh lime rind
2 tablespoons fresh lime juice
1 teaspoon prepared refrigerated finely chopped fresh ginger
¼ teaspoon salt

1. Cook rice according to package directions for microwave, omitting salt and fat. Stir in cilantro and remaining ingredients. **YIELD: 4 SERVINGS (SERVING SIZE: ABOUT ½ CUP).**

PER SERVING: Calories 81; Fat 0.3g (sat 0g, mono 0g, poly 0g); Protein 1.7g; Carb 18.9g; Fiber 0.5g; Chol 0mg; Iron 0.8mg; Sodium 149mg; Calc 2mg

SPICED JASMINE RICE

PointsPlus value per serving: 3

HANDS-ON TIME: 16 min. ■ **TOTAL TIME:** 16 min.

The spices in this recipe create an intense fragrance during cooking. Use boil-in-bag rice and matchstick-cut carrots to make this dish with little trouble.

1 (3½-ounce) bag boil-in-bag jasmine rice
Cooking spray
½ cup matchstick-cut carrots
½ cup frozen petite green peas
2 tablespoons golden raisins
1 tablespoon water
1 teaspoon garam masala
½ teaspoon salt
¼ teaspoon freshly ground black pepper

1. Cook rice according to package directions, omitting salt and fat. Drain.
2. Heat a large nonstick skillet over medium-high heat. Coat pan with cooking spray. Add carrots to pan, and sauté 3 minutes. Add peas and remaining ingredients; cook 5 minutes or until peas are thoroughly heated and water is absorbed. Stir in rice. **YIELD: 4 SERVINGS (SERVING SIZE: ½ CUP).**

PER SERVING: Calories 119; Fat 0.1g (sat 0g, mono 0g, poly 0g); Protein 2.8g; Carb 27.6g; Fiber 1.5g; Chol 0mg; Iron 1.2mg; Sodium 325mg; Calc 12mg

GARAM MASALA

Garam masala is similar to curry powder in that it's not a spice itself, but rather a blend of spices. Found in Indian and South Asian cuisines, traditional garam masala is typically made of peppercorns, cinnamon, cloves, cumin seeds, and cardamom pods, but may also include turmeric, coriander, ginger, and star anise. The seeds are toasted and then ground to get a rich, spicy flavor. Exact mixtures of garam masalas will vary by region. Store-bought mixtures can be found in the spice aisles of most supermarkets.

LEMON RISOTTO WITH ASPARAGUS

PointsPlus value per serving: 5

HANDS-ON TIME: 50 min. ■ **TOTAL TIME:** 50 min.

Risotto is traditionally made with Arborio rice because of its high starch content and firm texture. Constant stirring helps release the rice's starches, creating a creamy texture with separate grains. A large skillet or sauté pan provides a broad surface to help the rice cook evenly.

3 (14½-ounce) cans fat-free, lower-sodium chicken broth
1 tablespoon olive oil
½ cup finely chopped onion
1½ cups uncooked Arborio rice
2 teaspoons grated fresh lemon rind
½ cup dry white wine
3 cups (1-inch) diagonally cut asparagus (about 1 pound)
2 ounces grated Parmigiano-Reggiano cheese (about ½ cup)
2 tablespoons fresh lemon juice
2 teaspoons fresh thyme leaves

1. Bring broth to a simmer in a large saucepan (do not boil). Keep warm over low heat.
2. Heat a large nonstick skillet over medium heat. Add oil to pan; swirl to coat. Add onion; cook 5 minutes or until tender, stirring frequently. Add rice and rind; cook 2 minutes, stirring constantly. Stir in wine, and cook 3 minutes or until the liquid is nearly absorbed, stirring constantly.
3. Add 3½ cups broth, ½ cup at a time, stirring constantly until each portion of broth is absorbed before adding the next (about 20 minutes). Stir in asparagus. Add remaining broth, ½ cup at a time, stirring constantly until each portion of broth is absorbed before adding the next (about 10 minutes). Remove from heat; stir in cheese and juice. Sprinkle with thyme. **YIELD: 10 SERVINGS (SERVING SIZE: ABOUT ¾ CUP)**

PER SERVING: Calories: 184; Fat 2.9g (sat 1.1g, mono 1.4g, poly 0.2g); Protein 7g; Carb 30.7g; Fiber 1.6g; Chol 4mg; Iron 0.7mg; Sodium 319mg; Calc 92mg

DIRTY RICE

PointsPlus value per serving: 4

HANDS-ON TIME: 10 min. ▪ **TOTAL TIME:** 10 min.

Stir andouille sausage and fresh veggies into precooked rice for this quick-and-easy accompaniment to Creole Chicken Thighs (page 74).

- 1 (8.8-ounce) pouch microwaveable precooked long-grain rice
- Cooking spray
- ½ cup refrigerated prechopped celery, onion, and bell pepper mix
- 4 ounces andouille sausage, chopped
- 2 garlic cloves, minced
- 2 tablespoons chopped fresh parsley
- ⅛ teaspoon salt
- ⅛ teaspoon ground red pepper

1. Microwave rice according to package directions.
2. Heat a large saucepan over medium-high heat. Coat pan with cooking spray. Add celery mix, sausage, and garlic; sauté 5 minutes or until sausage is browned and vegetables are tender. Remove from heat. Stir in rice, parsley, salt, and ground red pepper. **YIELD: 4 SERVINGS (SERVING SIZE: ½ CUP).**

PER SERVING: Calories 154; Fat 5.2g (sat 1.5g, mono 2.5g, poly 0.9g); Protein 7.1g; Carb 19.8g; Fiber 1g; Chol 17mg; Iron 1mg; Sodium 290mg; Calc 36mg

SPICY BLACK BEANS AND RICE

PointsPlus value per serving: 4

HANDS-ON TIME: 11 min. ▪ **TOTAL TIME:** 11 min.

Chipotle chile powder and jalapeño add the heat to this side dish. To decrease the heat, substitute regular chili powder for the chipotle version.

- 2 (8.8-ounce) pouches microwaveable precooked long-grain rice
- 2 teaspoons canola oil
- 1 cup chopped onion
- 2 garlic cloves, minced
- 1 jalapeño pepper, seeded and chopped
- 1 cup canned reduced-sodium black beans, drained and rinsed
- 1 teaspoon ground cumin
- ¼ teaspoon salt
- ¼ teaspoon chipotle chile powder

1. Microwave rice according to package directions; keep warm.
2. Heat a medium skillet over medium-high heat. Add oil to pan; swirl to coat. Add onion, garlic, and jalapeño to pan; sauté 4 minutes or until tender. Stir in rice, beans, and remaining ingredients. Cook 2 minutes or until thoroughly heated. **YIELD: 8 SERVINGS (SERVING SIZE: ABOUT ⅔ CUP).**

PER SERVING: Calories 136; Fat 2.5g (sat 0.1g, mono 1.4g, poly 0.6g); Protein 3.9g; Carb 25.9g; Fiber 2.4g; Chol 0mg; Iron 1.6mg; Sodium 117mg; Calc 50mg

REFRIED BLACK BEANS

PointsPlus value per serving: 4

HANDS-ON TIME: 15 min. ▪ **TOTAL TIME:** 15 min.

Serve these beans alongside Salsa Verde Chicken Enchiladas (page 81), atop nachos, or in burritos. Substitute pinto beans for the black beans, if desired.

- 2 (15-ounce) cans no-salt-added black beans, undrained and divided
- 1 tablespoon canola oil
- 2 teaspoons ground cumin
- 2 garlic cloves, minced
- ⅜ teaspoon salt
- 2 tablespoons chopped fresh cilantro
- 1 tablespoon fresh lime juice

1. Rinse and drain 1 can beans. Heat a medium saucepan over medium-high heat. Add oil to pan; swirl to coat. Add cumin and garlic to pan; cook 30 seconds, stirring constantly. Add drained beans, 1 can undrained beans, and salt. Bring to a boil, stirring frequently; reduce heat, and simmer, uncovered, 10 minutes, stirring occasionally. Partially mash bean mixture with a potato masher until slightly thick. Stir in cilantro and lime juice. **YIELD: 4 SERVINGS (SERVING SIZE: ABOUT ½ CUP).**

PER SERVING: Calories 174; Fat 3.7g (sat 0.3g, mono 2.2g, poly 1g); Protein 9.8g; Carb 25.7g; Fiber 8.5g; Chol 0mg; Iron 2.8mg; Sodium 244mg; Calc 92mg

desserts

Roasted Pears with Orange-Caramel Sauce, *page 161*

BROILED CITRUS WITH CRYSTALLIZED GINGER

PointsPlus value per serving: 4 *(pictured on page 141)*

HANDS-ON TIME: 21 min. ■ **TOTAL TIME:** 21 min.

Broiled grapefruit is a classic dish, but it's often cumbersome to eat if left in the skin. Here, you peel the grapefruit, slice into rounds, and pair with another plentiful winter fruit—navel oranges.

2 large navel oranges
1 red grapefruit
¼ cup packed light brown sugar
1½ tablespoons chopped pistachios
1½ tablespoons chopped crystallized ginger
⅛ teaspoon sea salt

1. Preheat broiler.
2. Peel oranges. Cut each crosswise into 5 slices. Peel grapefruit. Cut crosswise into 6 slices. Arrange fruit on a 15 x 10–inch jelly-roll pan. Sprinkle brown sugar evenly over fruit. Broil 5 inches from heat 4 minutes or until bubbly and sugar melts.
3. Sprinkle fruit evenly with pistachios, ginger, and salt. Broil 2 minutes or until nuts are toasted. YIELD: 4 SERVINGS (SERVING SIZE: 4 FRUIT SLICES).

PER SERVING: Calories 148; Fat 1.4g (sat 0.2g, mono 0.7g, poly 0.4g); Protein 1.8g; Carb 34.6g; Fiber 2.8g; Chol 0mg; Iron 1.3mg; Sodium 78mg; Calc 75mg

CRYSTALLIZED GINGER

Crystallized ginger is candied fresh ginger that can be chopped and sprinkled on the tops of cookies, pastries, and desserts. You can make your own crystallized ginger by boiling chopped gingerroot in simple syrup until crystals begin to form. You can also purchase it at most markets in the spice section.

BROILED GRAPEFRUIT WITH VANILLA BEAN CREAM

PointsPlus value per serving: 3 *(pictured on page 142)*

HANDS-ON TIME: 11 min. ■ **TOTAL TIME:** 11 min.

Brown sugar is caramelized on top of this citrus fruit and then topped with a creamy vanilla yogurt mixture.

1½ cups red grapefruit sections (about 2 large grapefruit)
¼ cup packed light brown sugar
¼ cup vanilla low-fat yogurt
¼ cup light sour cream
1 vanilla bean

1. Preheat broiler.
2. Divide grapefruit sections evenly among 4 (4- to 5-inch) shallow broiler-proof ceramic dishes. Sprinkle each serving with 1 tablespoon brown sugar. Broil, 5 inches from heat, 7 minutes or until sugar melts and begins to caramelize.
3. While grapefruit mixture broils, combine yogurt and sour cream in a small bowl. Split vanilla bean lengthwise; scrape seeds from half of pod. Add seeds to yogurt mixture; stir well. Reserve remaining half of pod for another use. Serve grapefruit warm with vanilla bean cream. YIELD: 4 SERVINGS (SERVING SIZE: ABOUT ⅓ CUP GRAPEFRUIT SECTIONS AND 2 TABLESPOONS VANILLA BEAN CREAM).

PER SERVING: Calories 112; Fat 1.5g (sat 0.9g, mono 0.5g, poly 0g); Protein 2.1g; Carb 23.6g; Fiber 0.9g; Chol 6mg; Iron 0.2mg; Sodium 22mg; Calc 67mg

ROASTED BROWN SUGAR PEARS

PointsPlus value per serving: 4

HANDS-ON TIME: 3 min. ■ **TOTAL TIME:** 15 min.

Use ripe, juicy pears for the best results with this fall dessert.

2 firm ripe Bosc pears (¾ pound), halved lengthwise and cored
⅓ cup water
¼ cup packed brown sugar
¾ teaspoon vanilla extract
¼ cup vanilla low-fat Greek yogurt
2 tablespoons turbinado sugar

1. Preheat oven to 500°.
2. Place pears, cut sides down, in an 11 x 7–inch glass or ceramic baking dish. Combine ⅓ cup water, brown sugar, and vanilla; pour over pears.

3. Bake at 500° for 12 minutes or until tender. Place 1 pear half in each of 4 bowls; spoon syrup evenly over pears. Top evenly with yogurt and turbinado sugar. YIELD: 4 SERVINGS (SERVING SIZE: 1 PEAR HALF, 2 TEASPOONS SYRUP, 1 TABLESPOON YOGURT, AND 1½ TEASPOONS TURBINADO SUGAR).

PER SERVING: Calories 135; Fat 0.3g (sat 0.2g, mono 0g, poly 0g); Protein 1.6g; Carb 33.3g; Fiber 3g; Chol 2mg; Iron 0.1mg; Sodium 11mg; Calc 50mg

ROASTED PEARS WITH ORANGE-CARAMEL SAUCE

PointsPlus value per serving: 4

HANDS-ON TIME: 9 min. ■ **TOTAL TIME:** 44 min.

Freshly grated orange rind and freshly ground black pepper give bottled caramel topping a surprising yum factor.

2 firm ripe Bosc pears (about ¾ pound), peeled, halved lengthwise, and cored
Cooking spray
3 tablespoons brown sugar
⅛ teaspoon ground cardamom (optional)
¼ cup fat-free caramel topping
½ teaspoon grated fresh orange rind
¼ teaspoon freshly ground black pepper
½ cup vanilla bean fat-free Greek yogurt
Grated fresh orange rind (optional)

1. Preheat oven to 400°.
2. Arrange pear halves in an 8-inch square baking dish coated with cooking spray. Bake, uncovered, at 400° for 10 minutes.
3. Combine brown sugar and, if desired, cardamom in a small bowl. Sprinkle brown sugar mixture over pears. Bake 25 additional minutes or just until pears are tender. Remove pears from dish, discarding syrup in bottom of dish.
4. Combine caramel topping, ½ teaspoon orange rind, and black pepper, stirring with a whisk. Spoon yogurt into cavity of each pear. Drizzle with caramel sauce, and garnish with orange rind, if desired. YIELD: 4 SERVINGS (SERVING SIZE: 1 PEAR HALF, 2 TABLESPOONS YOGURT, AND 1 TABLESPOON CARAMEL SAUCE).

PER SERVING: Calories 161; Fat 0g (sat 0g, mono 0g, poly 0g); Protein 2g; Carb 39.8g; Fiber 3.1g; Chol 1mg; Iron 0.4mg; Sodium 70mg; Calc 48mg

STORING BOSC PEARS

Fall is generally peak season for pears, but the wide variety ensures availability much of the year. Bosc pears can be ripened on the counter, but transfer them to the refrigerator for storage when they reach the ideal softness. Always place pears in the coldest part of your refrigerator.

TROPICAL FRUIT PARFAITS

PointsPlus value per serving: 4

HANDS-ON TIME: 8 min. ■ **TOTAL TIME:** 13 min.

This easy dessert can double as a filling breakfast and is an easy way of getting in a serving of fruit.

1 cup chopped peeled mango (about 1 mango)
¾ cup chopped peeled kiwifruit (about 2 kiwifruit)
½ cup cubed fresh pineapple
3 tablespoons pineapple juice
½ teaspoon grated fresh lime rind
1 tablespoon fresh lime juice
2 cups vanilla low-fat yogurt
4 teaspoons flaked sweetened coconut, toasted

1. Combine first 6 ingredients in a medium bowl; cover and let stand 5 minutes. Spoon ¼ cup yogurt into each of 4 dessert dishes. Top each with about ¼ cup fruit mixture. Repeat layers once; top each with 1 teaspoon coconut. Serve immediately. YIELD: 4 SERVINGS (SERVING SIZE: 1 PARFAIT).

PER SERVING: Calories 166; Fat 2.1g (sat 1.3g, mono 0.5g, poly 0.1g); Protein 4.9g; Carb 33.1g; Fiber 2.2g; Chol 8mg; Iron 0.3mg; Sodium 74mg; Calc 147mg

MIXED BERRY PAVLOVA PARFAITS

PointsPlus value per serving: 4 *(pictured on page 143)*

HANDS-ON TIME: 10 min. ■ **TOTAL TIME:** 10 min.

A light and fresh dessert option perfect for after dinner or a mid-afternoon snack.

1 cup vanilla fat-free yogurt
½ cup reduced-fat sour cream
¼ cup packed brown sugar
1 cup strawberries, halved
1 cup blackberries
1 cup raspberries
1⅓ cups crushed vanilla meringue cookies (about 7 cookies), divided
Mint sprigs (optional)

1. Combine first 3 ingredients in a medium bowl, stirring with a whisk. Combine strawberries, blackberries, and raspberries in a medium bowl.

2. Spoon 2 tablespoons yogurt mixture evenly into each of 6 (8-ounce) parfait glasses; top each with ¼ cup berry mixture and 2½ tablespoons crushed cookies. Top each with about 2 tablespoons yogurt mixture and ¼ cup berry mixture. Top each parfait with about 1 tablespoon crushed cookies. Cover and chill until ready to serve. Garnish with mint sprigs, if desired. **YIELD: 6 SERVINGS (SERVING SIZE: 1 PARFAIT).**

PER SERVING: Calories 165; Fat 2.8g (sat 1.6g, mono 0.7g, poly 0.3g); Protein 4g; Carb 31.8g; Fiber 3.1g; Chol 11mg; Iron 0.5mg; Sodium 51mg; Calc 132mg

RASPBERRIES

Ripe raspberries pair well with rich chocolate dishes as well as creamy parfait mixtures. Because they are highly perishable, plan to use raspberries within two days of purchasing. Store in the refrigerator in the container you purchase them in or in a container with a lid. If you don't think you will use the berries before they go bad, consider freezing them. Freeze in a single-layer on a cookie sheet; once frozen, place them in a freezer-safe plastic bag or container. Frozen raspberries will typically keep for up to one year. To thaw, simply let sit at room temperature.

SWEET POTATO CHEESECAKE PARFAITS

PointsPlus value per serving: 5

HANDS-ON TIME: 11 min. ■ **TOTAL TIME:** 11 min.

Try serving these parfaits in champagne glasses for an elegant presentation. Cover and chill the leftover sweet potatoes to serve as a side dish within 3 days of opening.

1 cup refrigerated mashed sweet potatoes
4 ounces ⅓-less-fat cream cheese (about ½ cup), softened
¼ cup packed brown sugar
½ teaspoon pumpkin pie spice
1½ cups plus 3 tablespoons frozen fat-free whipped topping, thawed and divided
½ cup low-fat cinnamon graham cracker crumbs (about 3 cookie sheets)

1. Combine first 4 ingredients in a bowl; beat with a mixer at medium speed 1 minute or until smooth. Gently fold in 1½ cups whipped topping. Spoon ¼ cup sweet potato mixture into each of 6 dessert glasses; sprinkle each with 1 tablespoon graham cracker crumbs. Top each with about ¼ cup sweet potato mixture, and 1 teaspoon graham cracker crumbs. Top each with 1½ teaspoons whipped topping. **YIELD: 6 SERVINGS (SERVING SIZE: 1 PARFAIT).**

PER SERVING: Calories 174; Fat 5g (sat 2.4g, mono 1.1g, poly 0.2g); Protein 2.9g; Carb 28.5g; Fiber 0.9g; Chol 15mg; Iron 0.6mg; Sodium 149mg; Calc 78mg

INDIVIDUAL PEACH CRISPS

PointsPlus value per serving: 7

HANDS-ON TIME: 7 min. ■ **TOTAL TIME:** 20 min.

In this version, egg whites bind the topping instead of butter. You can substitute pecans for almonds.

½ cup regular oats
⅓ cup packed brown sugar
¼ cup sliced almonds
Dash of salt
1 teaspoon vanilla extract
2 large egg whites
6 peaches, peeled, halved, and pitted
3 cups vanilla low-fat frozen yogurt

1. Preheat oven to 400°.

2. Combine first 4 ingredients in a medium bowl. Combine vanilla and egg whites in a small bowl; stir with a whisk until foamy. Add egg mixture to oat mixture, stirring until well blended.

3. Spoon about 1 tablespoon oat mixture into each peach half. Arrange peach halves on a baking sheet. Bake at 400° for 13 minutes or until oat mixture is set. Serve with frozen yogurt. **YIELD: 6 SERVINGS (SERVING SIZE: 2 PEACH HALVES AND ½ CUP YOGURT).**

PER SERVING: Calories 301; Fat 3.9g (sat 1.1g, mono 1.8g, poly 0.8g); Protein 9.1g; Carb 50.9g; Fiber 5.5g; Chol 5mg; Iron 1mg; Sodium 107mg; Calc 189mg

FRENCH VANILLA SUMMER TRIFLE

PointsPlus value per serving: 8

HANDS-ON TIME: 24 min. ■ **TOTAL TIME:** 5 hr., 9 min.

Once you've assembled this dessert, refrigerate it for several hours to allow the peach juices and rich custard to soak into the ladyfingers.

2½ cups finely chopped peeled ripe peaches
2 tablespoons brown sugar
¼ teaspoon ground cinnamon
⅔ cup granulated sugar
2 tablespoons cornstarch
⅛ teaspoon salt
3 large egg yolks
1⅔ cups 2% reduced-fat milk
1 cup evaporated fat-free milk
½ teaspoon vanilla extract
15 cakelike ladyfingers, halved lengthwise

1. Combine peaches, brown sugar, and cinnamon, tossing well to combine; let peach mixture stand at room temperature 30 minutes.

2. Combine granulated sugar, cornstarch, salt, and egg yolks in a medium bowl, stirring with a whisk until smooth. Heat milks in a medium, heavy saucepan over medium-high heat to 180° or until tiny bubbles form around edge (do not boil). Gradually add hot milk mixture to sugar mixture, stirring constantly with a whisk.

3. Return the milk mixture to saucepan. Cook mixture over medium heat 2 minutes or until thick and bubbly, stirring constantly. Remove from heat, and stir in vanilla extract.

4. Spoon the custard into a small bowl. Place the bowl in a large ice-filled bowl for 15 minutes or until the custard is cool, stirring occasionally. Remove bowl from ice.

5. Arrange 10 of the ladyfinger halves, cut sides up, in a single layer on the bottom of a 1½-quart soufflé or trifle dish. Spoon half of the peach mixture over ladyfingers. Spread half of custard over peach mixture. Arrange 10 ladyfinger halves, standing upright, around side of dish. Arrange remaining 10 ladyfinger halves, cut sides up, on top of custard. Spoon remaining peach mixture over ladyfingers. Spread remaining custard over peach mixture. Cover and refrigerate 4 hours or overnight. **YIELD: 6 SERVINGS (SERVING SIZE: ABOUT 1 CUP).**

PER SERVING: Calories 300; Fat 4.9g (sat 2g, mono 1.5g, poly 0.8g); Protein 8.8g; Carb 56.7g; Fiber 1.7g; Chol 144mg; Iron 1mg; Sodium 265mg; Calc 246mg

MAKE-AHEAD CAPPUCCINO-OREO TRIFLES

PointsPlus value per serving: 6

HANDS-ON TIME: 23 min. ■ **TOTAL TIME:** 2 hr., 23 min.

½ cup sugar
¼ cup cornstarch
1 tablespoon instant coffee granules
1 large egg
2½ cups 1% low-fat milk
1 tablespoon coffee-flavored liqueur
16 reduced-fat cream-filled chocolate sandwich cookies, divided
1½ cups frozen reduced-calorie whipped topping, thawed

1. Combine first 4 ingredients in a bowl; stir well with a whisk. Cook milk in a heavy saucepan over medium-high heat to 180° or until tiny bubbles form around edge (do not boil). Gradually add hot milk to egg mixture, stirring constantly with a whisk. Return milk mixture to pan; cook over medium heat until thick (3 minutes), stirring constantly. Reduce heat to low; cook 2 minutes. Remove from heat; stir in liqueur. Pour into a medium bowl; place bowl in a larger bowl of ice water, stirring occasionally until mixture is cool.

2. Coarsely chop 8 cookies; fold chopped cookies and whipped topping into pudding. Spoon about ½ cup cookie mixture into each of 8 small parfait glasses or (6-ounce) custard cups. Cover and chill at least 2 hours or until cold. Top each serving with a cookie. **YIELD: 8 SERVINGS (SERVING SIZE: 1 TRIFLE).**

PER SERVING: Calories 227; Fat 5.4g (sat 3g, mono 1.5g, poly 0.3g); Protein 5.1g; Carb 40.2g; Fiber 0.7g; Chol 31mg; Iron 1.4mg; Sodium 183mg; Calc 107mg

CHOCOLATE-RASPBERRY PUDDING

PointsPlus value per serving: 4

HANDS-ON TIME: 15 min. ■ **TOTAL TIME:** 15 min.

This creamy chocolate pudding is every bit as decadent as higher fat varieties thanks to rich Dutch process cocoa and bittersweet chocolate. If you choose to make this creamy pudding ahead of time, cover the surface with plastic wrap before chilling. It should be cold and set after about 3 hours.

½ cup fresh raspberries
3 tablespoons water
½ cup sugar
¼ cup unsweetened Dutch process cocoa
2½ tablespoons cornstarch
¼ teaspoon salt
1½ cups fat-free milk
1 (12-ounce) can evaporated fat-free milk
2 ounces bittersweet chocolate, coarsely chopped
1 teaspoon vanilla extract
Frozen fat-free whipped topping, thawed (optional)
Fresh raspberries (optional)
Mint sprigs (optional)

1. Place raspberries and 3 tablespoons water in a blender or food processor; process until smooth. Press raspberry mixture through a sieve over a bowl, reserving liquid; discard solids.
2. Combine sugar and next 3 ingredients (through salt) in a large saucepan, stirring with a whisk. Stir in milk, evaporated milk, and raspberry mixture. Bring to a boil over medium-high heat, stirring constantly. Reduce heat, and simmer 1 minute or until thickened. Remove from heat; add chocolate and vanilla, stirring until chocolate is melted and mixture is smooth.
3. Divide mixture evenly among 8 (4-ounce) ramekins. Serve immediately, or cover and chill. Garnish with whipped topping, additional raspberries, and mint, if desired. YIELD: 8 SERVINGS (SERVING SIZE: ABOUT ½ CUP).

PER SERVING: Calories 158; Fat 3.4g (sat 1.5g, mono 0.8g, poly 0.1g); Protein 5.3g; Carb 28.4g; Fiber 1.5g; Chol 1mg; Iron 1.2mg; Sodium 133mg; Calc 163mg

TOFFEE PUDDING

PointsPlus value per serving: 7

HANDS-ON TIME: 8 min. ■ **TOTAL TIME:** 13 min.

Enjoy comfort food at its best with this simple, easy-to-make pudding. If you omit the toffee bits, each serving has a *PointsPlus* value of 5.

⅓ cup packed light brown sugar
3 tablespoons cornstarch
⅛ teaspoon salt
2 cups evaporated fat-free milk
1 tablespoon light stick butter
½ teaspoon vanilla extract
3 tablespoons milk chocolate toffee bits

1. Combine first 3 ingredients in a medium, heavy saucepan; gradually add milk, stirring with a whisk. Bring to a boil over medium-high heat, and cook 2 minutes or until thick, stirring constantly. Remove from heat.
2. Add butter and vanilla; stir until butter melts. Spoon pudding into 4 individual bowls; let stand 5 minutes. Sprinkle evenly with toffee bits before serving. YIELD: 4 SERVINGS (SERVING SIZE: ABOUT ½ CUP PUDDING AND ABOUT 2 TEASPOONS TOFFEE BITS).

PER SERVING: Calories 266; Fat 5.3g (sat 2.8g, mono 1.4g, poly 0.3g); Protein 8g; Carb 46.2g; Fiber 0.1g; Chol 8mg; Iron 0.2mg; Sodium 262mg; Calc 335mg

PUDDING SUCCESS

Nothing's more decadent than creamy, homemade pudding. If you've never made pudding from scratch, there are a few tips to keep in mind to ensure pudding success. Pudding is basically a cooked mixture of milk or cream and sugar that is thickened by either starch or eggs. Cornstarch is the most common thickener and the key to its success is contant stirring. The cornstarch granules have to be cooked at a high temperature for 1 to 3 minutes in order to fully absorb the liquid. Scorching can easily occur unless you stir the mixture constantly. Puddings that use eggs as thickeners require a careful, slow addition of the eggs to the hot milk mixture to prevent the eggs from scrambling. This is best done by bringing the milk and sugar to a boil, removing the pan from the heat, and then slowly adding the eggs. Since egg-based puddings don't have to come to a boil, be sure to use pasteurized eggs when making this type of pudding.

CHOCOLATE ALMOND FUDGE POPS

PointsPlus value per serving: 4

HANDS-ON TIME: 9 min. ▪ **TOTAL TIME:** 3 hr. 9 min.

Make a batch over the weekend and you'll be set with a portion-controlled dessert all week.

1 (14-ounce) can fat-free sweetened condensed milk
1½ cups dark chocolate almond milk
10 (3-ounce) paper cups
2 tablespoons mini chocolate chips
2 tablespoons chopped sliced almonds
10 wooden sticks

1. Combine sweetened condensed milk and almond milk in a medium bowl, stirring until smooth.
2. Pour milk mixture evenly into paper cups. Sprinkle with chocolate chips and almonds. Cover tops of cups with foil, and insert a wooden stick through foil into center of each cup. Freeze at least 3 hours or until firm. To serve, remove foil; peel cups from pops. YIELD: 10 SERVINGS (SERVING SIZE: 1 POP).

PER SERVING: Calories 141; Fat 1.5g (sat 0.4g, mono 0.7g, poly 0.2g); Protein 3.6g; Carb 28.4g; Fiber 0.4g; Chol 5mg; Iron 0.3mg; Sodium 60mg; Calc 151mg

ALMOND MILK

Almond milk is a popular alternative to cow's milk. It's made by mixing ground almonds with water and is often sweetened and sometimes flavored with vanilla or chocolate. Because it's made with almonds, it offers the health benefits found in nuts, like vitamin E and omega-3 fatty acids. It also contains no lactose, the natural sugar found in cow's milk, making it a great beverage choice for lactose-intolerant individuals; because it contains no animal products, it's a great choice for vegetarians. Perhaps the biggest nutritional difference between the two is calcium content. Unlike cow's milk, almonds are not a rich source of calcium. However, many brands of almond milk are fortified to provide similar amounts; be sure to check the label.

BANANAS FOSTER SUNDAES

PointsPlus value per serving: 8 *(pictured on page 14)*

HANDS-ON TIME: 8 min. ▪ **TOTAL TIME:** 8 min.

Take the time to toast the walnuts, which add the perfect touch of crunch to the buttery brown sugar syrup topping.

2 large ripe bananas
6 tablespoons packed brown sugar
2 tablespoons dark rum
1 tablespoon light stick butter
⅛ teaspoon salt
2 cups vanilla light ice cream
¼ cup chopped walnuts, toasted

1. Peel bananas, and cut each banana in half lengthwise. Cut each half into 3 pieces.
2. Combine sugar and next 3 ingredients (through salt) in a medium nonstick skillet. Cook over medium-low heat 2 minutes or until mixture begins to bubble. Add bananas to pan; cook 2 minutes or until bananas begin to soften.
3. Spoon ½ cup ice cream into the bottom of each of 4 glasses. Divide banana mixture evenly among glasses. Top with walnuts. Serve immediately. YIELD: 4 SERVINGS (SERVING SIZE: ½ CUP ICE CREAM, 3 PIECES BANANA, AND 1 TABLESPOON SAUCE).

PER SERVING: Calories 312; Fat 10g (sat 3.4g, mono 2g, poly 3.8g); Protein 4.9g; Carb 51.8g; Fiber 2.3g; Chol 24mg; Iron 0.5mg; Sodium 150mg; Calc 88mg

PEAR-GINGER ICE CREAM

PointsPlus value per serving: 3

HANDS-ON TIME: 3 min. ■ **TOTAL TIME:** 15 min.

Freezing 12 minutes as directed gives you ice cream with a soft-serve consistency. For harder ice cream that you can scoop, freeze longer.

1 (15-ounce) can pear halves in juice, drained
1½ cups low-fat buttermilk
½ cup sugar
½ cup pear nectar
1 tablespoon prepared refrigerated finely chopped fresh ginger (from a 4-ounce tube)
1 teaspoon vanilla extract
⅛ teaspoon ground cinnamon

1. Place all ingredients in a food processor; process 2 minutes or until smooth, scraping sides of bowl occasionally.
2. Pour pear mixture into the freezer can of an ice-cream freezer; freeze 12 minutes. **YIELD: 6 SERVINGS (SERVING SIZE: ABOUT ½ CUP).**

PER SERVING: Calories 126; Fat 0.6g (sat 0.3g, mono 0.2g, poly 0g); Protein 2.2g; Carb 28.7g; Fiber 0.8g; Chol 3mg; Iron 0.2mg; Sodium 67mg; Calc 77mg

MAKING ICE CREAM

It's easy to make ice cream at home. The ice-cream base can be an uncooked option, like Pear-Ginger Ice Cream, or cooked. If it's the latter, you'll need to completely cool the cooked mixture before freezing it. You can do this quickly by placing the pan in a large ice-filled metal bowl.

1

2

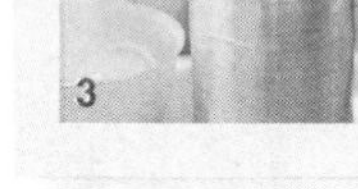

3

1. You'll need an ice-cream maker—either an old-fashioned bucket churn or a countertop freezer.
2. Traditional bucket-style freezers require rock salt and ice. Use coarse rock salt because it won't slip easily between the ice or drain through the cracks of the bucket.
3. Tabletop models rely strictly on a freezer bowl filled with a coolant. Place the mixture in the freezer can. Freeze according to manufacturer's instructions.

TURTLE ICE CREAM PIE

PointsPlus value per serving: 8

HANDS-ON TIME: 14 min. ■ **TOTAL TIME:** 5 hr. 29 min.

A thin layer of chocolate brownie batter forms the crust for this rich-tasting pie that is great for grown-ups, yet yummy enough for a kid's birthday party.

2.25 ounces all-purpose flour (about ½ cup)
¼ cup unsweetened cocoa
⅛ teaspoon salt
⅓ cup sugar
2½ tablespoons fat-free milk
½ teaspoon vanilla extract
1 large egg
2 tablespoons butter
2 tablespoons mini semisweet chocolate chips
Cooking spray
4 cups vanilla low-fat ice cream, softened
½ cup plus 3 tablespoons fat-free caramel sundae syrup
¼ cup chopped pecans, toasted

1. Preheat oven to 350°.
2. Weigh or lightly spoon flour into a dry measuring cup; level with a knife. Combine flour, cocoa, and salt in a medium bowl, stirring with a whisk; set aside. Combine sugar, milk, vanilla, and egg in a medium bowl, stirring with a whisk until well combined; set aside.
3. Place butter and mini chocolate chips in a small microwave-safe bowl. Microwave at high 1 minute or until butter and chocolate melt, stirring every 20 seconds. Add chocolate mixture to sugar mixture, stirring with a whisk. Fold in flour mixture. Spread batter into a 9-inch deep-dish pie plate coated with cooking spray. Bake at 350° for 15 minutes or until a wooden pick inserted in center comes out clean. Cool completely on a wire rack.

4. Place softened ice cream in a large bowl; beat with a mixer at medium speed until smooth. Spoon half of ice cream over cooled crust, and place remaining ice cream in refrigerator. Drizzle pie with ½ cup caramel. Freeze pie 30 minutes or until firm. Spread the remaining ice cream over caramel. Sprinkle evenly with pecans; drizzle with 3 tablespoons of caramel. Cover and freeze 4 hours or until firm. **YIELD: 8 SERVINGS (SERVING SIZE: 1 WEDGE).**

PER SERVING: Calories 308; Fat 10g (sat 4.3g, mono 3.9g, poly 1.2g); Protein 6.3g; Carb 50.5g; Fiber 1.8g; Chol 51mg; Iron 1.3mg; Sodium 181mg; Calc 104mg

POMEGRANATE SORBET

PointsPlus value per serving: 4 *(pictured on page 140)*

HANDS-ON TIME: 3 min. ■ **TOTAL TIME:** 2 hr. 38 min.

Pomegranates are full of vitamin C and phytochemicals with antioxidant properties, so you can feel good about this sweet and slightly tart dessert.

3 cups pomegranate juice, divided
¾ cup sugar
2 tablespoons fresh lime juice

1. Combine ½ cup pomegranate juice and sugar in a small saucepan over medium heat. Cook 2 minutes or until sugar dissolves, stirring frequently. Stir in 2½ cups pomegranate juice and lime juice.
2. Pour mixture into the freezer can of an electric ice-cream freezer; freeze according to manufacturer's instructions. Spoon ice cream into a freezer-safe container; cover and freeze 2 hours or until firm. **YIELD: 7 SERVINGS (SERVING SIZE: ½ CUP).**

PER SERVING: Calories 145; Fat 0g (sat 0g, mono 0g, poly 0g); Protein 0.5g; Carb 37g; Fiber 0g; Chol 0mg; Iron 0.2mg; Sodium 13mg; Calc 18mg

CARAMEL APPLE PUDDING PIE

PointsPlus value per serving: 5

HANDS-ON TIME: 14 min. ■ **TOTAL TIME:** 14 min.

Dulce de leche is a caramel sauce originating in South America. Look for it close to the cans of sweetened condensed milk in your local grocery store.

1 (12-ounce) package frozen harvest apples
8 low-fat cinnamon graham cracker sheets
⅔ cup dulce de leche
1 (1-ounce) box sugar-free, fat-free vanilla instant pudding
2 cups fat-free milk

1. Microwave apples according to package directions.
2. While apples cook, place graham cracker sheets in the bottom of a 9-inch square metal baking pan.
3. Place dulce de leche in a microwave-safe bowl; microwave at HIGH 30 seconds or until melted. Spread ½ cup dulce de leche over graham crackers.
4. Prepare pudding according to package directions using 2 cups fat-free milk. Spread pudding over dulce de leche. Top evenly with cooked apples. Drizzle with remaining dulce de leche. Cover and chill. Cut into 8 rectangles. **YIELD: 8 SERVINGS (SERVING SIZE: 1 RECTANGLE).**

PER SERVING: Calories 174; Fat 2.6g (sat 1.1g, mono 0.8g, poly 0.4g); Protein 3.6g; Carb 32.8g; Fiber 0.6g; Chol 8mg; Iron 0.2mg; Sodium 236mg; Calc 146mg

DULCE DE LECHE

Dulce de leche is sweetened milk that has been cooked and caramelized. Because the sugars in it have been caramelized, the thick milk product has a light brown color. Dulce de leche is commonly used to flavor candies, cakes, ice creams, and desserts such as flan. You can make your own dulce de leche by boiling a can of unopened, sweetened condensed milk for several hours, but it's also available ready-made in a can and usually found near the condensed and evaporated milks in the grocery.

CHOCOLATE–PEANUT BUTTER TARTS

PointsPlus value per serving: 1

HANDS-ON TIME: 10 min. ▪ **TOTAL TIME:** 15 min.

An easy way to pipe the whipped topping onto these indulgent tarts is to place the topping in a zip-top plastic bag and seal. After snipping off a small triangle from one corner of the bag, just squeeze the topping onto each tart.

2 tablespoons peanut butter
1 (4-ounce) container fat-free chocolate pudding
1 (1.9-ounce) package mini phyllo shells, thawed
½ cup frozen fat-free whipped topping, thawed

1. Combine peanut butter and pudding in small bowl; stir well. Spoon 1½ teaspoons peanut butter mixture into each phyllo shell; top with 1½ teaspoons whipped topping. Chill 5 minutes. **YIELD: 15 SERVINGS (SERVING SIZE: 1 TART).**

PER SERVING: Calories 39; Fat 2g (sat 0.2g, mono 1.1g, poly 0.6g); Protein 0.7g; Carb 4.6g; Fiber 0.2g; Chol 0mg; Iron 0.2mg; Sodium 33mg; Calc 8mg

PEANUT BUTTER

On average, 1 tablespoon of regular peanut butter (creamy or crunchy) has 100 calories and 8 grams of total fat. While the fat may seem high, the majority is good-for-your-heart unsaturated fats. One tablespoon also contains almost 4 grams of quality protein. Be sure to go for the real deal. The reduced-fat spreads offer little calorie savings, and you're losing healthy fats.

PEANUT BUTTER–BANANA PIE

PointsPlus value per serving: 8

HANDS-ON TIME: 16 min. ▪ **TOTAL TIME:** 4 hr., 28 min.

Bananas that are firm rather than extra-ripe work best in this pie.

1 cup reduced-calorie vanilla wafer crumbs (about 30 cookies)
2 tablespoons butter, melted and cooled
1 large egg white, lightly beaten
Cooking spray
⅔ cup sugar
3½ tablespoons cornstarch
¼ teaspoon salt
1⅓ cups 1% low-fat milk
2 large eggs, lightly beaten
2 tablespoons creamy peanut butter
1 teaspoon vanilla extract
2½ cups sliced banana
1½ cups frozen reduced-calorie whipped topping, thawed

1. Preheat oven to 350°.
2. Combine first 3 ingredients in a bowl, tossing with a fork until moist. Press into bottom and up sides of a 9-inch pie plate coated with cooking spray. Bake at 350° for 12 minutes; cool crust on a wire rack.
3. Combine sugar, cornstarch, and salt in a small heavy saucepan. Gradually add milk, stirring with a whisk until well blended. Cook over medium heat until mixture comes to a boil; cook 1 minute, stirring with a whisk. Gradually add about ⅓ cup hot custard to beaten eggs, stirring constantly with a whisk. Return egg mixture to pan. Cook over medium heat until thick (for about 1 minute); stir constantly. Remove from heat, and stir in peanut butter and vanilla. Cool slightly.
4. Arrange banana slices in bottom of prepared crust; spoon filling over bananas. Press plastic wrap onto the surface of filling; chill 4 hours. Remove plastic wrap. Spread whipped topping evenly over filling. Chill. **YIELD: 8 SERVINGS (SERVING SIZE: ⅛ OF PIE).**

PER SERVING: Calories 294; Fat 9.5g (sat 4.7g, mono 2.8g, poly 1.4g); Protein 5.9g; Carb 47.8g; Fiber 1.4g; Chol 65mg; Iron 0.8mg; Sodium 225mg; Calc 80mg

MINI PHYLLO-APPLE TARTS

PointsPlus value per serving: 1

HANDS-ON TIME: 13 min. ▪ **TOTAL TIME:** 13 min.

These sweet, cinnamon-infused apple pie bites will curb your pie cravings with only a fraction of the fat and sugar.

1½ teaspoons butter
1¼ cups diced peeled Granny Smith apple (about 8 ounces)
1½ tablespoons brown sugar
¼ teaspoon ground cinnamon
1½ teaspoons apple cider
1 (1.9-ounce) package mini phyllo shells, thawed
5 tablespoons refrigerated canned whipped topping
2½ tablespoons fat-free caramel topping

1. Melt butter in a medium skillet over medium-high heat. Add apple to pan; cook 3 minutes or until apple is tender. Sprinkle with brown sugar and cinnamon; cook 1 to 2 minutes or until mixture is syrupy, stirring frequently. Stir in cider; cook 1 minute.
2. Spoon apple mixture into phyllo shells. Top each tart with 1 teaspoon whipped topping and ½ teaspoon caramel topping. Serve warm. **YIELD: 15 SERVINGS (SERVING SIZE: 1 TART).**

PER SERVING: Calories 42; Fat 1.5g (sat 0.3g, mono 0.7g, poly 0.3g); Protein 0g; Carb 7.2g; Fiber 0.3g; Chol 2mg; Iron 0.2mg; Sodium 25mg; Calc 4mg

STORING APPLES

Though you may be tempted to display apples in a fruit bowl, resist the urge. Instead, store them in a plastic produce bag in the refrigerator. Apples emit ethylene, a gas that hastens ripening; the bag will help prevent them from accelerating the ripening of other produce.

FRESH CHERRY COBBLER

PointsPlus value per serving: 9

HANDS-ON TIME: 12 min. ▪ **TOTAL TIME:** 1 hr. 35 min.

½ (15-ounce) package refrigerated pie dough
Cooking spray
1 large egg white, lightly beaten
1 tablespoon sugar
4 cups pitted fresh cherries (about 1¾ pounds)
1 cup sugar
3 tablespoons uncooked quick-cooking tapioca
1 tablespoon fresh lemon juice
⅛ teaspoon salt
2 tablespoons chilled butter, cut into small pieces

1. Preheat oven to 375°.
2. Cut dough into 8 (9 x 1-inch) strips. Arrange dough strips in a lattice design on a baking sheet coated with cooking spray. Brush dough with egg white, and sprinkle evenly with 1 tablespoon sugar. Bake at 375° for 15 minutes or until crust is golden brown. Cool 10 minutes in pan on a wire rack. Carefully lift crust using 2 spatulas; cool completely on a wire rack.
3. Combine cherries, 1 cup sugar, tapioca, juice, and salt. Let stand 15 minutes. Spoon the cherry mixture into an 8-inch baking dish coated with cooking spray. Top with butter. Bake at 375° for 40 minutes or until hot and bubbly. Place crust on top of cherry mixture. **YIELD: 8 SERVINGS (SERVING SIZE: ⅛ OF COBBLER).**

PER SERVING: Calories 312; Fat 10.4g (sat 4.9g, mono 2.3g, poly 1.4g); Protein 2.3g; Carb 54g; Fiber 1.7g; Chol 13mg; Iron 0.3mg; Sodium 171mg; Calc 12mg

RED VELVET CUPCAKES

PointsPlus value per serving: 6

HANDS-ON TIME: 25 min. ■ **TOTAL TIME:** 1 hr. 15 min.

The red food coloring gives these cupcakes their signature color, but it can easily be omitted, if desired, to yield a light chocolate cake instead.

Cooking spray
10 ounces cake flour (about 2½ cups)
3 tablespoons unsweetened cocoa
1 teaspoon baking soda
1 teaspoon baking powder
1 teaspoon kosher salt
1½ cups granulated sugar
6 tablespoons unsalted butter, softened
2 large eggs
1¼ cups nonfat buttermilk
1½ teaspoons white vinegar
1½ teaspoons vanilla extract
2 tablespoons red food coloring (about 1 ounce)
5 tablespoons butter, softened
4 teaspoons nonfat buttermilk
1 (8-ounce) block cream cheese, softened
3½ cups powdered sugar (about 1 pound)
1¼ teaspoons vanilla extract

1. Preheat oven to 350°.
2. Place 30 paper muffin cup liners in muffin cups; coat with cooking spray.
3. Weigh or lightly spoon cake flour into dry measuring cups; level with a knife. Combine cake flour, unsweetened cocoa, baking soda, baking powder, and salt in a medium bowl; stir with a whisk. Place granulated sugar and unsalted butter in a large bowl; beat with a mixer at medium speed until well blended (about 3 minutes). Add eggs, 1 at a time, beating well after each addition. Add flour mixture and 1¼ cups buttermilk alternately to sugar mixture, beginning and ending with flour mixture. Add white vinegar, 1½ teaspoons vanilla, and food coloring; beat well.
4. Spoon batter into prepared muffin cups. Bake at 350° for 20 minutes or until a wooden pick inserted in center comes out clean. Cool 10 minutes in pan on wire rack; remove from pan. Cool completely on wire racks.
5. Beat 5 tablespoons butter, 4 teaspoons buttermilk, and cream cheese with a mixer at high speed until fluffy. Gradually add powdered sugar; beat until smooth. Add 1¼ teaspoons vanilla; beat well. Spread frosting evenly over cupcakes. **YIELD: 30 SERVINGS (SERVING SIZE: 1 CUPCAKE).**

PER SERVING: Calories 205; Fat 7.3g (sat 4.5g, mono 2g, poly 0.3g); Protein 1.6g; Carb 33.5g; Fiber 0.3g; Chol 34mg; Iron 0.9mg; Sodium 168mg; Calc 35mg

SALTED CARAMEL BROWNIES

PointsPlus value per serving: 5

HANDS-ON TIME: 30 min. ■ **TOTAL TIME:** 1 hr. 30 min.

With their rich, indulgent flavors, these layered caramel brownies dusted in sea salt are a definite crowd-pleaser.

3.38 ounces all-purpose flour (about ¾ cup)
1 cup granulated sugar
¾ cup unsweetened cocoa
½ cup packed brown sugar
½ teaspoon baking powder
6 tablespoons butter, melted
2 large eggs
1 teaspoon vanilla extract
Cooking spray
¼ cup butter
¼ cup packed brown sugar
3½ tablespoons evaporated fat-free milk, divided
¼ teaspoon vanilla extract
½ cup powdered sugar
1 ounce bittersweet chocolate, coarsely chopped
⅛ teaspoon coarse sea salt

1. Preheat oven to 350°.
2. Weigh or lightly spoon flour into dry measuring cups; level with a knife. Combine flour and next 4 ingredients (through baking powder) in a large bowl, stirring well with a whisk. Combine 6 tablespoons butter, eggs, and 1 teaspoon vanilla. Add butter mixture to flour mixture; stir to combine. Scrape batter into a 9-inch square metal baking pan lightly coated with cooking spray. Bake at 350° for 19 minutes or until a wooden pick inserted in center comes out with moist crumbs clinging. Cool in pan on a wire rack.
3. Melt ¼ cup butter in a saucepan over medium heat. Add ¼ cup brown sugar and 1½ tablespoons milk; cook 2 minutes. Remove from heat. Add vanilla and powdered sugar, stirring with a whisk until smooth. Spread mixture evenly over cooled brownies. Let stand 20 minutes or until set.

4. Combine 2 tablespoons milk and chocolate in a microwave-safe bowl; microwave at HIGH for 45 seconds or until melted, stirring after 20 seconds. Stir just until smooth; drizzle over caramel. Sprinkle with sea salt; let stand until set. Cut into squares. **YIELD: 20 SERVINGS (SERVING SIZE: 1 BROWNIE).**

PER SERVING: Calories 180; Fat 7.2g (sat 4.1g, mono 1.7g, poly 0.3g); Protein 2.1g; Carb 27.8g; Fiber 0.8g; Chol 37mg; Iron 0.9mg; Sodium 76mg; Calc 26mg

PEPPERMINT CHEESECAKE BROWNIES

PointsPlus value per serving: 6

HANDS-ON TIME: 16 min. ■ **TOTAL TIME:** 42 min.

Mint and chocolate lovers won't be able to resist these decadent brownies.

- **1 (8-ounce) block ⅓-less-fat cream cheese**
- **⅓ cup granulated sugar**
- **¼ teaspoon peppermint extract**
- **1 large egg**
- **1 large egg white**
- **1 tablespoon all-purpose flour**
- **4.5 ounces all-purpose flour (about 1 cup)**
- **½ cup unsweetened cocoa**
- **½ teaspoon salt**
- **1½ cups packed brown sugar**
- **¼ cup canola oil**
- **¼ cup buttermilk**
- **2 teaspoons vanilla extract**
- **2 large egg whites**
- **1 large egg**
- **Cooking spray**

1. Preheat oven to 350°.
2. Place cream cheese in a medium bowl; beat with a mixer at medium speed until smooth. Add granulated sugar and peppermint extract; beat well. Add 1 egg and 1 egg white; beat well. Add 1 tablespoon flour; beat mixture just until blended.
3. Weigh or lightly spoon 4.5 ounces (about 1 cup) flour into a dry measuring cup; level with a knife. Combine 4.5 ounces flour, cocoa, and salt in a medium bowl, stirring with a whisk. Combine brown sugar, oil, buttermilk, vanilla, 2 egg whites, and 1 egg in a large bowl; beat with a mixer at medium-high speed until well blended. Add flour mixture to brown sugar mixture; beat at low speed just until blended.
4. Reserve ½ cup of brownie batter. Pour remaining batter into a 9-inch square baking pan coated with cooking spray. Carefully pour cheesecake batter over top; spread evenly to edges. Dot cheesecake batter with reserved brownie batter. Swirl top two layers of batters together using the tip of a knife. Bake at 350° for 26 minutes or until top is set. Cool completely in pan on a wire rack. **YIELD: 16 SERVINGS (SERVING SIZE: 1 BROWNIE).**

PER SERVING: Calories 213; Fat 7.5g (sat 2.6g, mono 2.3g, poly 1.1g); Protein 4.4g; Carb 32.3g; Fiber 0.7g; Chol 37mg; Iron 1.3mg; Sodium 169mg; Calc 32mg

MAKING SWIRLED BROWNIES

Swirled brownies may look complicated but are actually quite easy to prepare. Spoon the first batter into the prepared pan, and then spoon the second batter evenly over the first. Using the tip of a knife, swirl the two batters together.

S'MORES TREATS

PointsPlus value per serving: 5

HANDS-ON TIME: 8 min. ■ **TOTAL TIME:** 8 min.

A fun spin on the classic kids' treat, honey graham cereal takes the place of crisped rice cereal in these s'more-inspired bars.

5 cups miniature marshmallows, divided
3 tablespoons light stick butter
4 cups honey graham ridged cereal
1 cup oven-toasted brown rice cereal
1 cup semisweet chocolate chips
Cooking spray

1. Place 4 cups marshmallows and butter in a large Dutch oven. Cook over medium heat until marshmallows and butter melt, stirring constantly. Remove from heat. Add remaining marshmallows, cereals, and chocolate chips, stirring to coat.
2. Press mixture firmly into a 13 x 9–inch metal baking pan coated with cooking spray using a spoon coated with cooking spray. Cool completely in pan on a wire rack. Cut into bars. **YIELD: 16 SERVINGS (SERVING SIZE: 1 BAR).**

PER SERVING: Calories 187; Fat 5.6g (sat 3.2g, mono 1.8g, poly 0.2g); Protein 1.6g; Carb 33.4g; Fiber 1.3g; Chol 3mg; Iron 1.5mg; Sodium 126mg; Calc 33mg

TOASTED COCONUT SHORTBREAD

PointsPlus value per serving: 2

HANDS-ON TIME: 22 min. ■ **TOTAL TIME:** 1 hr. 40 min.

Toasted coconut adds great flavor to these small shortbread cookies.

6.75 ounces all-purpose flour (about 1½ cups)
¼ cup cornstarch
¼ cup flaked sweetened coconut, toasted
⅛ teaspoon salt
½ cup butter, softened
½ cup packed brown sugar
¼ cup ice water

1. Weigh or lightly spoon flour into dry measuring cups; level with a knife. Combine flour and next 3 ingredients (through salt), stirring well with a whisk. Place butter and sugar in a medium bowl; beat with a mixer at medium speed until light and fluffy (about 1 minute). Add flour mixture, beating at low speed. (Mixture will appear crumbly.) Sprinkle ice water over flour mixture; beat at low speed just until combined. Shape dough into 2 (6-inch-long) logs; wrap each log in plastic wrap. Chill 1 hour or until very firm.
2. Preheat oven to 350°.
3. Line baking sheets with parchment paper. Unwrap dough; cut each log into 16 slices using a serrated knife. Place dough circles 1 inch apart on prepared baking sheets. Bake at 350° for 18 minutes or until lightly browned. **YIELD: 32 SERVINGS (SERVING SIZE: 1 COOKIE).**

PER SERVING: Calories 67; Fat 3.1g (sat 2g, mono 0.8g, poly 0.1g); Protein 0.7g; Carb 9.2g; Fiber 0.2g; Chol 8mg; Iron 0.3mg; Sodium 38mg; Calc 5mg

CHOCOLATE CHIP CAKE COOKIES

PointsPlus value per serving: 3 *(pictured on page 144)*

HANDS-ON TIME: 6 min. ■ **TOTAL TIME:** 56 min.

Cake mix allows you to throw together a batch of cookie bars in just minutes.

1 (15.25-ounce) package golden vanilla cake mix
¼ cup nonfat buttermilk
3 tablespoons butter, melted
1 tablespoon water
1 large egg, lightly beaten
1 cup semisweet chocolate chips
Cooking spray

1. Preheat oven to 350°.
2. Combine first 5 ingredients in a large bowl. Beat with a mixer at medium-high speed until smooth. Stir in chocolate chips.
3. Spread batter into a 13 x 9–inch metal baking pan coated with cooking spray. Bake at 350° for 20 minutes or until set. Cool 30 minutes in pan on a wire rack. Cut into squares. **YIELD: 36 SERVINGS (SERVING SIZE: 1 BAR).**

PER SERVING: Calories 91; Fat 3.9g (sat 2.1g, mono 0.6g, poly 0.1g); Protein 1.3g; Carb 13.6g; Fiber 0.3g; Chol 8mg; Iron 0.2mg; Sodium 91mg; Calc 20mg

OATMEAL-ALMOND LACE COOKIES

PointsPlus value per serving: 1

HANDS-ON TIME: 16 min. ▪ **TOTAL TIME:** 20 min.

1 cup old-fashioned rolled oats, toasted
⅓ cup light-colored corn syrup
1 tablespoon canola oil
2 tablespoons butter
⅓ cup sugar
1 large egg
¼ teaspoon vanilla extract
3 tablespoons all-purpose flour
1 teaspoon baking powder
¼ teaspoon salt
¼ cup chopped blanched almonds, toasted

1. Preheat oven to 400°.
2. Combine the first 3 ingredients in a medium bowl. Melt butter in a small saucepan over low heat. Cook 2 minutes or until butter begins to brown (do not burn). Pour into oat mixture; stir well.
3. Place sugar and egg in a medium bowl; beat with a mixer at medium speed until light and fluffy (about 2 minutes). Beat in vanilla.
4. Combine flour, baking powder, and salt, stirring with a whisk. Stir flour mixture into egg mixture. Stir egg mixture into oat mixture. Add almonds; stir well to combine.
5. Drop dough by heaping teaspoonfuls 2 inches apart onto 2 baking sheets lined with parchment paper. Bake at 400° for 4 minutes or until golden. Cool on pans 2 minutes. Transfer parchment to cooling rack; cool completely. **YIELD: 36 SERVINGS (SERVING SIZE: 1 COOKIE).**

PER SERVING: Calories 42; Fat 1.7g (sat 0.5g, mono 0.7g, poly 0.3g); Protein 0.7g; Carb 6.4g; Fiber 0.3g; Chol 2mg; Iron 0.2mg; Sodium 38mg; Calc 12mg

PB&J BUTTONS

PointsPlus value per serving: 2

HANDS-ON TIME: 12 min. ▪ **TOTAL TIME:** 32 min.

Oats and flaxseed boost the nutritional value of these cookies. Substitute any flavor of jam.

½ cup creamy peanut butter
¼ cup honey
½ teaspoon vanilla extract
¼ cup nonfat dry milk
1 cup quick-cooking oats
2 tablespoons flaxseed meal
2½ tablespoons strawberry jam

1. Cover a baking sheet with parchment paper; set aside. Combine first 6 ingredients in bowl, stirring until well blended. Shape mixture into 28 (1-inch) balls; place on prepared baking sheet.
2. Press thumb into center of each ball, leaving an indentation. Spoon about ¼ teaspoon jam into each indentation. Refrigerate 20 minutes or until firm. **YIELD: 28 BUTTONS (SERVING SIZE: 1 BUTTON).**

PER SERVING: Calories 58; Fat 2.7g (sat 0.4g, mono 1.1g, poly 0.8g); Protein 1.9g; Carb 7.1g; Fiber 0.8g; Chol 0mg; Iron 0.3mg; Sodium 25mg; Calc 10mg

HONEY

Although honey is a natural sweetener, it is a source of added sugar when added to foods and recipes. However, it does offer some extra perks that ordinary sugar does not. First, honey is slightly sweeter than granulated sugar which means you can use slightly less honey to get the same level of sweetness. Second, because of its consistency, honey can act as a thickener or emulsifier in recipes. Lastly, honey is a source of vitamin B_6 and iron, and it has been shown to have possible antioxidant properties. Honey will brown more quickly than sugar, so reduce oven temperatures by 25° if baking with honey instead of sugar.

DARK CHOCOLATE–BLUEBERRY BARK

PointsPlus value per serving: 4 *(pictured on page 141)*

HANDS-ON TIME: 4 min. ▪ **TOTAL TIME:** 14 min.

10 ounces bittersweet chocolate, coarsely chopped
⅔ cup dried blueberries, divided
½ cup dried cherries, chopped and divided
2 tablespoons chopped pistachios

1. Place chocolate in a microwave-safe bowl; microwave at HIGH 1½ minutes or until melted, stirring after 1 minute. Stir in ½ cup blueberries and ¼ cup cherries.
2. Cover a baking sheet with parchment paper. Pour chocolate mixture onto prepared pan, and spread into an 11 x 9–inch rectangle (about ⅛ inch thick). Sprinkle about 2½ tablespoons blueberries, ¼ cup cherries, and pistachios over chocolate. Chill 10 minutes or until firm. Cut into 16 pieces. **YIELD: 16 SERVINGS (SERVING SIZE: 1 PIECE).**

PER SERVING: Calories 146; Fat 7.3g (sat 4g, mono 2.3g, poly 0.3g); Protein 1.7g; Carb 16.9g; Fiber 2.9g; Chol 2mg; Iron 1.2mg; Sodium 8mg; Calc 15mg

BITTERSWEET CHOCOLATE

Bittersweet chocolate is a type of dark chocolate that contains less sugar and a higher percentage of cacao, which gives it an intense chocolate flavor. Because of this intensity, bittersweet chocolate is a good choice when baking. Semisweet has more sugar and less cacao so it won't produce the same results as bittersweet chocolate.

PEANUT BUTTER AND CHOCOLATE–DIPPED PRETZELS

PointsPlus value per serving: 4

HANDS-ON TIME: 25 min. ▪ **TOTAL TIME:** 55 min.

This salty-sweet dessert is perfect as a snack, a pick-up dessert at a party, or as a gift. To make ahead, dip the pretzels, and store in the fridge on a parchment-lined tray up to five days ahead. Set them out shortly before serving.

4 ounces semisweet chocolate, chopped
¼ cup creamy peanut butter
30 braided honey-wheat pretzel twists

1. Line a jelly-roll pan with parchment paper.
2. Place chocolate in a small microwave-safe bowl. Microwave at HIGH 1 minute or until chocolate melts, stirring every 15 seconds. Stir in peanut butter until smooth.
3. Working with 1 pretzel at a time, dip and roll 1 end of each pretzel in chocolate mixture to coat. Place pretzel on prepared pan. Repeat procedure with remaining pretzels and chocolate mixture. Place in freezer for 30 minutes or until set. **YIELD: 10 SERVINGS (SERVING SIZE: 3 PRETZELS).**

PER SERVING: Calories 135; Fat 6.8g (sat 2.7g, mono 2.2g, poly 1g); Protein 3.2g; Carb 16.7g; Fiber 1.4g; Chol 0mg; Iron 0.5mg; Sodium 183mg; Calc 3mg

STRAWBERRY CHEESECAKE MILKSHAKE

PointsPlus value per serving: 5

HANDS-ON TIME: 5 min. ■ **TOTAL TIME:** 5 min.

Keep a package of frozen strawberries in the freezer so you can make this frosty treat all year long.

- **2 cups vanilla fat-free ice cream**
- **2 cups frozen whole strawberries**
- **1½ cups fat-free milk**
- **⅓ cup tub-style light cream cheese**
- **1 low-fat graham cracker sheet, crushed**

1. Place first 4 ingredients in a blender; process until smooth. Pour mixture evenly into 4 glasses. Sprinkle with crushed graham cracker. **YIELD: 4 SERVINGS (SERVING SIZE: ABOUT 1 CUP MILKSHAKE AND ABOUT 1 TABLESPOON CRUSHED GRAHAM CRACKER).**

PER SERVING: Calories 183; Fat 2.8g (sat 1.8g, mono 0.7g, poly 0.1g); Protein 8.4g; Carb 34g; Fiber 4.5g; Chol 11mg; Iron 0.4mg; Sodium 183mg; Calc 286mg

BANANA CREAM PIE SMOOTHIE

PointsPlus value per serving: 6

HANDS-ON TIME: 4 min. ■ **TOTAL TIME:** 1 hr. 4 min.

Frozen bananas, graham cracker crumbs, and vanilla extract are a few of the ingredients that make this smoothie a rich dessert in a glass. Because it calls for low-fat yogurt and fat-free milk, one serving gives you about the same amount of calcium as a glass of milk.

- **1 cup sliced ripe banana (about 1 large)**
- **1 cup vanilla low-fat yogurt**
- **½ cup 1% low-fat milk**
- **2 tablespoons whole-wheat graham cracker crumbs (about ½ cookie sheet)**
- **1 tablespoon nonfat dry milk**
- **½ teaspoon vanilla extract**
- **3 ice cubes (about ¼ cup)**
- **Graham cracker crumbs (optional)**

1. Arrange banana slices in a single layer on a baking sheet, and freeze until firm (about 1 hour).
2. Place frozen banana, yogurt, and next 5 ingredients (through ice cubes) in a blender; process until smooth. Pour evenly into 2 glasses. Sprinkle with graham cracker crumbs, if desired. Serve immediately. **YIELD: 2 SERVINGS (SERVING SIZE: 1 CUP).**

PER SERVING: Calories 216; Fat 2.8g (sat 1.5g, mono 0.8g, poly 0.3g); Protein 9.8g; Carb 39.3g; Fiber 1.9g; Chol 9mg; Iron 0.4mg; Sodium 145mg; Calc 315mg

BANANAS

Bananas are one of the most popular fruits thanks to their easy portability, low cost, and mild sweet flavor. Bananas are widely known to be a great source of potassium, but they're also a good source of vitamin C, vitamin B_6, manganese, and fiber. Bananas vary in sweetness based on ripeness, and the color of the peel is the key indicator of ripeness. Unripe green bananas are hard and not very sweet, but it will sweeten as the skin turns from green to yellow to brown.

To speed up the ripening process of bananas:
Place unripe bananas in a paper bag with an apple. The apple emits a gas that speeds up the bananas' ripening process.
To slow down the ripening process of bananas:
Place ripe bananas that you are not ready to eat in the refrigerator. The cool temperatures will turn the skin a slightly brown color, but the texture and sweetness will remain the same.
What to do with extra ripe bananas on hand:
Rather than let them go bad, slice them or break them into smaller pieces and freeze in a single layer on a cookie sheet. Once frozen, place in a zip-top freezer bag. You can use them as needed to add flavor and creaminess to smoothies.

	MONDAY	TUESDAY	WEDNESDAY	THURSDAY
BREAKFAST	**whole-wheat English muffin,** 1 **cantaloupe,** 1 wedge **fat-free milk,** 1 cup	**grits,** 1 cup **egg,** 1 scrambled **strawberries,** 1 cup	**whole-wheat English muffin,** 1 **all-fruit spread,** 2 tablespoons **turkey bacon,** 3 slices **fat-free milk,** 1 cup	**oatmeal,** 1 cup **raspberry nonfat Greek yogurt,** 1 (6-ounce) container **grapefruit sections,** 1 cup
LUNCH	**minestrone soup,** 1 cup canned **herbed pita chips,** 1 ounce **Quick Spinach Salad** (Toss together 1 cup baby spinach leaves, ¼ cup diced tomato, 2 tablespoons crumbled blue cheese, 1 piece cooked and crumbled center-cut bacon, and 2 tablespoons light olive oil vinaigrette - ***PointsPlus* value per serving: 4)**	**Pesto Chicken Sandwich** (Combine 2 teaspoons each fat-free mayonnaise and pesto; spread over 1 slice of high-fiber bread. Top with 3 ounces skinless rotisserie chicken breast, ½ cup arugula leaves, 1 large tomato slice, and 1 slice of bread. - ***PointsPlus* value per serving: 8)** **honeydew cubes,** 1 cup **fat-free milk,** 1 cup	**Chicken Panzanella Salad,** 1 serving, page 98 **plum,** 1 **blueberry nonfat Greek yogurt,** 1 (6-ounce) container	**Barbecued Chicken–Stuffed Potatoes,** 1 serving, page 81 **pear,** 1 medium **mixed salad greens,** 2 cups **light balsamic vinaigrette,** 2 tablespoons
DINNER	**grilled salmon fillet,** 5 ounces cooked **Parmesan Polenta with Garlic,** 1 serving, page 156 **Broccoli Slaw with Mustard Vinaigrette,** 1 serving, page 84	**Herbed Lamb Chops,** 1 serving, page 42 **Roasted Sweet Potatoes** (Cut a small sweet potato into 6 wedges. Toss with 1 teaspoon olive oil, ¼ teaspoon garlic powder, and ⅛ teaspoon salt. Roast potato cubes at 450° for 30 minutes, or until crisp, stirring occasionally. - ***PointsPlus* value per serving: 4)** **steamed asparagus,** 12 spears	**Spinach and White Bean Rotini,** 1 serving, page 28 **Gingered Tropical Fruit Salad,** 1 serving, page 84	**Taco Burgers,** 1 serving, page 108 **baked potato chips,** 1 ounce **banana,** 1 small **fat-free milk,** 1 cup
SNACK	**vanilla nonfat Greek yogurt,** 1 (6-ounce) container **apple,** 1 medium	**Chocolate-Raspberry Pudding,** 1 serving, page 164 **fat-free milk,** 1 cup	**popcorn,** 2 cups light microwave **part-skim mozzarella cheese stick,** 1	**baby carrots,** 1 cup **light Ranch dressing,** 2 tablespoons
PointsPlus VALUE	**Total *PointsPlus* value for the day: 31**	**Total *PointsPlus* value for the day: 32**	**Total *PointsPlus* value for the day: 31**	**Total *PointsPlus* value for the day: 30**

One day's menu provides at least two servings of dairy and at least five servings of fruits and/or vegetables.

7-Day Menu Planner

WEEK 1

	FRIDAY	SATURDAY	SUNDAY
BREAKFAST	**Open-Faced PB & Banana Sandwich** (Top cut halves of a toasted whole-wheat English muffin with 1 tablespoon peanut butter and 1 small sliced banana. - ***PointsPlus* value per serving: 5)** **fat-free milk,** 1 cup	**blueberry nonfat Greek yogurt,** 1 (6-ounce) container **high-fiber oat and nut bar,** 1 **honeydew cubes,** 1 cup	**Honey-Blueberry Oatmeal** (Stir ⅓ cup blueberries and 1 tablespoon honey into 1 cup hot cooked oatmeal. - ***PointsPlus* value per serving: 5)** **fat-free milk,** 1 cup
LUNCH	**hummus,** ¼ cup **whole-wheat pita,** 1 small, warmed **cucumber slices,** 1 cup **watermelon cubes,** 1 cup **strawberry nonfat Greek yogurt,** 1 (6-ounce) container	**Southwestern Frittata** (Saute ¼ cup each onion and bell pepper in 1 teaspoon olive oil in a small skillet. Whisk together 1 egg, 3 egg whites, and a dash each salt and pepper; stir in 3 tablespoons chopped lean deli ham and 3 tablespoons reduced-fat cheddar cheese. Pour egg mixture into pan; cook until set. Serve with salsa. - ***PointsPlus* value per serving: 6)** **fat-free milk,** 1 cup	**hamburger,** 1 small fast food with lettuce and tomato **orange,** 1 medium **side salad,** 1 small **light Italian dressing,** 2 tablespoons
DINNER	**Mediterranean Chicken with Zucchini,** 1 serving, page 80 **red wine,** 5 ounces	**Salmon Cobb Salad,** 1 serving, page 89 **whole-wheat crackers,** 5 **grapes,** 1 cup	**Turkey Chili,** 1 serving, page 146 **corn muffin,** 1 **raspberries,** 1 cup
SNACK	**Curried Chicken Lettuce Wraps,** 1 serving, page 25 **pineapple chunks,** 1 cup	**hummus,** ¼ cup **mixed raw vegetables,** 1 cup **orange,** 1 medium	**pomegranate nonfat Greek yogurt,** 1 (6-ounce) container
PointsPlus VALUE	**Total *PointsPlus* value for the day: 29**	**Total *PointsPlus* value for the day: 31**	**Total *PointsPlus* value for the day: 29**

	MONDAY	TUESDAY	WEDNESDAY	THURSDAY
BREAKFAST	**poached egg,** 1 **turkey bacon,** 3 slices **raspberries,** 1 cup	**whole-wheat English muffin,** 1 half **peanut butter,** 1 tablespoon **pomegranate nonfat Greek yogurt,** 1 (6-ounce) container	**bran flakes cereal,** 1 cup **raisins,** 2 tablespoons **fat-free milk,** 1 cup **light cranberry juice,** 1 cup	**scrambled eggs,** 1 egg and 3 egg whites **turkey bacon,** 3 slices **fat-free milk,** 1 cup
LUNCH	**spaghetti with meat sauce,** 1 light frozen entrée **steamed broccoli,** 1 cup **fat-free milk,** 1 cup	**chicken soft taco,** 1 fast food **baby carrots,** 1 cup **apple slices,** 1 cup	**Sausage and Spinach Soup,** 1 serving, page 145 **herbed pita chips,** 1 ounce **pear,** 1 medium	**Deluxe Roast Beef Sandwich** (Spread 2 teaspoons each of fat-free mayo and Dijon mustard over 2 slices high-fiber bread. Place 2 ounces sliced deli roast beef; 1 [¾-ounce] reduced-fat provolone cheese slice; 2 lettuce leaves; 2 tomato slices; and 2 slices cooked turkey bacon, halved, on 1 bread slice. Top with remaining slice of bread. - ***PointsPlus* value per serving: 10)** **grapes,** 1 cup
DINNER	**Curried Chicken Thighs,** 1 serving, page 75 **Moroccan Couscous,** 1 serving, page 154 **sautéed zucchini,** 1 cup	**broiled flank steak,** lean and trimmed, 3 ounces cooked **baked sweet potato,** 1 medium **Spinach-Orange Salad** (Combine 2 cups baby spinach leaves; ¼ cup drained, no-sugar-added mandarin oranges, and 1 tablespoon each of chopped walnuts and feta cheese. Top with 2 tablespoons light balsamic vinaigrette. - ***PointsPlus* value per serving: 5)**	**Broiled Tilapia with Avocado-Radish Salsa,** 1 serving, page 32 **Cilantro Rice,** 1 serving, page 156 **steamed sugar snap peas,** 1 cup	**Rotini with Chicken, Asparagus, and Tomatoes,** 1 serving, page 69 **baby spinach leaves,** 2 cups **light balsamic vinaigrette,** 2 tablespoons
SNACK	**Salted Caramel Brownies,** 1 serving, page 170 **fat-free milk,** 1 cup	**fat-free cottage cheese,** 1 cup **mixed fruit salad,** 1 cup	**Peanut Butter and Chocolate–Dipped Pretzels,** 1 serving, page 174 **fat-free milk,** 1 cup	**strawberry nonfat Greek yogurt,** 1 (6-ounce) container
PointsPlus VALUE	Total ***PointsPlus*** value for the day: 32	Total ***PointsPlus*** value for the day: 30	Total ***PointsPlus*** value for the day: 31	Total ***PointsPlus*** value for the day: 30

One day's menu provides at least two servings of dairy and at least five servings of fruits and/or vegetables.

7-Day Menu Planner

WEEK 2

	FRIDAY	SATURDAY	SUNDAY
BREAKFAST	**bran flakes cereal,** 1 cup **blueberries,** 1 cup **fat-free milk,** 1 cup	**Peaches and Cream Waffles** (Toast 2 low-fat whole-grain waffles; top with 1 cup sliced peaches, ¼ cup vanilla nonfat Greek yogurt, and 2 tablespoons light syrup. - ***PointsPlus* value per serving: 7**) **fat-free milk,** 1 cup	**honey nonfat Greek yogurt,** 1 (6-ounce) container **high-fiber oat and nut bar,** 1 **light orange juice,** 1 cup
LUNCH	**margherita pizza,** 1 light frozen entrée **baby carrots,** 1 cup **banana,** 1 small **fat-free milk,** 1 cup	**black bean soup,** 1½ cups **light sour cream,** 2 tablespoons **mixed salad greens,** 2 cups **light olive oil vinaigrette,** 2 tablespoons **fat-free milk,** 1 cup	**Loaded Chicken Nachos,** 1 serving, page 82 **pineapple chunks,** 1 cup **fat-free milk,** 1 cup **cucumber slices,** 1 cup
DINNER	**steamed shrimp,** 6 ounces **Warm Fingerling Potatoes with Feta,** 1 serving, page 152 **steamed green beans,** 1 cup	**Beef Filets with Caramel Brandy-Rosemary Sauce,** 1 serving, page 35 **mashed potatoes,** ½ cup **Blue Cheese Asparagus,** 1 serving, page 148	**Herbed Mushroom Ragout over Cheesy Polenta,** 1 serving, page 29 **mixed salad greens,** 2 cups **light Ranch dressing,** 2 tablespoons
SNACK	**Creamy Spinach Dip,** 1 serving, page 18 **tortilla chips,** 1 ounce	**apple,** 1 medium **part-skim mozzarella cheese stick,** 1	**Parmesan-Pepper Popcorn** (Toss 2 cups popped light microwave popcorn with 1 tablespoon grated Parmesan cheese and ¼ teaspoon ground pepper. - ***PointsPlus* value per serving: 2**)
PointsPlus VALUE	**Total *PointsPlus* value for the day: 28**	**Total *PointsPlus* value for the day: 30**	**Total *PointsPlus* value for the day: 32**

	MONDAY	TUESDAY	WEDNESDAY	THURSDAY
BREAKFAST	**low-fat multi-grain waffles,** 2 frozen **light syrup,** 2 tablespoons **vanilla nonfat Greek yogurt,** 1 (6-ounce) container	**bran flakes cereal with raisins,** 1 cup **fat-free milk,** 1 cup **banana,** 1 small **light orange juice,** 1 cup	**low-fat multi-grain waffles,** 2 frozen **light syrup,** 2 tablespoons **fat-free milk,** 1 cup	**scrambled eggs,** 1 egg and 3 egg whites **high-fiber whole-wheat bread,** 1 slice **light orange juice,** 1 cup
LUNCH	**macaroni and cheese,** 1 low-fat frozen entrée **mixed salad greens,** 2 cups **reduced-fat Italian dressing,** 2 tablespoons	**Balsamic Chicken and White Beans,** 1 serving, page 79 **plum,** 1 medium **pomegranate nonfat Greek yogurt,** 1 (6-ounce) container	**high-fiber whole-wheat bread,** 2 slices **peanut butter,** 1 tablespoon **fruit spread,** 2 tablespoons **orange,** 1 medium **fat-free milk,** 1 cup	**Beef and Pepper Melt** (Toast two slices high-fiber whole-wheat bread. Spread 2 teaspoons each fat-free mayonnaise and Dijon mustard over one side of bread; top with 2 ounces lean deli roast beef, ¼ cup drained roasted red peppers, and 1 ounce reduced-fat provolone cheese. Broil until cheese melts; top cheese with 1 tomato slice and remaining bread slice. - ***PointsPlus* value per serving: 9)**
DINNER	**Turkey Pilaf–Stuffed Peppers,** 1 serving, page 77 **fat-free milk,** 1 cup **pineapple cubes,** 1 cup	**grilled tuna steak,** 6 ounces cooked **Sun-Dried Tomato–Pesto Orzo** (Toss 1 cup hot cooked orzo pasta with 2 teaspoons pesto and ⅛ teaspoon salt; gently stir in 2 tablespoons chopped sun-dried tomato. - ***PointsPlus* value per serving: 6)** **steamed asparagus,** 12 spears	**Pork Medallions with Rosemary Pan Sauce,** 1 serving, page 39 **wild rice,** 1 cup **steamed peas and carrots,** 1 cup	**Black Bean and Kale Quesadillas,** 1 serving, page 28 **grapes,** 1 cup **fat-free milk,** 1 cup
SNACK	**apple,** 1 medium **peanut butter,** 1 tablespoon	**fat-free cottage cheese,** 1 cup **blueberries,** 1 cup	**hummus,** ¼ cup **baby carrots,** 1 cup **strawberries,** 1 cup	**Double Berry Smoothie** (Place 1 [6-ounce] container blueberry nonfat Greek yogurt, 1 cup frozen blueberries, and ½ cup light cranberry juice in blender; process until smooth. - ***PointsPlus* value per serving: 5)**
PointsPlus VALUE	**Total *PointsPlus* value for the day: 30**	**Total *PointsPlus* value for the day: 32**	**Total *PointsPlus* value for the day: 33**	**Total *PointsPlus* value for the day: 30**

One day's menu provides at least two servings of dairy and at least five servings of fruits and/or vegetables.

7-Day Menu Planner

WEEK 3

	FRIDAY	SATURDAY	SUNDAY
BREAKFAST	**bran flakes cereal with raisins,** 1 cup **fat-free milk,** 1 cup **strawberries,** 1 cup	**hard-boiled egg,** 1 **high-fiber whole-wheat bread,** 1 slice **honey nonfat Greek yogurt,** 1 (6-ounce) container	**low-fat multi-grain waffle,** 1 frozen **light syrup,** 2 tablespoons **fat-free milk,** 1 cup **cantaloupe wedge,** 1
LUNCH	**Salmon Corn Chowder,** 1 serving, page 121 **mixed salad greens,** 2 cups **light balsamic vinaigrette,** 2 tablespoons	**grilled vegetable burger,** 1 patty **lite wheat hamburger bun,** 1 **lettuce leaf and tomato slice,** 1 each **baked potato chips,** 1 ounce **blueberries,** 1 cup	**Greek Tuna Wrap** (Toss 2 cups salad greens with 2 tablespoons light balsamic vinaigrette; spoon onto 1 [8-inch] low-fat whole-wheat tortilla. Top with 2 ounces canned and drained light chunk tuna, ¼ cup chopped tomato, and 2 tablespoons feta cheese; roll up to serve. - ***PointsPlus* value per serving: 10)** **cucumber slices,** 1 cup **banana,** 1 small
DINNER	**rotisserie chicken breast,** 3 ounces with skin removed **steamed new potatoes,** 2 small **Bacon-Walnut Brussels Sprouts,** 1 serving, page 150	**Feta Shrimp,** 1 serving, page 33 **brown rice,** ½ cup **steamed green beans,** 1 cup	**Southwestern Smothered Chicken,** 1 serving, page 66 **Refried Black Beans,** 1 serving, page 158 **watermelon cubes,** 1 cup
SNACK	**fat-free cottage cheese,** 1 cup **apple,** 1 medium	**Roasted Brown Sugar Pears,** 1 serving, page 160 **fat-free milk,** 1 cup	**cherry nonfat Greek yogurt,** 1 (6-ounce) container **orange,** 1 medium
PointsPlus VALUE	**Total *PointsPlus* value for the day: 29**	**Total *PointsPlus* value for the day: 32**	**Total *PointsPlus* value for the day: 30**

	MONDAY	TUESDAY	WEDNESDAY	THURSDAY
BREAKFAST	**whole-grain puffed cereal,** 1½ cups **raspberries,** 1 cup **fat-free milk,** 1 cup **light orange juice,** 1 cup	**oatmeal,** 1 cup cooked **scrambled eggs,** 1 egg and 3 egg whites **light orange juice,** 1 cup	**Strawberry-Orange Smoothie** (Place 1 [6-ounce] container strawberry nonfat Greek yogurt, 1 cup sliced frozen strawberries, and ½ cup light orange juice in blender; process until smooth. - ***PointsPlus* value per serving: 5)**	**whole-grain puffed cereal,** 1½ cups **blueberries,** 1 cup **fat-free milk,** 1 cup
LUNCH	**Turkey Bean Burrito** (Combine ⅓ cup cooked ground turkey with ½ cup fat-free refried beans; spoon down center of a 7-inch whole-wheat tortilla. Top with 3 tablespoons reduced-fat shredded cheddar cheese. Microwave at HIGH 20 seconds; roll up, serve over shredded lettuce, and top with salsa. - ***PointsPlus* value per serving: 9)** **strawberry nonfat Greek yogurt,** 1 (6-ounce) container	**French bread pepperoni pizza,** 1 light frozen entrée **baby carrots,** 1 cup **light Ranch dressing,** 2 tablespoons **fat-free milk,** 1 cup	**chicken tortilla soup,** 1 medium fast food **baked tortilla chips,** 1 ounce **fat-free milk,** 1 cup	**Tuscan Tuna Salad** (Combine 2 ounces drained light chunk tuna, ½ cup rinsed and drained cannellini beans, and ¼ cup each chopped tomato and chopped cucumber. Whisk together 1 tablespoon olive oil, 1 teaspoon lemon juice, and a dash each garlic powder and salt; pour over tuna mixture, and toss. Serve over bed of lettuce. - ***PointsPlus* value per serving: 7)** **pineapple cubes,** 1 cup
DINNER	**lean pork loin,** 4 ounces trimmed and cooked **Goat Cheese and Spinach Polenta,** 1 serving, page 156 **steamed green beans,** 1 cup	**Chicken Cutlets with Warm Lemon-Artichoke Relish,** 1 serving, page 72 **mashed potatoes,** 1 cup **steamed broccoli,** 1 cup	**Linguine with Spicy Beef and Olives,** 1 serving, page 38 **baby spinach leaves,** 2 cups **light balsamic vinaigrette,** 2 tablespoons	**ground turkey patty,** made with 4 ounces 93% lean ground turkey **lite wheat hamburger bun,** 1 **tomato slice and lettuce leaf,** 1 each **baked potato chips,** 1 ounce **watermelon cubes,** 1 cup
SNACK	**Chocolate Almond Fudge Pops,** 1 serving, page 165	**fat-free cottage cheese,** 1 cup **cubed melon,** 1 cup	**apple,** 1 medium **peanut butter,** 1 tablespoon	**whole-wheat pita,** 1 small **hummus,** ¼ cup
PointsPlus VALUE	**Total *PointsPlus* value for the day: 29**	**Total *PointsPlus* value for the day: 33**	**Total *PointsPlus* value for the day: 28**	**Total *PointsPlus* value for the day: 29**

One day's menu provides at least two servings of dairy and at least five servings of fruits and/or vegetables.

7-Day Menu Planner

WEEK 4

	FRIDAY	SATURDAY	SUNDAY
BREAKFAST	**Maple-Walnut Oatmeal** (Stir 1 tablespoon each light syrup and chopped toasted walnuts into 1 cup hot cooked oatmeal. - ***PointsPlus* value per serving: 7)** **fat-free milk,** 1 cup **grapefruit sections,** 1 cup	**whole-grain puffed cereal,** 1½ cups **banana,** 1 small **fat-free milk,** 1 cup	**Ham & Cheese Breakfast Wrap** (Whisk together 3 egg whites, 2 tablespoons diced ham, and a dash of salt; scramble egg mixture in hot skillet. Spoon eggs down center of a warm 8-inch whole-wheat tortilla; top with 2 tablespoons reduced-fat shredded cheddar cheese. Roll up to serve. - ***PointsPlus* value per serving: 6)** **blueberries,** 1 cup
LUNCH	**rotisserie chicken breast,** 3 ounces with skin removed **deli coleslaw,** ½ cup **raspberry nonfat Greek yogurt,** 1 (6-ounce) container	**BLT Salad** (Top 1½ cups torn romaine lettuce with 2 slices cooked and crumbled center-cut bacon and ⅓ cup each diced tomato and avocado. Top with 2 tablespoons light Ranch dressing. - ***PointsPlus* value per serving: 6)** **whole-grain French bread,** 1 ounce	**chili with beans,** 1 cup **corn muffin,** 1 **baby spinach leaves,** 2 cups **light balsamic vinaigrette,** 2 tablespoons **fat-free milk,** 1 cup
DINNER	**Meatless Tex-Mex Tostadas,** 1 serving, page 29 **orange,** 1 medium **sautéed squash,** 1 cup	**Miso-Glazed Scallops with Wilted Kale,** 1 serving, page 33 **steamed brown rice,** ½ cup **honeydew cubes,** 1 cup	**Chicken Supreme Calzone,** 1 serving, page 76 **fat-free milk,** 1 cup **nectarines,** 2 small
SNACK	**cherries,** 1 cup **light cheese wedge,** 1	**pomegranate nonfat Greek yogurt,** 1 (6-ounce) container **popcorn,** 2 cups light microwave	**Blue Cheese and Chive Straws,** 2 servings, page 20 **grapes,** 1 cup
PointsPlus VALUE	Total ***PointsPlus*** value for **the day: 30**	Total ***PointsPlus*** value for **the day: 27**	Total ***PointsPlus*** value for **the day: 32**

GENERAL RECIPE INDEX

PointsPlus® Value Index

1 *PointsPlus* value

2 *PointsPlus* value

3 ***PointsPlus*** value

4 ***PointsPlus*** value

5 ***PointsPlus*** value

6 ***PointsPlus*** value

7 ***PointsPlus*** value

8 ***PointsPlus*** value

9 ***PointsPlus*** value

10 ***PointsPlus*** value

11 ***PointsPlus*** value

10 SIMPLE SIDE DISHES

Vegetable	Servings	Preparation	Cooking Instructions
Asparagus	3 to 4 per pound	Snap off tough ends. Remove scales, if desired.	To steam: Cook, covered, on a rack above boiling water 2 to 3 minutes. To boil: Cook, covered, in a small amount of boiling water 2 to 3 minutes or until crisp-tender.
Broccoli	3 to 4 per pound	Remove outer leaves and tough ends of lower stalks. Wash; cut into spears.	To steam: Cook, covered, on a rack above boiling water 5 to 7 minutes or until crisp-tender.
Carrots	4 per pound	Scrape; remove ends, and rinse. Leave tiny carrots whole; slice large carrots.	To steam: Cook, covered, on a rack above boiling water 8 to 10 minutes or until crisp-tender. To boil: Cook, covered, in a small amount of boiling water 8 to 10 minutes or until crisp-tender.
Cauliflower	4 per medium head	Remove outer leaves and stalk. Wash. Break into florets.	To steam: Cook, covered, on a rack above boiling water 5 to 7 minutes or until crisp-tender.
Corn	4 per 4 large ears	Remove husks and silks. Leave corn on the cob, or cut off kernels.	To boil: Cook, covered, in boiling water to cover 8 to 10 minutes (on cob) or in a small amount of boiling water 4 to 6 minutes (kernels).
Green beans	4 per pound	Wash; trim ends, and remove strings. Cut into 1½-inch pieces.	To steam: Cook, covered, on a rack above boiling water 5 to 7 minutes. To boil: Cook, covered, in a small amount of boiling water 5 to 7 minutes or until crisp-tender.
Potatoes	3 to 4 per pound	Scrub; peel, if desired. Leave whole, slice, or cut into chunks.	To boil: Cook, covered, in boiling water to cover 30 to 40 minutes (whole) or 15 to 20 minutes (slices or chunks). To bake: Bake at 400° for 1 hour or until done.
Snow peas	4 per pound	Wash; trim ends, and remove tough strings.	To steam: Cook, covered, on a rack above boiling water 2 to 3 minutes. Or sauté in cooking spray or 1 teaspoon oil over medium-high heat 3 to 4 minutes or until crisp-tender.
Squash, summer	3 to 4 per pound	Wash; trim ends, and slice or chop.	To steam: Cook, covered, on a rack above boiling water 6 to 8 minutes. To boil: Cook, covered, in a small amount of boiling water 6 to 8 minutes or until crisp-tender.
Squash, winter *(including acorn, butternut, and buttercup)*	2 per pound	Rinse; cut in half, and remove all seeds. Leave in halves to bake, or peel and cube to boil.	To boil: Cook cubes, covered, in boiling water 20 to 25 minutes. To bake: Place halves, cut sides down, in a shallow baking dish; add ½ inch water. Bake, uncovered, at 375° for 30 minutes. Turn and season, or fill; bake an additional 20 to 30 minutes or until tender.